FIDIC users' guide
A practical guide to the
1999 Red and Yellow Books

Brian W. Totterdill

thomas telford

Published by Thomas Telford Publishing, Thomas Telford Ltd,
40 Marsh Wall, London E14 9TP
URL: www.thomastelford.com

Distributors for Thomas Telford books are
USA: ASCE Press, 1801 Alexander Bell Drive, Reston, VA 20191-4400, USA
Japan: Maruzen Co. Ltd, Book Department, 3–10 Nihonbashi 2-chome,
Chuo-ku, Tokyo 103
Australia: DA Books and Journals, 648 Whitehorse Road, Mitcham 3132,
Victoria

First published 2006
Reprinted 2007, 2008 (twice), 2009, 2010

Also available from Thomas Telford Books
FIDIC users' guide: A practical guide to the 1999 Red Book. B. W. Totterdill.
ISBN: 0 7277 2885 7
FIDIC Conditions of Contract for Construction. ISBN: 2 8843 2022 9

A catalogue record for this book is available from the British Library

ISBN: 978 0 7277 3441 9

© Brian W. Totterdill and Thomas Telford Limited 2006

Typeset by Academic + Technical, Bristol
Printed and bound in Great Britain by CPI Antony Rowe, Chippenham, Wiltshire

Preface to the second edition

This second edition of the *FIDIC Users' Guide* has been extended to include the Conditions of Contract for Plant and Design-Build, known as the 1999 Yellow Book. It also reviews the other FIDIC Contracts which have been published since the first edition was written, together with further discussion based on experience with the practical use of the 1999 Contracts.

During 2005 FIDIC published the *Multilateral Development Banks Harmonised Conditions of Contract for Construction*, commonly known as the MDB Edition. This Contract has been prepared in conjunction with The World Bank and a group of Multilateral Development Banks and is included in their procurement documents. The MDB Edition includes some significant changes to the Conditions of Contract for Construction and is reviewed in Part 4 of this book.

Since the publication of the first edition there has been an increased use of the 1999 FIDIC Contracts. The Plant and Design-Build Contract has become popular, particularly with Employers considering Contractor design for water-related and environmental projects. This Contract is very similar in layout and content to the Contract for Construction but differs in detail due to the different requirements for Contractor design rather than Employer design and the greater emphasis on electrical and mechanical plant. These differences are extremely important and require detailed study when deciding which Contract to use and when preparing and administering the Contract. Hence this second edition includes a detailed comparison between the Red and Yellow Books and a guide to the differences at each Sub-Clause of the Plant and Design-Build Contract.

Also, since the publication of the first edition, the European International Contractors (EIC) have published a very useful series of EIC Contractor's Guides to the different FIDIC Contracts. I must acknowledge the assistance I have received from these Guides, not just in understanding the Contractor's point of view, but also from their suggestions that potential disputes could be avoided by clarification of the meaning of certain clauses. Further details of these Guides can be obtained from EIC at www.eicontractors.de.

I am also most grateful to FIDIC for allowing the Clauses in the Conditions of Contract to be reproduced and for assistance from The FIDIC Contracts Guide. Copies of the Conditions of Contract and other FIDIC publications can be obtained from the FIDIC Bookshop, Box 311 CH-1215 Geneva 15, Switzerland (tel: +41 22 799 49 00; fax: +41 22 799 49 01; fidic.pub@pobox.com; http://www.fidic.org/bookshop).

Preface to the first edition

In recent years the role of the Conditions of Contract in a construction project has undergone a radical change. The Conditions of Contract were originally a legal document, giving the rights and obligations of the Parties, and were only consulted when a claim or dispute became a serious problem. Resident Engineers and Contractor's Project Managers were probably aware that such documents existed, but most of them had never even seen the Conditions of Contract, much less used it as a reference to guide their actions on the site.

In more recent years, the increase in the size and complexity of projects and the increasing demand from Clients and Employers that projects should finish on time and within budget have increased the pressures for improved management techniques on construction sites. The current emphasis on improved procedures for the avoidance or resolution of claims and disputes has added to these pressures on the staff on site.

One of the consequences of the movement towards improving efficiency and reducing costs has been the increasing use of the Conditions of Contract as a manual of good project management procedures. This development has been evident in the successive revisions to the Federation Internationale des Ingenieurs-Conseils (FIDIC) Conditions of Contract for Works of Civil Engineering Construction, the traditional FIDIC 'Red Book', and experienced a major leap forward with the publication of the New Engineering Contract by The Institution of Civil Engineers in London. The New Engineering Contract not only incorporated procedures which virtually formed a manual of good project management techniques and encouraged a less adversarial approach to the relationship between Contractor and Employer but also was written in good English, in a style and format that could be readily understood by construction professionals.

The Conditions of Contract, which were published by FIDIC in 1999, mark a further step forward in the process of the incorporation of management procedures expressed in a practical style and format. Hence, it is now inconceivable that Resident Engineers, Contractor's

Managers and the other construction professionals who prepare documents and administer projects on site should not have the Conditions of Contract on their desks and refer to its requirements and procedures on almost a daily basis.

This book is a practical guide for the people who actually use FIDIC Conditions of Contract, based on the author's practical experience of construction projects, conducting training courses and the resolution of disputes. It is intended to assist the people who are preparing Contract documents as well as those who are administering the project on the Site or dealing with claims and disputes. The book includes a detailed review of the Conditions of Contract for Construction and comparisons with the other FIDIC Conditions which were published in 1999. The review must be read together with the wording of the actual Sub-Clause. The interrelation of the actions and notices by the Employer, Contractor and Engineer with the milestone events during the construction of the project are shown in a series of flow charts. There is also a comparison with previous FIDIC Conditions and a comparison of Clause numbers to assist those who are familiar with the traditional FIDIC Red Book. The book is not intended to be a legal analysis of the new FIDIC Conditions or a comparison of the correct interpretation of the conditions of contract in different jurisdictions. That task can be left for those who are better qualified to analyse and speculate on the correct legal interpretation of controversial Clauses.

Contents

Part 1

The Traditional and the 1999 FIDIC Conditions of Contract

Chapter 1

Introduction to the FIDIC Conditions of Contract

1.1 Construction Contracts

Any construction Contract is a legally binding agreement between two Parties – the Owner, who is generally referred to as the Employer, and the Contractor. The Employer initiates the project, decides what he wants, gives instructions, supervises the construction, pays for the project and occupies the completed project. The Contractor builds the project and is paid for his work.

The Contract controls the relations between the Employer and the Contractor and includes a substantial bundle of documents. These documents include details of the work which the Contractor has offered to construct and the payments that will be made from the Employer to the Contractor. The Contract includes Conditions of Contract, which lay down the responsibilities and obligations of both Parties. When unexpected problems arise, which often result in delays and additional costs, the Conditions of Contract determine which of the Parties must bear the consequences.

A typical construction contract will include the following.

(a) *The Contractor's Tender*, which is the Contractor's offer to carry out the work for a certain price. The Tender will be based on information and documents provided by the Employer, and includes the Contractor's proposal for the rates of payment for the different items of work.

(b) *The Contract Agreement*, which is the document that confirms the offer and acceptance and establishes the formal Contract. Under some jurisdictions the Contract Agreement is required in order to establish a legally binding agreement between the Parties.

(c) *The Employer's Letter of Acceptance*, which is the letter from the Employer to the Contractor in which the Employer accepts the Contractor's offer to carry out the work. This offer and acceptance constitute a legally binding agreement, within the terms which are

3

stated in the Letter of Acceptance. The Letter of Acceptance will refer to the Contractor's Tender and any subsequent agreements.

(d) *The Conditions of Contract*, which are generally based on a standard document, modified to suit the requirements of the Employer for the particular project.

(e) *The Technical Documents*, which include drawings, specifications, bills of quantities and other schedules and give the Employer's technical requirements for the project, together with the detailed calculations which make up the Accepted Contract Amount. When the design is to be prepared by the Contractor the drawings and specifications are replaced by the Employer's Requirements and Contractor's Proposals.

1.2 The FIDIC Conditions of Contract

The most commonly used Conditions of Contract for international construction projects are published by the Federation Internationale des Ingenieurs-Conseils (FIDIC), the International Federation of Consulting Engineers. The Traditional FIDIC Contract for civil engineering construction is the FIDIC 'Conditions of Contract for Works of Civil Engineering Construction', commonly known as 'The Red Book'. In 1999 this was superseded by the FIDIC 'Conditions of Contract for Construction', which are the subject of this book, together with the Conditions of Contract for Plant and Design-Build.

The FIDIC Conditions of Contract include:

- the General Conditions, and
- the Particular Conditions.

The General Conditions are intended to be used unchanged for every project. The Particular Conditions are prepared for the particular project and include any changes or additional clauses which the Employer has decided to include to suit the local and project requirements. Some employers have printed their own versions of the General Conditions, with changes to suit their own requirements. This procedure cannot be recommended. One of the advantages of using standard Conditions of Contract is that contractors tendering for the project and contract administrators are familiar with the standard Conditions and are aware of their responsibilities and of the consequences of any failure to meet their obligations. Any changes or additions are in a separate document and so everyone's attention is drawn to the changes. When the General Conditions have been reprinted with small but significant changes then the changes may be overlooked and the project will suffer as a consequence.

The General Conditions also include the Appendix to Tender, which is a schedule of essential information, most of which must be completed by the Employer before he issues the Tender documents and a few items which are completed by the Tenderer.

In any project, there will be problems and to overcome these problems it will be necessary to carry out additional work. This will take time and money. The most common situation is that the Contractor spends money and then claims it back from the Employer. When this situation arises it is necessary to decide whether the Employer must reimburse the Contractor, or whether the Contractor must bear the additional cost. If this cannot be agreed by the Parties' representatives on the site then an initial decision will be made by the Engineer or other Employer's Representative. This is an interim decision and is subject to appeal to an arbitrator or the Courts. However, reference to arbitration or the Courts is a slow and expensive procedure. Under the 1999 FIDIC Conditions of Contract if either Party is not satisfied with the Engineer's initial acceptance or rejection of a claim then the dispute can be referred immediately, on site, for a decision by a Dispute Adjudication Board (DAB). This decision must be implemented, but the dispute can then be referred to arbitration for a final decision.

The basis on which all such decisions must be made is laid down in the Conditions of Contract. The Conditions of Contract give the procedural rules and lay down the rights and obligations of the Parties to the Contract. Successive revisions to the standard Conditions of Contract have increased the complexity of these rules and procedures so that the current Conditions of Contract are virtually manuals of good project management practice, rather that purely legal statements of party rights and obligations.

1.3 The Traditional FIDIC Conditions of Contract

FIDIC publishes a family of different Conditions of Contract to suit the requirements of different types of construction projects. Since 1999 there have been two separate and distinct sets of FIDIC Conditions of Contract available for use – the Traditional FIDIC Conditions of Contract and the new 1999 FIDIC Conditions of Contract.

The Traditional FIDIC Conditions of Contract are as follows.

- *Conditions of Contract for Works of Civil Engineering Construction,* fourth edition 1987, reprinted 1992 with further amendments, known as 'The Red Book'. A supplement to the fourth edition was published in 1996.
- *Conditions of Contract for Electrical and Mechanical Works,* third edition 1987, known as 'The Yellow Book'.

- *Conditions of Contract for Design-Build and Turnkey,* first edition 1995, known as 'The Orange Book'.
- *Client/Consultant Model Services Agreement,* third edition 1998, known as 'The White Book'.

Other FIDIC publications include:

- *Conditions of Subcontract for Works of Civil Engineering Construction,* first edition 1994.
- *Tendering Procedure,* second edition 1994.
- *Guides to the Use of the Different FIDIC Conditions of Contract.*
- *Amicable Settlement of Construction Disputes,* first edition 1992.
- *Mediation; Explanation and Guidelines,* first edition 1993.
- *Insurance of Large Civil Engineering Projects,* 1981 plus 1997 update.
- Other publications on different aspects of the construction of engineering projects and the work of FIDIC.

All the FIDIC publications use English as the official and authentic text. Translations into some other languages have been published by FIDIC and other translations are also available. A list of all their publications is available from FIDIC (FIDIC Bookshop, Box 311, CH-1215 Geneva 15, Switzerland) or can be found at their website (www.fidic.org).

1.4 The 1999 FIDIC Conditions of Contract

A publication such as a standard Conditions of Contract needs to be revised every few years. Construction procedures develop with changes to the size and complexity of projects and with experience of the use of the Contract procedures to overcome problems. These changes are reflected in the different editions of the FIDIC Conditions of Contract. However, around 1997, FIDIC decided that the time had come for a major review of all its Conditions of Contract. FIDIC decided that they would not just revise the existing editions, or even publish new editions, but would change the basic purpose of each of the Contracts and completely rearrange the layout of the Conditions of Contract.

The original FIDIC Conditions of Contract were for Works of Civil Engineering, followed by the Contract for Electrical and Mechanical Works. The principle of different Conditions of Contract to suit different types of engineering was modified in 1995 by the publication of the Conditions of Contract for Design-Build and Turnkey. The Design-Build and Turnkey Contract included detailed provisions for design by the Contractor, but was also written in a different style and the layout of Clauses and Sub-Clauses was different to the earlier Contracts.

The style and layout of the Design-Build Contract was developed further when, following test editions in 1998, FIDIC published the first edition of a new set of Conditions of Contract in 1999. These are:

- *The Conditions of Contract for Construction.* This Contract is for Building and Engineering Works which have been designed by the Employer and replaces the traditional FIDIC Red Book.
- *The Conditions of Contract for Plant and Design-Build.* This Contract is for Electrical and Mechanical Plant and for Building and Engineering Works, designed by the Contractor and replaces the traditional FIDIC Yellow and Orange Books. The publication is yellow in colour.
- *The Conditions of Contract for EPC/Turnkey Projects.* This Contract is for Engineering, Procurement and Construction or Turnkey Projects where the Contractor takes total responsibility for the design and execution of the project, providing a completed project ready for occupation. This is a new FIDIC Contract and the publication is silver in colour.
- *The Short Form of Contract.* This Contract is for Building or Engineering Works of relatively small capital value or time period or for relatively simple works where a much shorter form of contract is suitable. This is a new FIDIC Contract and is green in colour.
- *The Form of Contract for Dredging and Reclamation Works.* At the time of writing only the test edition (2001) has been published and is blue in colour.

In 2000 FIDIC published The FIDIC Contracts Guide, which gives detailed guidance on the use of the three principal 1999 Contracts. The Contracts Guide was written by Mr Peter L. Booen, who was the principal drafter of the 1999 Contracts. Hence it gives an authoritative guide to the intentions of the panels who drafted these Contracts. The Contracts Guide includes the complete texts of these three contracts, printed side-by-side for easy comparison, together with comments on the background to each Sub-Clause. The Guide also includes a very useful guide to the FIDIC Procurement Procedures, including notes on standard forms and letters. Flow Charts are provided showing the recommended procedures for Prequalification, Obtaining Tenders and Evaluating Tenders.

1.5 The MDB Harmonised Construction Contract

During 2005 FIDIC published the Multilateral Development Banks Harmonised Edition of the Conditions of Contract for Construction (the MDB Edition). This Contract was prepared and agreed with a group of Development Banks who have been licensed to include it in their procurement procedures.

1.6 Social clauses

The Conditions of Contract give the rights and obligations of the Parties to the Contract. The Parties' rights are expressed in detail in order to facilitate the allocation of liability in the event of any delays or additional costs being incurred by either Party. The detailed obligations, particularly the obligations of the Contractor, are aimed at delivering the completed Works within the requirements for quality, time and cost. In recent years standard Conditions of Contract, particularly FIDIC, have incorporated additional clauses which are intended to avoid, or restrict, corruption and the impact of the construction work on the environment and the local community, as well as improving disease avoidance and the care and facilities for the workers on the Site. The MDB Edition includes a number of additional clauses for this purpose.

This trend is increasing and some organisations are now talking about including additional clauses in the Particular Conditions which would require the Contractor to execute the Works in a manner that may not be the most economic method, but would bring additional benefits to the country of the project. For example:

- dividing the project into smaller Contracts, thus enabling them to be carried out by local Contractors, which would assist in the development of local industry;
- the construction of labour camps and other temporary works in such a way that they can be handed over to the local community on completion of the project;
- clauses requiring the use of local Subcontractors and local labour, even if this means providing training and other requirements;
- clauses discouraging the import of machinery, in order to oblige the Contractor to use local labour rather than machines.

Any such clauses will add to the cost of the project, and possibly require a longer time period for construction, so they will only be included on the initiative of the Employer, with the agreement of any funding institution. However, construction projects are built for the benefit of the community so, if additional benefits can be obtained for a reasonable additional cost, this must be a worthwhile investment.

1.7 Contents of this book

A further review of each of these Contracts is given in Chapter 3 of this book. Parts 2 and 3 include a Clause-by-Clause review of the Conditions of Contract for Construction and for Plant & Design-Build, together with copies of the FIDIC Clauses. Part 4 gives a review and Clause comparison between the MDB Edition and the Construction Contract. Part 5 gives a comparison of Sub-Clause numbers between the fourth Edition of the Red Book and the Conditions of Contract for Construction.

Chapter 2

Comparisons between the different FIDIC Conditions of Contract

2.1 The Traditional and the 1999 Conditions of Contract

The most commonly used FIDIC Conditions of Contract have always been referred to as 'The Red Book' for Works of Civil Engineering Construction. This has now been replaced by the Conditions of Contract for Construction 'The New Red Book'. The other traditional FIDIC Conditions of Contract have also been replaced by 1999 Conditions of Contract. With the increasing use of FIDIC Contracts, many users of the 1999 Contracts will be using FIDIC for the first time. These people may have an advantage over those of us who have used the traditional Contracts and are now having to convert to the 1999 Contracts. There are many similarities between the new and the old FIDIC Conditions and some Sub-Clauses are identical but have been rearranged and renumbered. However, there are also many changes, some of which are significant new requirements and others which constitute just a minor change of wording, possibly to clarify the previously intended meaning. It is very easy, but very dangerous, to assume that a Sub-Clause that looks familiar is unchanged from the traditional Conditions of Contract.

2.2 The Traditional 'Red Book' and the Conditions of Contract for Construction

Part 2 of this book refers to the 1999 Conditions of Contract for Construction and avoids the temptation to make frequent comparisons between the new and the old contracts. Comparisons of individual Sub-Clauses are particularly difficult, because some Sub-Clauses have changes in wording that may not be immediately apparent. Also, each of the Sub-Clauses must be read in conjunction with other Sub-Clauses and the rearrangement of the layout adds to the difficulty in identifying all the Sub-Clauses that relate to a particular subject. While the previous Contracts will obviously remain in use for some considerable time, measured in years rather than months, when the 1999 Contracts are used it is essential to concentrate on the Contract for the particular project rather than to make constant comparisons with the Contract that was used for a previous project.

The reduction from 72 to 20 main Clauses, with the consequent re-arrangement and increase in the number of Sub-Clauses, makes a direct comparison impossible. Whilst it is not possible to list all the significant changes from the Traditional to the 1999 Contract, the most important changes include the following.

(a) The General Conditions and the Guidance for the Preparation of Particular Conditions are now included in the same publication and are no longer referred to as Part I and Part II. Whilst it may be convenient for people who are preparing Contract documents to have both the FIDIC Conditions in one publication it is certainly not conducive to the inclusion of General Conditions into the Contract by reference, or helpful to the people who are using the Contracts. The Contractor and site supervisory staff only require the General Conditions and the inclusion of other sections in the same publication can only cause confusion. It will be necessary to separate the General Conditions from the other documents and combine them with the Particular Conditions, Appendix to Tender and other documents that make up the Conditions of Contract for a particular project. When the General Conditions are being translated into a different language it will be necessary to identify exactly which documents are required. The omission of the designations Part I and Part II is also to be regretted as it linked the different parts together and gave a convenient short title for reference purposes.

(b) New terms have been introduced and defined at Clause 1, includ-ing the following.

   (i)   'Schedules', which is defined at Sub-Clause 1.1.1.7, is used to describe the Bills of Quantities and other Schedules sub-mitted by the Contractor with the Letter of Tender and included in the Contract.

   (ii) 'Base Date', at 1.1.3.1, is the date 28 days prior to the latest date for submission of the Tender.

   (iii) 'Defects Notification Period', at 1.1.3.7, replaces the Defects Liability Period and is a more accurate description.

   (iv) 'Accepted Contract Amount', at 1.1.4.1, is the amount accepted in the Letter of Acceptance, whereas 'Contract Price' includes adjustments.

   (v)   'Goods', at 1.1.5.2, includes the Contractor's Equipment, Materials, Plant and Temporary Works.

(vi) A procedure has been introduced at Sub-Clause 2.5 for use when the Employer wishes to claim against the Contractor.

(vii) The role of the Engineer has been changed, at Clause 3 and in various other Sub-Clauses.

(viii) The term 'Engineer's Representative' has been abolished and is apparently replaced by a reference, at Sub-Clause 3.2, to a possible resident engineer.

(ix) Provisions for Quality Assurance have been introduced at Sub-Clause 4.9.

(x) There is provision, at Sub-Clause 4.20, for the Employer to provide equipment and free-issue materials for the use of the Contractor.

(xi) The Contractor is required to submit detailed monthly progress reports, at Sub-Clause 4.21.

(xii) The delay causes listed at Sub-Clause 8.4, which entitle the Contractor to an extension of time, have changed. Delay caused by the Employer's other Contractors on the site and unforeseeable shortages in the availability of personnel or goods caused by epidemic or government actions have been added. Other special circumstances that may occur have been omitted. However, the provision for extensions as a result of delays caused by authorities at Sub-Clause 8.5 and the Force Majeure provision at Clause 19 may cover some of the situations which would previously have been regarded as special circumstances.

(xiii) Provisions for Value Engineering have been introduced at Sub-Clause 13.2.

(xiv) Sub-Clause 13.8 includes a complex formula for calculating adjustments for changes in Cost.

(xv) Provision for Force Majeure is included at Clause 19.

(xvi) Provision for a Dispute Adjudication Board (DAB) has been included at Sub-Clauses 20.2–20.4, together with changes to the role of the Engineer and to the procedures for dealing with Contractor's claims.

The fact that the role of the Engineer has changed is immediately apparent from the removal of the traditional Clause 67 reference of any dispute for an Engineer's decision, but the changes also affect a large number of other Sub-Clauses. The impact on the actual performance of the Engineer's duties may be less than would be expected from an initial study of the new conditions. When carrying out his duties the Engineer is deemed to act for the Employer, as Sub-Clause 3.1(a), and is, by definition at Sub-Clause 1.1.2.6, considered part of the

'Employer's Personnel'. However, the Engineer is still required to be 'fair' as discussed later in this chapter. The Contractor is no longer required to send copies of some notices direct to the Employer but other notices and information must still be sent direct to the Employer, with a copy to the Engineer.

While the Clause 67 reference of disputes to the Engineer has been replaced by the Dispute Adjudication Board, a new requirement has been introduced for claims to be determined by the Engineer. Sub-Clause 3.5 gives the procedure for the Engineer to decide matters such as Contractor's claims and requires him to consult with each Party 'in an endeavour to reach agreement' and then 'make a fair determination in accordance with the Contract, taking due regard of all relevant circumstances'. This suggests that the Engineer will not necessarily take the action that would be preferred by the Employer. This task is expected to be carried out by the Engineer and not delegated to an assistant. Similarly, Sub-Clause 14.6 requires Interim Payment Certificates to show the amount which the Engineer 'fairly determines to be due'.

Many improvements and other changes have been introduced but some small changes in wording can only be identified by a detailed comparison of Sub-Clauses. For example, the definition of 'Cost', at Sub-Clause 1.1.4.3 is based on 'all expenditure reasonably incurred' compared with the previous reference to 'all expenditure properly incurred'. The full implications of all the changes will only become apparent when the new Conditions have been in use for several years.

However, some comparisons are inevitable and people who are familiar with The Red Book may wish to locate the equivalent Clause in the new contracts. A direct comparison of Sub-Clauses is not always possible due to the rearrangement of Clauses and the rearrangement of material within clauses. A table of Sub-Clause comparisons is included in Part 5 of this book.

2.3 Comparison between the different 1999 Conditions of Contract

The traditional FIDIC Conditions of Contract appear to have been written by different committees, at different times, with very little attempt at co-ordination. However, the 1999 Conditions of Contract have been properly co-ordinated, the style and layouts are identical and many of the provisions are the same throughout the family of Contracts. This co-ordination will bring considerable benefits to the users of the Contracts. Anyone who is familiar with one Contract will be able to convert to a different Contract with the minimum of effort.

The Conditions of Contract for Construction (The Red Book)

This is the basic 1999 FIDIC Conditions of Contract and is reviewed Clause-by-Clause in Part 2 of this book, together with the Conditions of Contract for Plant and Design-Build.

As a change from the previous Red Book, the 1999 Conditions of Contract are also intended for use for Electrical and Mechanical Works which are designed by the Employer. Provision has been added, at Clause 9, for Tests on Completion, which are likely to be required for mechanical plant, and follows the previous Yellow Book for Electrical and Mechanical Works. A definition of 'Tests after Completion' has also been added at Sub-Clause 1.1.3.6 although details are to be provided in the Particular Conditions and Specification.

Although this Contract is intended for use when the Works are designed by the Employer, it recognises that some design may be required from the Contractor. The requirements are given at Sub-Clause 4.1, but rely on further details in the Specification. Clause 5 of the Conditions of Contract for Plant and Design-Build provides useful guidance for additional requirements that could be included in the Particular Conditions.

The Conditions of Contract for Plant and Design-Build (The Yellow Book)

This Contract is intended for use for Electrical and Mechanical Plant and for Building and Engineering Works, designed by the Contractor. It has been developed from the previous Orange Book for Design-Build and Turnkey. A Clause-by-Clause review and comparison with the Conditions of Contract for Construction is included in Part 2 of this book.

The majority of Clauses in this Contract are identical to Clauses in the Conditions of Contract for Construction. This will be a considerable help to the users of FIDIC Contracts. Anyone who is familiar with the Conditions of Contract for Construction should have no difficulty in adapting to the Plant and Design-Build Conditions of Contract. The main differences derive from the Contractor being responsible for the design of the Works and the Plant and Design-Build Conditions being for a lump sum contract with payments from Schedules rather than by remeasurement of the quantities of work which have been executed.

The main differences can be summarised as follows.

- The Definitions at Sub-Clause 1.1 change to replace 'Specification' and 'Drawings' by 'Employer's Requirements' and 'Contractor's Proposal'. 'Bill of Quantities' and 'Daywork Schedule' are replaced by 'Schedule of Guarantees' and 'Schedule of Payments'. However, Sub-Clause 13.6 still refers to a Daywork Schedule.

- At Sub-Clause 1.5 the priority of documents changes to suit the different documents as defined at Sub-Clause 1.1.
- Sub-Clause 1.9 'Delayed Drawings or Instructions' is replaced by 'Errors in the Employer's requirements', which is the equivalent terminology for the different situations.
- At Sub-Clause 4.1 the Contractor's obligations change to suit different situations.
- Sub-Clause 4.5 'Assignment of Benefit of Subcontract' is omitted and replaced by a very short Sub-Clause on 'Nominated Subcontractors'.
- Clause 5 'Nominated Subcontractors' is cancelled. The Clause number has been used for a detailed Clause 'Design'.
- Sub-Clause 8.3 'Programme', sub-paragraph (a) requires the programme to include trial operation.
- Sub-Clause 9.1 'Contractor's Obligations' for 'Tests on Completion' includes additional requirements for pre-commissioning tests, commissioning tests and trial operation.
- Clause 12 'Measurement and Evaluation' is not required. The Clause number has been used for a new Clause for 'Tests after Completion'.
- Sub-Clauses 13.1 'Right to Vary' and 13.2 'Value Engineering' are reduced in scope to suit the different circumstances.
- Clause 14 is changed to suit the different payment procedures for the lump sum contract.
- Sub-Clause 20.2 'Appointment of the Dispute Adjudication Board' is changed so that the DAB is only appointed after a party gives notice to the other party of its intention to refer a dispute to the DAB. The Guidance for the Preparation of Particular Conditions suggests that for certain types of project, particularly those involving extensive work on Site, it would be appropriate for the DAB to visit the Site on a regular basis. A permanent DAB should then be appointed as in the Conditions of Contract for Construction. Obviously a DAB which has to be appointed after the dispute has arisen will not be available immediately and will take longer to consider the problem and reach a decision.

    The reason for this difference is not clear but it seems to create problems and reduce the effectiveness of the DAB. If the reason is that different people may be appropriate for design and construction disputes then the problem could be overcome in the composition of the DAB. For a very large project it may be appropriate to appoint additional people to the DAB and for the Chairman to select the people who will deal with a particular dispute.

These changes are generally a consequence of the change to a lump sum contract with all the design being provided by the Contractor. Work which has been designed by the Contractor is not normally measured for payment because payment for measured quantities could lead to uneconomic design. Also, Contractor design is generally specified on a performance basis and is subject to testing after completion to check the operation and performance. However, there seems no good reason why FIDIC published two separate Contracts. The alternative provisions could surely have been incorporated into a single document, either as alternative Clauses, or in the Guidance for the Preparation of Particular Conditions.

The Conditions of Contract for Construction can be used when there is some design by the Contractor. It may sometimes be desirable to import the more detailed Contractor design Clauses and procedures into those contracts which combine Contractor design with Employer design.

The problems of preparing Employer's Requirements and of evaluating Tenders for design work must not be underestimated. Some Employers use a two-stage tender procedure for evaluating different design proposals but this may not be permitted by the funding agency.

The Conditions of Contract for EPC/Turnkey Projects (The Silver Book)

The Conditions of Contract for EPC (Engineering, Procurement and Construction) and Turnkey Projects are intended for use when the Employer gives his overall requirements and the Contractor takes a much greater share of the risks, carries out all the design and construction and hands over the completed project, ready for operation 'at the turn of a key'. FIDIC state, in the Introduction to these Conditions, that they may be suitable when the Employer wants a greater degree of certainty in price and time and is prepared to pay a higher price in order to achieve that certainty. The Contractor takes virtually all the risks and must be paid a premium for taking the risks. This procedure could be appropriate where the EPC Contract is a critical part of a larger commercial venture. The Introduction also refers to situations where this Contract would not be suitable. An EPC/Turnkey Contract will involve more negotiation than an Employer Design or Design-Build Contract, before the Contract terms are agreed. Contractors must consider very carefully the implications of this allocation of risk before agreeing to the Contract Price.

In the Introductory Note to the Silver Book, FIDIC emphasis the additional requirements at tender stage if the Contractor is being required to take additional risks, and continues

> Thereafter the Contractor should be given freedom to carry out the work in his chosen manner, provided the end result meets the performance criteria specified by the Employer. Consequently the Employer should only

exercise limited control over and should in general not interfere with the Contractor's work.

The layout and content of the Clauses and Sub-Clauses is similar to the Plant and Design-Build Contract. The question to be considered is whether these Clauses are appropriate for a Contract under which the Contractor is being paid to take more of the risk. If the Contractor is to achieve the certainty of price and time stipulated then the involvement of the Employer during construction must be reduced to an absolute minimum. Whilst the opportunities for Employer involvement, or interference, have been reduced from the Conditions of Contract for Construction, the Contract still allows more Employer involvement than is consistent with the above requirement, or is desirable in order to achieve the overall requirement for the project.

Comparing this Contract with the Plant and Design-Build Contract, most of the changes reflect the greater allocation of risk to the Contractor. The wording of some clauses, such as 4.12, must be queried as to whether the Contractor should be expected to allow for risks that could not be foreseen when he prepared his Tender. In general, the Employer transfers risk to the Contractor but maintains his rights to be involved in administration and supervision. The changes include the following.

- The Appendix to Tender and Letter of Acceptance are not used. The information given in the Appendix to Tender under other Contracts must be included in the Employer's Requirements. The Letter of Acceptance is incorporated into the Contract Agreement which, by definition at Sub-Clause 1.1.1.2, can include annexed memoranda.
- Sub-Clause 1.1 'Definitions' includes changes to reflect the different requirements.
- Sub-Clauses 1.5 'Priority of Documents' and 1.6 'Contract Agreement' are changed because there is no Letter of Acceptance.
- Sub-Clause 1.9 'Errors in the Employer's Requirements' is deleted.
- A new Sub-Clause 1.9 'Confidentiality' has been introduced.
- Sub-Clause 1.12 'Confidential Details' reduces the information that the Contractor is obliged to disclose.
- Clause 3 'The Engineer' is replaced by 'The Employer's Administration'. Throughout the Contract it is the Employer who carries out the duties allocated to the Engineer in other Contracts.
- Sub-Clauses 4.7 'Setting Out', 4.10 'Site Data', 4.11 'Sufficiency of the Contract Price', 4.12 'Unforeseeable Difficulties', 7.2 'Samples', 7.3 'Inspection' and 8.1 'Commencement of Works' are all reduced in length or modified to reflect the different risk allocation, often removing the Contractor's right to claim.
- Sub-Clause 8.4 'Extension of Time for Completion' is changed to remove the right to an extension of time in the event of exceptionally

17

adverse climatic conditions or unforeseeable shortages. The other extension situations remain, which implies that it is still necessary to allow for the situation that the Contractor does not complete the Works on time, but is not responsible for the delay.

- The provisions of Sub-Clause 10.2 'Taking Over of Parts of the Works' are greatly reduced and only permitted by agreement.
- Sub-Clause 10.4 'Surfaces Requiring Reinstatement' is deleted.
- Sub-Clause 12.2 'Delayed Tests after Completion' is changed.
- The provisions in Sub-Clause 13.8 'Adjustments for Changes in Costs' are removed and it just refers to the Particular Conditions.
- Clause 14 'Contract Price and Payment' has major changes to reflect the greater risk taken and additional guarantees that have been given by the Contractor.
- Sub-Clause 17.3 'Employer's Risks' has been reduced.

The FIDIC Contracts Guide includes a note that a two-stage tender procedure may be adopted for some tenders which include Contractor design. The first stage would comprise technical proposals, on which the Employer may comment before he invites one or more of them to submit final priced offers. This is particular appropriate for EPC/Turnkey projects and will need to allow time for investigations and discussion on a more detailed design proposal. Some Employers make a payment to tenderers for the additional work in preparing a second stage tender. It may be necessary to discuss and modify the Particular Conditions in order to satisfy the tenderer.

The Silver Book is becoming popular with Employers, who see the advantages of a firm price and time. However the Tender price will be higher than for a Yellow Book Contract, because the Contractor is taking more of the risks and has to allow for this in his Tender. In order to maintain these benefits it is essential that the Employer does not interfere with the Contractor's work. FIDIC have published a warning that the EPC/Turnkey Contract is not advised when there is high unforeseen risk.

The Short Form of Contract (The Green Book)

According to the FIDIC Foreword to the Short Form of Contract, it is suitable not only for work of relatively small capital value, but also for 'fairly simple or repetitive work or work of short duration without the need for specialist sub-contracts'. In other words, it is suitable for projects which will not have too many problems. However, it should only be used after proper consideration of the consequences of using a shorter Contract. If, or when, problems do arise the Parties must be ready to negotiate an agreed solution, rather than rely on their interpretation of the Conditions of Contract. The role of an Adjudicator will be important.

The Short Form will serve a useful purpose but should be used with some caution. In particular, Employers who are not accustomed to using FIDIC Conditions of Contract must resist the temptation to regard the Short Form as being a simple Contract that will be easy to use. The other FIDIC Contracts, being longer and more complex, include more detailed procedures and give more guidance to Employers who encounter problems. The Short Form is more suitable for use by experienced Employers. Whilst it does not include provision for an Engineer, it will be necessary to designate experienced people as 'Authorised Person' under Sub-Clause 3.1 and 'Employer's Representative' under Sub-Clause 3.2.

The Guidance Notes for the Short Form confirm that the Employer's Representative acts for and in the interests of the Employer, without any dual-role requirement to be impartial. However, the Employer's Representative will be making immediate decisions on any problems or claims and these decisions will be subject to review by the Adjudicator. The Employer's Representative should therefore act fairly and in accordance with the provisions of the applicable law and the Contract.

The Short Form of Contract is, as might be expected, a shorter form of the Conditions of Contract for Construction. The Short Form has only 15 Clauses and 52 Sub-Clauses instead of 20 Clauses and 163 Sub-Clauses. This is not just a matter of some Sub-Clauses being omitted and others retained, but also involves a rearrangement of the essential requirements with some requirements being omitted.

A detailed analysis and comparison with the Conditions of Contract for Construction would be longer than the Short Form of Contract itself and would serve no useful purpose here. The Short Form must be studied and judged on its own and the FIDIC publication includes a very useful section 'Notes for Guidance'. However, the following points of comparison are important.

- There are no Particular Conditions. If changes or additional Clauses are required then Particular Conditions must be added. Particular Conditions are already included in the priority list in the Appendix to the Agreement, with a high priority.
- The Appendix to Tender and Letter of Acceptance are not used and the Contract Agreement is replaced by a more general 'Agreement'. The Agreement refers to the Employer's request for Tender, the Contractor's Tender offer and the Employer's acceptance in a single document. The essential information that is normally in the Appendix to Tender is included in the Appendix, which is issued with the request for Tender and becomes part of the Agreement.
- Sub-Clause 6.1 gives a list of Employer's Liabilities, which would entitle the Contractor to an extension of time under Sub-Clause 7.3 and/or reimbursement of Cost under Sub-Clause 10.4. Whilst

this list appears to repeat the similar claims causes which are scattered throughout The Red Book, the use of the word 'liability' and the absence of detail means that it will be more difficult for claims to be rejected and the Employer could find that he has an increased liability under the Short Form.

- The Dispute Adjudication Board is replaced by a single 'Adjudicator'. The Adjudicator is only appointed after the dispute has arisen. The shorter contract with fewer provisions could make the task of the Adjudicator more difficult. The Parties should consider selecting and appointing a suitable person at the start of the project so that that person is available to visit the Site if required before a claim develops into a dispute.

Employers considering the use of the Short Form should also look at the FIDIC Dredging Contract. This is similar to the Short Form but includes a number of improvements. Some of these improvements could usefully be introduced into the Short Form.

The Contract for Dredging and Reclamation Works (The Blue Book)

The Test Edition of the FIDIC Form of Contract for Dredging and Reclamation Works was published in 2001. The layout and content of this Contract is similar to the FIDIC Short Form of Contract, modified to suit the particular requirements for dredging work. It also incorporates several changes and improvements, presumably with the benefit of experience of use of the Short Form.

The MDB Harmonised Conditions of Contract for Construction (The MDB Edition)

During 2005, FIDIC licensed Multilateral Development Banks (MDB) to use a revised version of the Conditions of Contract for Construction. This is known as the Multilateral Development Banks Harmonised Conditions of Contract for Construction, and is referred to here as the MDB Edition. The MDB Edition can only be used for Contracts that are financed by one of the participating Banks. The MDB Edition includes a number of changes to the 1999 Red Book. Some of these changes incorporate Clauses from previous MDB Contracts and the intention is to standardise and reduce the need for further Particular Conditions.

The participating Banks are listed and the changes are reviewed in Part 4 of this book. Some of these changes relate specifically to actions that involve the Bank. Others include improvements which could usefully be incorporated into the Particular Conditions for other projects. The complete wording must be consulted, but some of the more important changes can be summarised as follows:

(a) General changes of layout and wording
  (i) The Appendix to Tender has become the Contract Data and is Part A of the Particular Conditions.
  (ii) The DAB has become the Dispute Board (DB).
  (iii) The Bank and Borrower are defined and named in the Contract Data.
(b) Changes to Sub-Clauses related to the Bank
  (i) The Contractor must permit the Bank or its appointee to inspect or audit the Contractor's accounts (Sub-Clause 1.15).
  (ii) If the Bank suspends disbursements under its loan, the Employer must notify the Contractor (Sub-Clause 2.4).
  (iii) All equipment, material and services to be incorporated in or required for the Works shall have their origin in any eligible source country as defined by the Bank (Sub-Clause 4.1).
  (iv) Payment if the loan is suspended (Sub-Clause 14.7).
  (v) Suspension and termination if the loan is suspended (Sub-Clauses 16.1 and 16.2).
(c) Other changes
  (i) Reasonable profit has become 5% (Sub-Clause 1.2).
  (ii) Constraints on the Engineer's authority are listed (Sub-Clause 3.1).
  (iii) The Contractor shall give fair and reasonable opportunity for contractors from the Country to be appointed as Subcontractors (Sub-Clause 4.4).
  (iv) The Contractor is encouraged to employ staff and labour from within the Country (Sub-Clause 6.1).
  (v) Additional Health and Safety, welfare and similar clauses (Sub-Clauses 6.7, 6.12–6.22).
  (vi) Includes a Retention Money guarantee (Sub-Clause 14.9).
  (vii) A Clause against Corrupt or fraudulent practices (Sub-Clause 15.6).
  (viii) Procedures for the appointment of the Dispute Board have been improved (Sub-Clause 20.2).

Chapter 3

The 1999 FIDIC Red and Yellow Books

3.1 Contents of the FIDIC Publication

The 1999 FIDIC Conditions of Contract for Construction (The Red Book or RB) and the 1999 Conditions of Contract for Plant and Design-Build (The Yellow Book or YB) have the same layout and most of the Clauses are identical, or with small changes. Clauses 5 and 12 are completely different and other Clauses have changes due to the different requirements for Employer design and Contractor design.

The FIDIC publications are arranged in three sections – General Conditions, Guidance and Forms – and include far more than just the Conditions of Contract. All these sections are important for the Employer or Consultant who is preparing Contract documents. However, only the General Conditions and the other documents that are included in the Contract documents are important for the Contractor and the staff on the Site who will administer the Contract.

The FIDIC publications include:

(a) Foreword
(b) General Conditions
    (i) Contents
    (ii) The General Conditions, as Clauses 1 to 20
    (iii) Appendix: General Conditions of Dispute Adjudication Agreement
    (iv) Annex: Procedural Rules
    (v) Index of Sub-Clauses
(c) Guidance for the preparation of Particular Conditions
    (i) Contents
    (ii) Introduction
    (iii) Notes on the preparation of Tender documents
    (iv) Comments and examples of alternative and additional Sub-Clauses
    (v) Annexes: Forms of Securities

  Annex A: Example Form of Parent Company Guarantee
  Annex B: Example Form of Tender Security
  Annex C: Example Form of Performance Security – Demand
    Guarantee
  Annex D: Example Form of Performance Security – Surety
    Bond
  Annex E: Example Form of Advance Payment Guarantee
  Annex F: Example Form of Retention Money Guarantee
  Annex G: Example Form of Payment Guarantee by Employer

(d) Forms for
  (i) Letter of Tender
  (ii) Appendix to Tender
  (iii) Contract Agreement
  (iv) Dispute Adjudication Agreement (for one-person DAB)
  (v) Dispute Adjudication Agreement (for each member of a
  three-person DAB).

These documents are set out in Appendix A4 (Part 3 of this book) and their content is reviewed in Part 2 but, in general, they cover the following subjects.

(a) The *Foreword* includes a brief review of the different 1999 Contracts with introductory comments on the use of the FIDIC Conditions of Contract. This is followed by three charts giving the typical sequence of events during the Contract, for payment and for disputes. The charts are useful, but have been over-simplified. Expanded and additional charts are provided in Chapter 5 of this book.

(b) The *General Conditions* comprise Clauses 1 to 20 together with the Appendix and Annex for the Dispute Adjudication Board agreements. These are the General Conditions which should be included unchanged in the Contract.

(c) The *Guidance* includes brief comments on the preparation of Tender documents, together with detailed guidance and proposals for changes and additional Sub-Clauses which may be required for a particular project and will form the Particular Conditions. This is followed by examples of forms for the securities and guarantees which are referred to in the General and Particular Conditions. Copies of any forms which are required for the particular Contract should be included with the Particular Conditions. The Guidance is of interest to the Employer or Consultant who is preparing the Contract documents, rather than to the people who will be administering the Contract on Site.

(d) The *Forms* include examples of the letters and agreements referred to in the General Conditions. Copies should be included with the

Particular Conditions as appropriate. The Appendix to Tender is particularly important because this document gives figures and information that are essential to complete the Clauses in the Conditions of Contract.

For the efficient administration of a FIDIC Contract the pages which make up the General Conditions, Particular Conditions and Appendix to Tender should be combined and used as a single document.

3.2 Preparation of the Contract documents

The Conditions of Contract do not just give the rights and obligations of the Parties as a legal framework to be used for the resolution of disputes. They also include project management procedures which are essential for the administration of the project, whether or not there are any problems. For example, the procedures for the Engineer to issue additional drawings and for the Contractor to receive payments are laid down in the Conditions of Contract. The proper use of the procedures in the Conditions of Contract can avoid problems becoming disputes and assist the fast and economic resolution of any disputes which do arise.

The Conditions of Contract on their own are not complete. Certain information must be provided in other documents in order to complete the Contract documents. Lists of the Sub-Clauses that refer to information being provided in other parts of the documents which make up the Contract are given in Tables 3.1–3.6. If, for any reason, this information is being provided in a different document then the Sub-Clause should be amended in the particular Conditions. This information must be co-ordinated with other documents in order to ensure that the Contract, as a whole, will serve its intended purpose.

In order to prepare the Contract documents for a project using the FIDIC procedures it is necessary to do the following.

- Incorporate the FIDIC General Conditions unchanged, together with the General Conditions of Dispute Adjudication Agreement and the Annex: Procedural Rules. The General Conditions include numerous references to information given in other documents, referring to:
  - the Appendix to Tender;
  - the Particular Conditions;
  - the Specification (RB) or Employer's Requirements (YB); the Schedules; and
  - 'in the Contract'.

  If this information is not provided then the particular Sub-Clause may have been deleted, possibly unintentionally.

Table 3.1.   Sub-Clauses that refer to the Appendix to Tender

Sub-Clause	
1.1.2.2	Definition of 'Employer'
1.1.2.3	Definition of 'Contractor'
1.1.2.4	Definition of 'Engineer'
1.1.3.3	Definition of 'Time for Completion'
	Time for Completion of Sections
1.1.3.7	Definition of 'Defects Notification Period'
1.1.5.6	Definition of 'Section'
1.3(a)	Systems of electronic transmission
1.3(b)	Addresses for communications
1.4	Governing Law
	Ruling Language
	Language for Communications
2.1	Times for access and possession of Site
4.2	Amount of Performance Security
5.1	Period for notice of errors (YB only)
6.5	Normal working hours
8.7	Delay damages, Works and Sections
13.5(b)	Percentage for Provisional Sums
13.8	Table of Cost adjustment data
14.2	Advance payment, currencies, proportions, repayment provisions
14.3(c)	Retention percentage and limit
14.5	Lists for Plant and Materials payments
14.6	Minimum Interim Payment Certificate
14.9	Percentage value of Sections (YB only)
14.15	Currencies of payment
18.1	Submission of insurance information
18.2(d)	Maximum insurance deductible
18.3	Minimum limit per occurrence for insurance
20.2	Date for appointment of DAB (RB only)
	Number of DAB members
20.3	DAB appointing authority

- Insert essential information in the Appendix to Tender, which is printed near the end of the FIDIC publication. The Employer must insert most of the information required in order to complete the documents for calling Tenders. Other information will be inserted by the Tenderer. Each item in the Appendix to Tender relates to a Sub-Clause in the General Conditions and the requirements in relation to particular Sub-Clauses are considered in Part 2 of this book. A list of the Sub-Clauses that refer to information in the Appendix to Tender is given in Table 3.1.

Table 3.2.   Sub-Clauses that refer to the Particular Conditions

Sub-Clause	
1.1.3.6	Definition of 'Tests after Completion' (RB only)
1.13	Compliance with Laws
3.1	Engineer to obtain Employer's approval
4.1	Procedures for design by Contractor (RB only)
4.2	Form for Performance Security
4.4	Procedures for consent to Subcontractors
4.16	Procedures for delivery of Goods to Site
4.21	Procedures for progress reports
4.22	Security of the Site
8.1	Period for Commencement Date from Letter of Acceptance
12.1	Alternative details of tests after Completion (YB only)
14.1	Evaluation of Contract Price
14.2	Form for advance payment guarantee
14.8	Percentage for financing charges
17.6	Amount for limitation of liability
18.1	Insurance details
18.2	Insurance details
18.3	Insurance procedures
20.3	DAB appointing authority

- Prepare Particular Conditions to suit the Employer's requirements for the particular project. The preparation of the Particular Conditions is considered later in this chapter, with discussion of the relevant Sub-Clauses in Part 2 of this book.
- Many of the Sub-Clauses in the General Conditions rely on other Sub-Clauses, both for their application and to maintain a fair balance between the interests of the Parties. When considering changes and additions to the FIDIC Sub-Clauses it is important to consider the relationship between different Sub-Clauses and to maintain this balance. Any attempt to change this balance by amending Sub-Clauses which appear to favour the Contractor generally causes problems and additional costs in either the Tender or in the resolution of the resulting claims and disputes. A list of the Sub-Clauses that refer to the Particular Conditions is given in Table 3.2.
- Check the Sub-Clauses that refer to information in the Specification (RB) or Employer's Requirements (YB) and ensure that they include the necessary information. A list of these Sub-Clauses is given in Table 3.3. In addition, there are Sub-Clauses which may be amplified or require additional information in the Specification (RB) or Employer's Requirements (YB) and a list of these Sub-Clauses is given in Table 3.4. If a Red Book Contract includes significant

Table 3.3.   Sub-Clauses that refer to the Specification (RB) or Employer's Requirements (YB)

Sub-Clause	
1.13(a)	Permissions obtained by Employer
1.1.6.3	Definition of 'Employer's Equipment'
4.6	Opportunities for work by others
4.18	Values for emissions and discharges
4.19	Details and prices of services available on the Site
4.20	Details of Employer's Equipment and free-issue materials
5.1	Criteria for designers (YB only)
5.2	Technical documents to be included in Contractor's Documents (YB only)
	Language for Contractor's Documents (YB only)
5.3	Contractor's Documents to be submitted for review and/or approval (YB only)
	Review periods (YB only)
5.4	Other standards for compliance (YB only)
5.5	Training to be provided for Employer's Personnel (YB only)
5.6	Numbers and types of copies of as-built drawings (YB only)
5.7	Manuals for operation and maintenance (YB only)
6.1	Arrangements for staff and labour
6.6	Facilities for staff and labour
7.8	Payment of royalties
	(a) natural materials from outside the Site
	(b) disposal of demolition, excavation and surplus materials

Contractor's design then some of the Yellow Book Clauses may have been included in the Particular Conditions.

- Check the Sub-Clauses that refer to the Schedules and ensure that these Schedules are provided. The Schedules are prepared by the Employer, completed by the Tenderer, and included in the Contract. A Yellow Book Contract may include additional Schedules for information which in required to be included in the Tenderer's proposal. A list of these Sub-Clauses is given in Table 3.5.
- Check the Sub-Clauses that refer to information which may be included elsewhere in the Contract and ensure that any necessary information is included in the appropriate document. The General Conditions do not state in which document this information should be included. Some of this information may have been included in supplementary documents which were agreed after the Tender was submitted and are attached to the Letter of Acceptance or Contract Agreement. A list of these Sub-Clauses is given in Table 3.6.

Table 3.4.   Sub-Clauses that may usefully be amplified in the Specification (RB) or Employer's Requirements (YB)

Sub-Clause

1.8	Requirements for Contractor's Documents (RB only)
1.8	Number of copies of Contractor's Documents (YB only)
1.13	Permissions being obtained by the Employer
2.1	Phased possession foundations, etc.
4.1	Contractor's designs (RB only)
4.1	Intended purposes for which the Works are required (YB only)
4.6	Other contractors, etc. on the Site
4.7	Setting out points, etc.
4.14	Third parties
4.18	Environmental constraints
4.19	Services available on the Site
4.20	Employer's equipment and free issue material
5.1	Nominated Subcontractors (RB only)
5.1	Criteria for design personnel (YB only)
5.2	Contractor's documents required and whether for approval (YB only)
5.4	Technical standards and building regulations (YB only)
5.5	Operational training for the Employer's Personnel (YB only)
5.6	As-built drawings and other records (YB only)
5.7	Operation and maintenance manuals (YB only)
6.6	Facilities for personnel
7.2	Samples
7.4	Testing during manufacture and/or construction
9.1	Tests on Completion
9.4	Damages for failure to pass Tests on Completion (YB only)
12.1	Tests after Completion (YB only)
12.4	Damages for failure to pass Tests after Completion (YB only)
13.5	Provisional Sums

Table 3.5.   Sub-Clauses that refer to Schedules

Sub-Clause

1.1.1.1	Contract includes schedules
1.1.1.6	Defines Schedules (YB only)
1.1.1.7	Defines Schedules, which may include Bill of Quantities (RB only)
1.1.1.10	Daywork schedule (RB only)
1.1.1.10	Schedule of Guarantees and Schedule of Payments (YB only)
1.5	Schedules are the lowest priority (RB only)
1.5	Schedules have priority above Contractor's Proposals
13.6	Daywork Schedules
14.1	Refers to quantities and price data in Schedules (YB only)
14.4	Schedule of Payments

Table 3.6. Sub-Clauses that refer to the Contract

Sub-Clause	
1.1.1.1	List of Contract documents
1.1.2.3	Contractor as named in Letter of Tender
1.1.2.5	Contractor's Representative as named in Contract
1.1.2.8	Subcontractors named in Contract
1.1.2.9	DAB members named in Contract
1.1.3.4	Tests on Completion specified in Contract
1.1.3.6	Tests after Completion specified in Contract
1.1.4.1	Accepted Contract Amount in Letter of Acceptance
1.1.4.10	Provisional Sum specified in Contract
1.1.6.7	Site as specified in the Contract
1.8	Number of copies of Contractor's Documents
4.1	Contractor's obligations to the extent in the Contract (RB only)
	Plant and Contractor's Documents specified in Contract
	Contractor's design as specified in Contract (RB only)
4.3	Contractor's Representative may be named in Contract
4.7	Setting out points specified in Contract
4.9	Quality assurance system stated in Contract
4.11	Obligations covered by Accepted Contract Amount
4.15	Access route arrangements unless otherwise stated in Contract
5.1(a)	Nominated Subcontractors stated in Contract (RB only)
6.5	Working hours stated otherwise in Contract
7.1(a)	Manner of execution specified in Contract
7.1(c)	Unless otherwise specified in Contract
7.2	Samples specified in Contract
7.4	Tests specified in Contract
7.6	Plant, Materials or other work not in accordance with Contract
8.2	Work for completion stated in Contract
8.3(c)	Inspections and Tests specified in Contract
9.4	Other obligations under the Contract
12.1	Measurement records by Engineer unless otherwise in Contract (RB only)
12.1	Requirements for Tests after Completion (YB only)
12.2	Method of measurement except as otherwise stated in Contract (RB only)
12.3	Engineer's valuation except as otherwise stated in Contract (RB only)
13.4	Currencies provided for in Contract
13.6	Daywork Schedule included in Contract
14.4	Schedule of payments in Contract
14.7	Payment country specified in Contract
17.3(f)	Part of Permanent Works occupied by Employer specified in Contract
18.1	Insurance requirements
20.2	List of potential DAB members in Contract

- Consider the need for a Contract Agreement. The FIDIC standard agreement form may need to be modified to suit the Employer's standard agreement, but the information contained in the FIDIC form must be included.
- Decide whether a one-person or three-person Dispute Adjudication Board is required and decide whether to nominate potential members in the Tender documents. Any amendments to the General Conditions of Dispute Adjudication Agreement or the Annex: Procedural Rules must be included in the Particular Conditions.
- Consider the use of FIDIC Annexes A to G for the Forms of Securities and Guarantees which are referred to in the General Conditions and the Appendix to Tender. The FIDIC standard forms may need to be modified to suit the Employer's standard forms and any applicable law.
- Consider the inclusion of a standard Letter of Tender for use by Tenderers when submitting their Tender. If the FIDIC standard form is not used then the Instructions to Tenderers should include the requirement that the appropriate information must be confirmed by the Tenderer.
- Check that all relevant data in the Employer's possession on sub-surface and hydrological conditions has been made available to the Tenderers for their information, as Sub-Clause 4.10, including any additional information which came into the Employer's possession after the Base Date.
- Review the FIDIC Tender procedures as given in The FIDIC Contracts Guide. Adopt or modify as appropriate.

3.3 The layout of the General Conditions

The General Conditions include 20 main Clauses with approximately 160 Sub-Clauses. The arrangement of information in Sub-Clauses is more logical than in previous FIDIC Conditions, but is far from perfect. When the user requires information to help resolve a particular problem it may be necessary to consult several different Sub-Clauses. The Index, which is located after the General Conditions, is a considerable help in locating references to a particular subject but detailed study and experience in the use of the General Conditions will often reveal important information in unexpected places.

The main Clauses can be considered in groups of Clauses dealing with related subjects.

- *Clause 1: General Provisions* covers subjects that apply to the Contract in general, such as definitions, the applicable language and law, the priority of the different documents which make up the Contract and the use of the different documents.

- *Clauses 2 to 4: The Employer; The Engineer; The Contractor* deal with the duties and obligations of the different organisations that play a part in the execution of the Works. It is significant that the Contractor's Clause contains more Sub-Clauses than all the others added together. It is the Contractor who is responsible for executing the Works and so is the most active of the people who are involved with the project. Many other Sub-Clauses throughout the General Conditions refer to the Contractor's obligations.
- *Clause 5 (RB): Nominated Subcontractors* deals with the requirements for Subcontractors who have been nominated either in the Contract or as a variation under Clause 13. In the Yellow Book nominated Subcontractors can only be instructed as a Variation and this is covered at Sub-Clause 4.5.
- *Clause 5 (YB): Design* gives the requirements concerning the Contractor's design obligations.
- *Clauses 6 and 7: Staff and Labour; Plant, Materials and Workmanship* deal with the requirements for the items of men and materials which the Contractor brings to the Site and uses to execute the project.
- *Clauses 8, 9, 10 and 11: Commencement, Delays and Suspension; Tests on Completion; Employer's Taking Over; Defects Liability* follow the sequence of events during the construction of the project.
- *Clause 12 (RB): Measurement and Evaluation* gives the procedures when the work is to be paid by measurement of actual quantities.
- *Clause 12 (YB): Tests after Completion* gives the procedures for any performance tests that are required after the Works have been handed over and occupied by the Employer.
- *Clauses 13 and 14: Variations and Adjustments; Contract Price and Payment* give the procedures for the Employer to pay the Contractor for his work.
- *Clauses 15 and 16: Termination by Employer; Suspension and Termination by Contractor* refer to events which may occur at any time during the construction sequence and may bring the Contract to a close.
- *Clause 17: Risk and Responsibility* relates to the project as a whole and includes Sub-Clauses which are only used rarely, together with matters which are critical to the Parties' responsibilities and overlap with the requirements of other important Sub-Clauses.
- *Clause 18: Insurance* includes important procedures which must be implemented at or before the commencement of the Works in addition to the procedures to be used when a problem occurs which will give rise to an insurance claim.
- *Clause 19: Force Majeure* is a general Clause which will only be used when the particular problem occurs. The final Sub-Clause refers to

release from performance in a wider context than just due to Force Majeure.

- *Clause 20: Claims, Disputes and Arbitration* will probably be the most frequently used Clause in the whole Conditions of Contract. It includes procedures such as the submission and response to Contractor's claims, which must be used when a problem has arisen, as well as the procedures for the resolution of claims and disputes. Clause 20 also includes the procedures for the appointment of the Dispute Adjudication Board.

3.4 The sequence of construction operations

The Sub-Clauses that refer to events during the construction period are generally arranged in the order in which the events occur:

- Commencement
- Progress
- Completion
- Defects Period
- Disputes.

Other Clauses have then been included to cover particular subjects, such as the duties of the Engineer, the submission of claims and the provisions for payment. These matters can arise at any time during the construction period and are arranged in a reasonably logical order.

Due to the complexity of the General Conditions it is impossible to follow a logical sequence for all the Sub-Clauses. Many Sub-Clauses will be found in unexpected places and some essential information is difficult to locate. Additional cross-references have been included in the review of Sub-Clauses in Part 2 of this book, in order to assist the user to locate the different Sub-Clauses which are relevant to a particular situation.

A series of flow charts (Figs. 1 to 14) is included in Chapter 5 in order to show the sequence of events and the relevant Sub-Clauses for certain important operations. These flow charts must be read together with the relevant Sub-Clauses.

3.5 Preparation of the Particular Conditions

The Conditions of Contract give the rights and obligations of the Parties, including project management obligations. The technical requirements are given in the other documents which make up the Contract. The FIDIC General Conditions are the standard document which must be included, unchanged, in every Contract. Any changes or additional obligations required by the Employer can be included in the Particular Conditions. Any changes must be kept to a minimum, must not disturb the balance between the Employer and the Contractor, and must be carefully checked to ensure that there is no conflict with any other Clause. Changes which are just a matter of personal preference should be avoided.

FIDIC, in the Guidance for the Preparation of Particular Conditions, give suggested wording for clauses to meet some of the most common requirements. This Guidance is extremely valuable and should be studied carefully when preparing Particular Conditions. If the FIDIC Clauses are used then there should not be a problem of conflicting Clauses, but there may be a need for additional cross-references and additional links in flow charts. FIDIC Contracts published since the 1999 Contracts should also be reviewed because they include some improvements which could be included in particular Conditions.

The major matters which make further Clauses in the Particular Conditions essential are:

- conflict with the applicable law and Laws which must be co-ordinated with the Contract;
- the requirements of the financing authority;
- regulations and the Employer's procedures which must be co-ordinated with the Contract;
- the need to import Clauses from another FIDIC Contract.

Examples of these requirements are given in the review of Sub-Clauses in Part 2 of this book. Examples of financing authority requirements are given in the review of the MDB Edition in Part 4 of this book.

The need to co-ordinate the Contract with applicable law is particularly important in countries with a Civil Law jurisdiction. For example the countries in Central Europe, which are making extensive use of the FIDIC Contracts, generally have detailed laws that govern all construction in that country. The full list of requirements varies from country to country, but some typical examples are:

- the need for the design to be approved before construction can start on Site, which causes additional problems with the use of Design-Build Contracts;
- the power to give the Contractor possession of the Site may lie with a regional authority, rather than with the Employer;
- the need for the Contractor to keep a 'Site Diary' – this is a legal document in which any authorised person or authority can make an entry;
- certain authorities may have the power to issue instructions to the Contractor; this, of course, is in conflict with the FIDIC procedure

under which only the Engineer can issue instructions to the Contractor;

- legal restrictions on the power of any non-Government employee to authorise instructions and payments to the Contractor for a Government-financed contract, which may also affect Variations and the measurement of quantities.

If this study and co-ordination of the standard Contract with the Laws of the Country is carried out by a national authority or organisation then the same provisions could be used for all Contracts in that country.

Chapter 4

Claims and dispute procedures

4.1 Introduction

The procedures for the resolution of claims are arguably the most important part of any Conditions of Contract. Certainly the claims provisions are the most frequently used Clauses in any Contract. The FIDIC Conditions include provisions for the submission, consideration and resolution of claims and disputes in a number of different Clauses. Successive revisions to the traditional Red Book and the publication of the Orange Book, for Design-Build and Turnkey Contracts, introduced additional provisions and more complicated procedures. The 1999 Conditions of Contract have continued this process, introduced further provisions and even more complicated procedures. Whilst Clause 20 is headed 'Claims, Disputes and Arbitration', there is also a large number of other Clauses that include procedures which must be followed by the Employer, the Engineer and the Contractor, for the submission and response to claims.

The claims procedures in individual Clauses are reviewed in Part 2 of this book. This chapter gives a general review of the procedures for the submission, response and resolution of claims, draws attention to the need for co-ordination between different Clauses, and lists some of the Clauses which include similar procedures. These procedures may have been modified in the Particular Conditions and the actual Contract should be checked to ascertain the detailed procedures for the particular project.

Unexpected situations are an inevitable feature of every construction project. Delays and additional costs may result, leading to claims from either Party to the Contract. Claims may arise under any of the Contracts for a particular project, and may be Employer–Contractor, Contractor–Subcontractor or Employer–Consultant, whether the Contract is for construction based on a Consultant design, Design and Build or a Turnkey project. The procedures under all the 1999 FIDIC Contracts are similar, but may differ in detail from the procedures described in this chapter.

If the Particular Conditions include provision for management meetings, as discussed under Clause 3 in Part 2 of this book, then meetings may be called to discuss the situation and how to avoid further problems. Such meetings would be extremely valuable to resolve technical and contractual problems and prevent minor differences from developing into major disputes.

The 1999 FIDIC Conditions of Contract include procedures which must be followed for the Employer to claim against the Contractor as well as for the Contractor to claim against the Employer. This is a new procedure for FIDIC, which will help with the efficient administration of the project but will need to be studied carefully by both the Employer and the Engineer.

4.2 Claims and the Conditions of Contract

The Conditions of Contract give the rights and obligations of the Parties to the Contract, i.e. the Employer and the Contractor. Other people, such as the Engineer, a Consultant or a Subcontractor may be involved in the preparation, analysis or administration of the claim but cannot be the principal who makes or receives the claim. While it may be legally possible for an outside person to claim that either the Employer or the Contractor has caused them damage by negligence or failing to comply with some legal obligation, any such claim would be outside the scope of this book. However, attention is drawn to Sub-Clause 17.1 in which the Parties indemnify each other with respect to claims from third parties.

All claims that are made because of problems which arose under or in connection with a particular Contract must follow the procedures laid down in that Contract. The claim may be made:

- in accordance with a Clause which states that the Contractor may be entitled to additional time or money in certain circumstances, or the Employer may be entitled to claim money from the Contractor;
- because one Party alleges that the other Party has failed to fulfil an obligation which is required by a Clause in the Contract;
- because one Party alleges that it is entitled to payment for some other reason, possibly because of some legal entitlement, which applies regardless of whether it is mentioned in the Contract.

4.3 Claims by the Contractor

Most claims are made by the Contractor and may be claims for an extension of time for completion of the Works, or for reimbursement of money that has been spent or will be spent. If the claim is for money that is expected to be spent then, even if liability is agreed, money will not be certified by the Engineer until it has actually been spent by the Contractor. Claims for additional time frequently result in a claim for additional payment which, under the FIDIC Conditions, must be submitted as a separate claim.

In general, the sequences of procedures for the submission of claims, in accordance with Clause 20 and other Clauses, can be summarised as follows.

(a) In certain circumstances the Contractor must give notice that he is aware of a situation which may arise and cause problems. The Engineer can then take action to avoid or resolve the problems.

(b) The Contractor gives notice that he considers himself to be entitled to additional time for completion or additional payment.

(c) The Contractor gives notice when he has actually suffered delay or additional cost.

(d) The Contractor keeps contemporary records to support his claim and the details are inspected by the Engineer. Factual records are checked at the time, to establish and agree the facts, regardless of any query or objections on liability.

(e) The Contractor submits his fully detailed claim with supporting particulars.

(f) The Engineer responds and approves or disapproves the claim. The Engineer must give his response on the principle, regardless of whether he has asked for further information.

(g) The Engineer will then certify for interim payment any amount which has been substantiated.

(h) The Engineer proceeds in accordance with Sub-Clause 3.5, to determine any extension of time or additional payment.

(i) If the Contractor does not agree with the Engineer and negotiation fails to achieve agreement, then the claim becomes a dispute and the procedures of Sub-Clauses 20.4 to 20.6 are followed, basically: (i) a decision by the Dispute Adjudication Board, followed by (ii) an attempt at amicable settlement, followed by (iii) arbitration.

In the above list the Engineer's determination under Sub-Clause 3.5 has been included as point (h). This follows the order of events in Sub-Clause 20.1. However, there are a number of situations when the Engineer may wish to make an earlier determination, or the Contractor may ask for an earlier determination. The FIDIC Conditions do not specifically allow the Contractor to request a determination, but action under Sub-Clause 3.5 may avoid the need to refer a dispute to the DAB under Sub-Clause 20.4.

Situations which may be suitable for an immediate determination under Sub-Clause 3.5 include:

- any claim which the Resident Engineer has stated will be rejected;

- any claim which has been rejected by the Engineer in principle as point (f);
- the Engineer's review of Contractor's Document under Clause 5 (YB);
- adverse comments by the Engineer on the Contractor's programme as Sub-Clause 8.3;
- a requirement to increase production under Sub-Clause 8.6;
- a rejection under the second paragraph of Sub-Clause 20.1;
- any other action by the Engineer which is disputed by the Contractor.

In practice these procedures may be simplified and meetings will be held to try to resolve any problems. However, it is important that all the appropriate notices are issued referring to all the relevant clauses. The people who are working on the Site will be subject to pressure not to delay the Works and to co-operate in resolving any claims in a non-adversarial manner. However, if a claim does end in arbitration then any failure to submit a notice or comply with a procedure will be used against the Party who failed to follow the correct procedure.

All claims for additional time or money must follow the procedures of Sub-Clause 20.1, which requires a notice to the Engineer 'as soon as practicable, and not later than 28 days after the Contractor became aware, or should have become aware, of the event or circumstance'. Failure to comply with this requirement may result in the Contractor losing his entitlement to the claim, under the second paragraph of Sub-Clause 20.1. Failure to comply with the requirements of other Sub-Clauses will result in the evaluation of the claim being reduced if the investigation of the claim was prevented or prejudiced by this failure, under the final paragraph of Sub-Clause 20.1.

Sub-Clause 20.1, which is reviewed in detail in Part 2 of this book, requires the Contractor to submit his claim in detail and to submit contemporary records. This information is essential for the Engineer, and any subsequent DAB or arbitrator, to make a fair assessment of the claim. Many justifiable claims have been lost, or costs have escalated to a totally unreasonable extent, due to a failure by the Contractor to keep proper records at the time the claim occurred. Similarly, unjustified claims have been successful because the Engineer failed to keep proper records on behalf of the Employer.

The definition of a dispute at Sub-Clause 20.4 is wider than the requirement for a notice under Sub-Clause 20.1. For example, if the Contractor objects to an instruction by the Engineer then the Contractor would have to obey the instruction, under Sub-Clause 3.3, but there may be a dispute which could be referred direct to the DAB under Sub-Clause 20.4. Disputes concerning additional time or money must follow the procedures of Sub-Clause 20.1. This procedure could take several months before the problem could be referred to the DAB, unless both sides agree to ask the DAB for an opinion, under the seventh paragraph of Sub-Clause 20.2.

Under the MDB Edition revision to item 2 of the Annex: Procedural Rules, the DAB can, at a site visit, endeavour to prevent a problem or claim developing into a dispute. This is an extremely useful procedure which could benefit the project and save considerable costs.

The requirements for the submission of claims are summarised in Figs. 12, 13 and 14 (Chapter 5). These requirements could result in parallel procedures and more than one referral to the Engineer under Sub-Clause 3.5 from the same situation. The referral under Sub-Clause 3.5 is particularly important because:

- the Engineer does not just determine liability or any payments but consults both Parties and acts like a mediator to try to reach agreement between them;
- this task should be carried out by the Engineer himself and cannot be delegated without the agreement of both Parties.

In some circumstances it may be desirable for the Engineer to proceed under Sub-Clause 3.5 as quickly as possible after the situation has arisen, in order to avoid further argument, or at least to establish the clear boundaries of any difference of opinion. From a practical point of view the extent to which the Engineer will want to use this procedure may depend on whether his office is located near the Site or in some country on the other side of the world.

Notices are issued, as Sub-Clause 1.3, to the Engineer or to a designated assistant, who is preferably resident on the Site. Notices may be required under several different Sub-Clauses for the same claim. The Sub-Clause 20.1 notice is a requirement for all claims, both for extension of time and for additional payment. Claims for an extension of time must also comply with the requirements of Sub-Clause 8.4.

Sub-Clause 8.3 includes a general requirement for the Contractor to give notice of any 'specific probable events or circumstances which may adversely affect the work, increase the Contract Price or delay the execution of the Works'.

Other Sub-Clauses that include specific requirements for claims are reviewed in Part 2 of this book and include the following.

- Sub-Clauses that require the Contractor to give notice of an event which may cause delay or additional cost:
  1.9 (RB)   Delayed Drawings or Instructions
  1.9 (YB)   Errors in the Employer's Requirements
  4.12   Unforeseeable Physical Conditions

4.24	Fossils
5.4 (YB)	Change in technical standard
16.1	Contractor's Entitlement to Suspend Work 17.4
	Consequences of Employer's Risks
19.4	Consequences of Force Majeure

- Sub-Clauses that entitle the Contractor to an extension of time and/ or additional payment:

1.9 (RB)	Delayed Drawings or Instructions
1.9 (YB)	Errors in the Employer's Requirements
2.1	Right of Access to the Site
4.7	Setting Out
4.12	Unforeseeable Physical Conditions
4.24	Fossils
7.4	Testing
10.2	Taking-Over of Parts of the Works
10.3	Interference with Tests on Completion
11.8	Contractor to Search
12.2 (YB)	Delayed Tests after Completion
12.4 (YB)	Delay in giving access to investigate failure of Tests after Completion
13.7	Adjustments for Changes in Legislation
16.1	Contractor's Entitlement to Suspend Work
17.4	Consequences of Employer's Risks
19.4	Consequences of Force Majeure

- Sub-Clauses that involve valuation or similar requirements:

12.3 (RB)	Evaluation
12.4 (RB)	Omissions
15.3	Valuation at Date of Termination
16.4	Payment on Termination
18.1	General Requirements for Insurances

- Sub-Clauses that provide for the Contractor to claim profit as well as cost:

1.9 (RB)	Delayed Drawings or Instructions
1.9 (YB)	Errors in the Employer's Requirements
2.1	Right of Access to the Site
4.7	Setting Out
7.4	Testing
10.2	Taking-Over of Parts of the Works
10.3	Interference with Tests on Completion
11.8	Contractor to Search
12.2 (YB)	Delayed tests after Completion
12.4 (YB)	Delay in giving access to investigate failure of tests after Completion
16.1	Contractor's Entitlement to Suspend Work

16.4	Payment on Termination
17.4	Consequences of Employer's Risks.

When submitting a claim the Contractor should include reference to all the Sub-Clauses that may be relevant. Some claims situations are covered by more than one Sub-Clause and the Contractor's entitlement may vary dependent on which Sub-Clause is used as the justification for the claim. Some Engineers may ask that a claim notice includes reference to specific Sub-Clauses. However, this is frequently not possible and is not essential. Claims are submitted 'under any Clause of these Conditions or otherwise in connection with the Contract', as stated at Sub-Clause 20.1. Claims may also be made under the governing law, which is referred to at Sub-Clause 1.4 and stated in the Appendix to Tender.

4.4 Claims by the Employer

Previous FIDIC Contracts did not include procedures for claims by the Employer. In practice, the Employer probably deducted any money he thought he was entitled to claim and the Contractor had to submit a claim to recover the deduction. This situation inevitably caused problems and disputes and procedures for claims by the Employer are now given at Sub-Clause 2.5.

Either the Employer or the Engineer must give notice to the Contractor of any claim as soon as practicable after he became aware of the event or circumstance. These procedures are much less onerous than the procedures for Contractor's claims. The Engineer then makes a determination under Sub-Clause 3.5. Either Party can then refer the matter to the DAB if they are not satisfied with the Engineer's determination.

Sub-Clause 2.5 is clear that if the Employer 'considers himself to be entitled to any payment under any Clause of these Conditions or otherwise in connection with the Contract, and/or to any extension of the Defects Notification Period' then notice must be given and the Sub-Clause 2.5 procedure followed. Sub-Clause 2.5 lists specific deductions for which notice is not required. There are a number of Sub-Clauses that refer to Sub-Clause 2.5, but other Sub-Clauses refer to claims or deduction due to the Employer and do not refer to Sub-Clause 2.5. Clearly, the Employer should follow these procedures before making a deduction under any Sub-Clause.

Sub-Clauses that refer to claims by the Employer are as follows.

- Sub-Clauses that require notice under Sub-Clause 2.5:
  - 7.5 Rejection
  - 7.6 Remedial Work
  - 8.6 Rate of Progress

> 11.3   Extension of Defects Notification Period
> 15.4   Payment after Termination
- Sub-Clauses under which notice is not required:
  > 4.19   Electricity, Water and Gas
  > 4.20   Employer's Equipment and Free-Issue Material
  > Other services requested by the Contractor
- Sub-Clauses which allow for claims or deductions by the Employer include:
  > 4.2   Performance Security
  > 5.4   Evidence of Payments to nominated Subcontractors
  > 9.2   Delayed Tests
  > 10.2   Taking Over of Parts of the Works
  > 11.4   Failure to Remedy Defects
  > 11.6   Further Tests
  > 11.11 Clearance of Site
  > 18.1   General Requirements for Insurances
  > 18.2   Insurance for Works and Contractor's Equipment.

4.5 The Dispute Adjudication Board (DAB)

If a dispute arises between the Employer and the Contractor then it is referred to the DAB, under Clause 20.4. The wording of Sub-Clause 20.4 is not restricted to disputes as a result of a claim being rejected, but includes disputes of any kind whatsoever, in connection with or arising out of the Contract or the execution of the Works.

The World Bank has, for several years, required major contracts to include procedures for a Dispute Review Board (DRB), which is similar to the DAB. The difference is that the DAB gives a decision which must be implemented, whereas the DRB just gives a recommendation.

Detailed provisions and procedures for the DAB are included at Sub-Clauses 20.2 to 20.4, the Appendix 'General Conditions of Dispute Adjudication Agreement' and the Annex: Procedural Rules. These provisions are reviewed in Parts 2 and 3 of this book.

The DAB comprises either one or three people. The one-person Board is chosen by agreement at the start of the project. For the three-person Board each side proposes one person for the other side's agreement and the Chairman is chosen by agreement. Failing agreement, the selection is made by an independent organisation, such as FIDIC or The Institution of Civil Engineers, named in the Appendix to Tender.

The DAB procedure described in this section is the procedure from the Conditions of Contract for Construction. This is the preferred procedure, although the Conditions of Contract for Plant and Design-Build include a procedure under which the DAB is only appointed after the dispute has arisen and is only appointed for that dispute. This procedure is described in Chapter 30 of this book.

The detailed procedures for the selection of the DAB members are mentioned in a number of different documents. The FIDIC Guidance for the Preparation of Particular Conditions states the important principle which should govern the process as 'it is essential that candidates for this position are not imposed by either Party on the other Party'. Sub-Clause 20.2 and the Appendix to Tender state that the Parties shall jointly appoint the DAB by the date 28 days after the Commencement Date.

The fourth paragraph of Sub-Clause 20.4 and the FIDIC standard form for the Letter of Tender to be submitted by the Contractor include reference to a list of members for the DAB being included in the Contract. The list appears to have been prepared by the Employer and the Contractor can either accept, reject or add to the suggested list in his Tender. For the Employer to suggest names in the Tender documents, to be accepted or rejected by the Contractor before his Tender has even been considered will inevitably imply, rightly or wrongly, that these people are being imposed on the Contractor by the Employer. To ensure that the procedure is seen to be fair, and hence to establish confidence in the DAB, it is preferable that names are not accepted or rejected until the Tender has been accepted. The Parties can then exchange names and details of candidates and negotiate on an equal basis.

From a practical point of view, to insert the names of candidates in the documents at too early a stage can cause problems. The work of a DAB member requires a commitment to be available to spend time for the project as and when required. Most potential DAB members also have other commitments and will only be able to accept a limited number of DAB appointments at any one time. To be asked to allow one's name to be put forward involves some commitment and so the time between the name being put forward and the appointment being confirmed should be kept to a minimum.

The members of the DAB sign an Agreement and must be independent of both Parties. They are appointed at the start of the project and visit the Site every three or four months. The DAB will have been sent copies of correspondence, notices and minutes of meetings and so will be aware of progress and familiar with problems which may have arisen. During visits the DAB will inspect the work in progress and meet the Parties. Any potential problems may be raised jointly by the Parties and the DAB asked to express an opinion. These visits have been found to assist with the resolution of claims and other problems before they escalate into serious disputes.

Any dispute can be referred to the DAB for its decision and the DAB proceeds as Sub-Clause 20.4. The DAB decision must be implemented but if either Party is not satisfied it can give a notice of dissatisfaction within 28 days. This notice prevents the decision becoming final and binding and enables the dispute to be referred to arbitration.

Both FIDIC and The Institution of Civil Engineers provide lists of potential members for Dispute Boards.

4.6 Amicable settlement

Sub-Clause 20.5 provides for a 56-day period after the issue of the notice of dissatisfaction before arbitration can be commenced. This is to allow time for the Parties to attempt to settle the dispute amicably.

The Contract does not stipulate any particular procedure for the attempt at amicable settlement. It may be a further attempt by the Engineer, or a direct negotiation between senior managers of the Contractor and the Employer. Taking the dispute away from the people who are directly involved and who have established fixed positions may help to achieve a settlement that is acceptable to both sides.

Alternatively, an independent Mediator or Conciliator may be appointed to try to help the Parties reach an agreed settlement. FIDIC has published a report on Mediation, which gives a procedure for an independent person to help with the negotiation using a form of shuttle diplomacy. The Institution of Civil Engineers, several Arbitration Centres and the United Nations Commission for International Trade Law (UNCITRAL) have published procedures for Conciliation. These procedures are similar to Mediation, but the Conciliator or Tribunal may also give a recommendation, which is often used as a basis for further negotiation.

While the FIDIC Conditions do not require any particular procedure during the amicable settlement period, the Particular Conditions could require that conciliation, or some other procedure, should be tried.

4.7 Arbitration

Sub-Clause 20.6 gives the provisions for a dispute to be settled by arbitration. The FIDIC Contract refers to the Arbitration Rules of the International Chamber of Commerce in Paris, but the rules of a different arbitral organisation may have been included in the Particular Conditions. Any arbitration will be subject to the applicable arbitration law as well as the Arbitration Rules and the governing law as stated in the Contract.

Arbitration is a very thorough procedure which is outside the scope of this book. It has a legal basis and should achieve the correct legal decision on a dispute. However, legal procedures are never straightforward and several years of legal arguments may only produce the solution which was apparent to any reasonable person at the time the dispute started. During negotiation, both sides should remember that the legal and managerial costs of arbitration are considerable, are never fully recovered even by the winner, and so could logically be added to or subtracted from any offer to settle.

4.8 The Courts

A Contract is, by definition, a legally binding agreement and the governing law is stated in the Contract. Hence, any disagreement or dispute may eventually be referred to the Courts of the country of the governing law.

If the provision for arbitration has been deleted in the Particular Conditions then any dispute which is not settled by the Engineer or the DAB must be referred to the Courts. However, most international contractors prefer international arbitration because it is seen to be completely independent of the country of the project. Furthermore, arbitration is conducted by technical people or legal professionals with experience of construction law, and is generally conducted in the language of the project. The Courts may require that all the project paperwork is translated into the language of the country. Any dispute that may arise concerning the conduct or result of an arbitration may also be referred to the Courts.

Chapter 5

Flow charts

During the administration of a project, any major activity or procedure will involve a sequence of events that are covered by different Clauses in the Contract. FIDIC have attempted to arrange the Sub-Clauses in a logical order so as to assist the user to identify the relevant sequence of Sub-Clauses. However, owing to the complexity of the situations that arise and the need to refer to certain Sub-Clauses in a variety of different situations, it has not been possible to achieve a sequence to suit all circumstances. The following flow charts (Figs. 1–14) show the sequence of events and the relevant Sub-Clauses for certain important operations. These flow charts must be read together with the relevant Sub-Clauses.

The flow charts given in Figs. 3 and 4, and the reference to Clause 12 in Fig. 7 only apply to the Yellow Book. However, if the relevant Sub-Clauses have been included in the Particular Conditions for a Red Book Contract then the flow charts will apply.

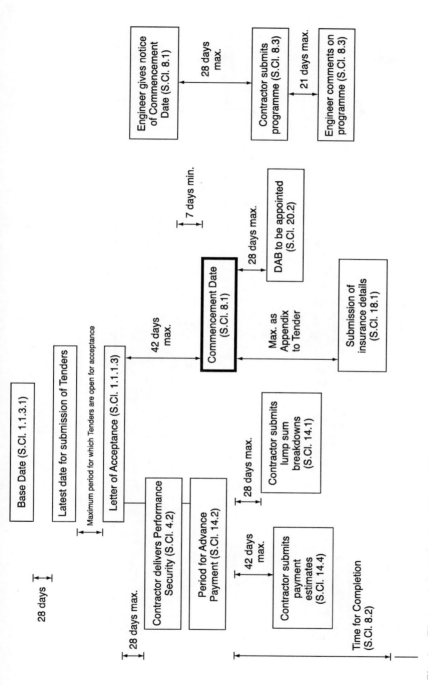

Fig. 1. Time periods in the Conditions of Contract

Fig. 1. Continued

Fig. 2.   Progress requirements

Fig. 2.   Continued

Fig. 3.   Errors in Employer's Requirements (YB only)

Notes:
1. All boxes refer to SCl. 5.1(YB) unless noted otherwise.
2. 'Document' refers to Contractor's Documents as S.Cl. 1.1.6.1 (YB)

Fig. 4   Design procedures (YB only)

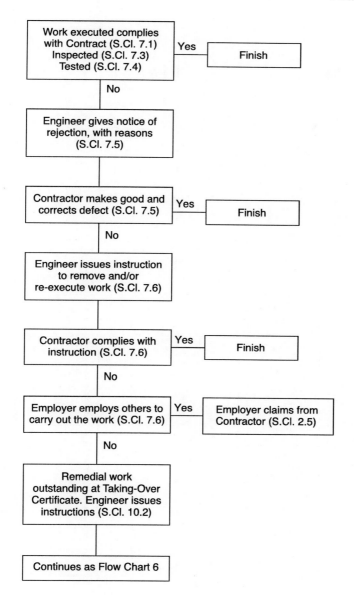

Notes:
1. If the Contractor questions an instruction by an assistant to the Engineer he may refer the matter to the Engineer (S.Cl. 3.2(b)).
2. The Contractor must comply with an instruction from the Engineer (S.Cl. 3.3), but may request payment as a Variation (Clause 13).
3. If a dispute arises it may be referred to the Dispute Adjudication Board (S.Cl. 20.4).

Fig. 5. Workmanship procedures

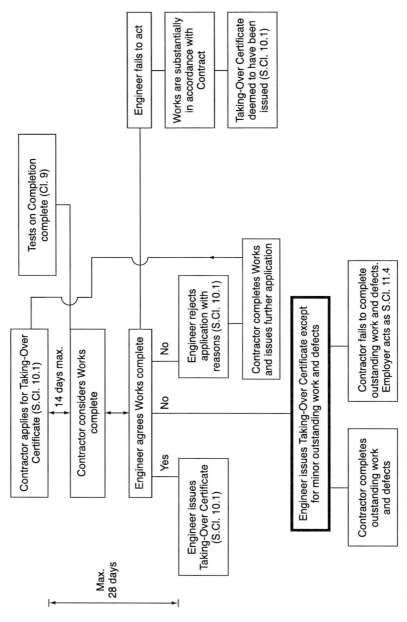

Fig. 6. Procedures at Completion of Works

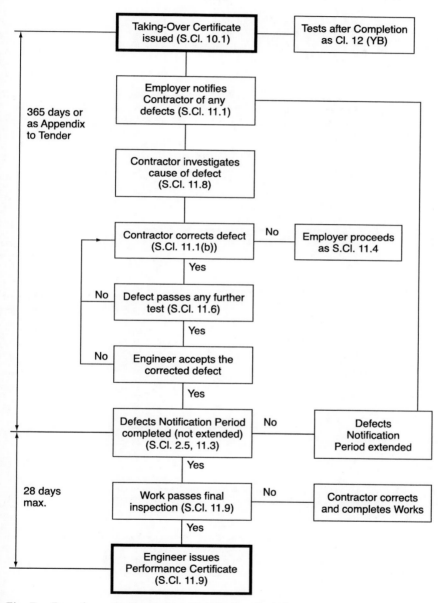

Fig. 7. Procedures during Defects Notification Period

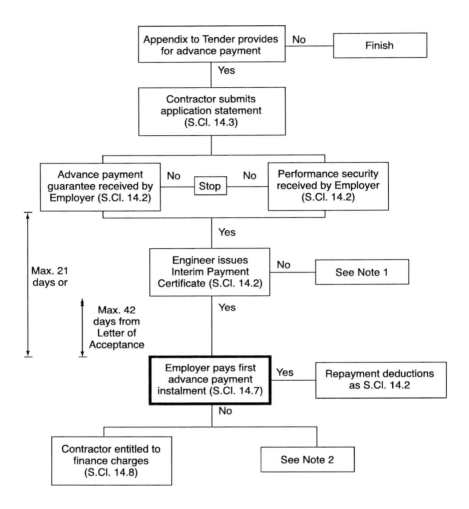

Note 1:
(i)   If the Engineer fails to issue the Interim Payment Certificate, the Contractor may give 21 days notice and then suspend or reduce the rate of work (S.Cl. 16.1).
(ii) If the Engineer fails to issue the Interim Payment Certificate within 56 days from the Contractor's application statement, the Contractor may terminate the Contract (S.Cl. 16.2(b)).
Note 2:
(i)   If the Employer fails to make the payment, the Contractor may give 21 days notice and then suspend or reduce the rate of work (S.Cl. 16.1).
(ii) If the Contractor does not receive payment within 42 days of the due date, the Contractor may terminate the Contract (S.Cl. 16.2(c)).

Fig. 8.   Procedures for advance payment

Note 1:
(i) If the Engineer fails to issue the Interim Payment Certificate, the Contractor may give 21 days notice and then suspend or reduce the rate of work (S.Cl. 16.1).
(ii) If the Engineer fails to issue the Interim Payment Certificate within 56 days from the Contractor's application statement, the Contractor may terminate the Contract (S.Cl. 16.2(b)).
Note 2:
(i) If the Employer fails to make the payment, the Contractor may give 21 days notice and then suspend or reduce the rate of work (S.Cl. 16.1).
(ii) If the Contractor does not receive payment within 42 days of the due date, the Contractor may terminate the Contract (S.Cl. 16.2(c)).

Fig. 9. Payment procedures

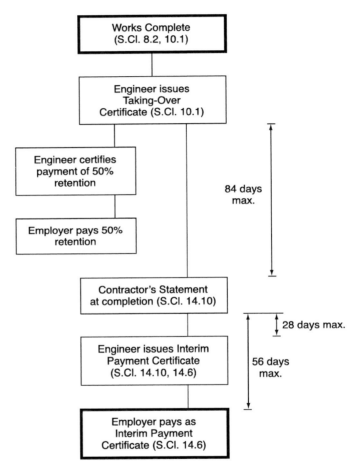

Note:
Sanctions for failure to certify or pay the Interim Payment Certificates are as Fig. 6.

Fig. 10.   Procedures for payment at Completion of Works

Fig. 11.   *Procedures for final payment*

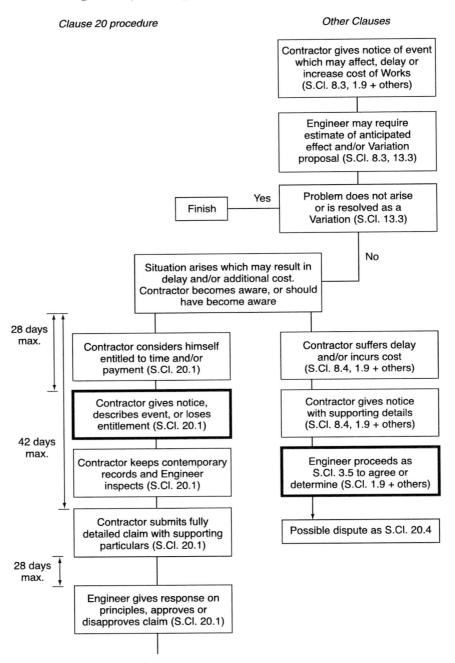

Fig. 12. Claims by the Contractor

Engineer certifies any
amount substantiated
(S.Cl. 20.1, 14.6)

Engineer proceeds as
S.Cl. 3.5 to agree or
determine (S.Cl. 20.1)

Possible dispute as
S.Cl. 20.4

Continue as Flow Chart 11

Notes:
1. S.Cl. 20.1 notice is obligatory for all claims.
2. Engineer's determination as S.Cl. 3.5 can be made at any time in the sequence as appropriate.
3. Notices etc. should be given as soon as possible within the stated period.
4. Consents and determinations must not be unreasonably withheld or delayed (S.Cl. 1.3).

Fig. 12. Continued

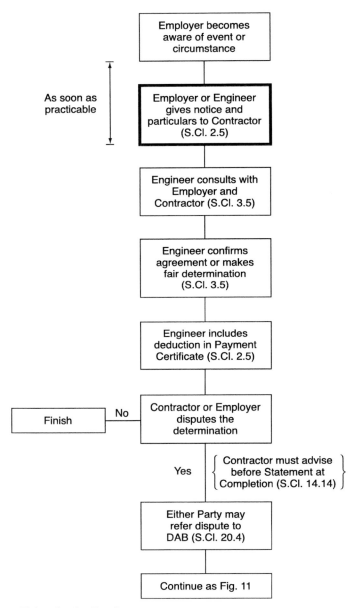

Fig. 13.   Claims by the Employer

Part 2

The FIDIC Conditions of Contract for Construction and for Plant and Design-Build

Chapter 6

Introduction to Part 2

The purpose for which each of these Contracts is intended is stated on the title page of each of the FIDIC documents:

- the Conditions of Contract for Construction is for building and engineering works designed by the Employer;
- the Conditions of Contract for Plant and Design-Build is for electrical and mechanical plant, and for building and engineering works, designed by the Contractor.

Part 2 of this book includes a detailed review of the Sub-Clauses in the FIDIC Conditions of Contract for Construction and for Plant and Design-Build. The commentary on each Sub-Clause starts with the Contract for Construction and is followed by a review of any changes in the Contract for Plant and Design-Build. The commentary includes suggestions for possible changes which could be made in the Particular Conditions, together with cross-references to other Sub-Clauses that may be relevant.

This review does not attempt to give a detailed legal analysis of every Sub-Clause, but to draw readers' attention to problems that may arise in the interpretation and use of the Sub-Clause. These comments and any references to the content of the Sub-Clauses must be read in relation to the complete Sub-Clause, which is reproduced in the text.

Part 1 of this book includes fourteen flow charts (Figs. 1 to 14 in Chapter 5). These flow charts show the procedures required by the Conditions in certain sequences of events and should be consulted in connection with the Sub-Clauses as listed below.

- Fig. 1. *Time periods in the Conditions of Contract*: Sub-Clauses 1.1.1.3, 1.1.3.1, 4.2, 8.1, 8.2, 8.3, 8.4, 8.7, 9, 10.1, 11, 11.3, 11.9, 11.10, 14.1, 14.2, 14.4, 20.2.
- Fig. 2. *Progress Requirements*: Sub-Clauses 2.1, 2.5, 3.5, 8.1, 8.3, 8.4, 8.6, 14.6, 20.1, 20.4.
- Fig. 3. *Errors in Employer's Requirements (YB only)*: Sub-Clauses 1.9, 5.1, 8.1, 13.1, 20.1.

- Fig. 4. *Design procedures (YB only)*: Sub-Clauses 1.1.6.1, 1.13, 5.1.
- Fig. 5. *Workmanship procedures*: Sub-Clauses 2.5, 7.1, 7.3, 7.4, 7.5, 7.6, 10.2.
- Fig. 6. *Procedures at Completion of Works*: Sub-Clauses 9, 10.1, 11.4.
- Fig. 7. *Procedures during Defects Notification Period*: Sub-Clauses 2.5, 10.1, 11.1, 11.3, 11.6, 11.8, 11.9, 12 (YB).
- Fig. 8. *Procedures for advance payment*: Sub-Clauses 14.2, 14.3, 14.7, 14.8, 16.1, 16.2.
- Fig. 9. *Payment procedures*: Sub-Clauses 4.2, 14.3, 14.6, 14.7, 14.8, 16.1, 16.2.
- Fig. 10. *Procedures for Payment at Completion of Works*: Sub-Clauses 8.2, 10.1, 14.6, 14.10.
- Fig. 11. *Procedures for final payment*: Sub-Clauses 14.7, 14.9, 14.11, 14.12, 14.13.
- Fig. 12. *Claims by the Contractor*: Sub-Clauses 1.3, 1.9, 3.5, 8.3, 8.4, 13.3, 14.6, 20.1, 20.4.
- Fig. 13. *Claims by the Employer*: Sub-Clauses 2.5, 3.5, 14.14, 20.4.
- Fig. 14. *Procedures for disputes*: Sub-Clauses 20.4, 20.5, 20.6.

Chapter 7

Contents: General Conditions

6 STAFF AND LABOUR

7 PLANT, MATERIALS AND WORKMANSHIP

8 COMMENCEMENT, DELAYS AND SUSPENSION

9 TESTS ON COMPLETION

Chapter 8

Definitions listed alphabetically

Chapter 9

Clause 1: General Provisions

Clause 1 covers general matters such as definitions, the law and language of the Contract and various matters concerning the documents. Definitions which are given at Sub-Clause 1.1 and are relevant to this Clause include:

1.1.1.1	Contract
1.1.1.2	Contract Agreement
1.1.1.3	Letter of Acceptance
1.1.1.4	Letter of Tender
1.1.1.5 (RB)	Specification
1.1.1.5 (YB)	Employer's Requirements
1.1.1.6	Drawings
1.1.1.9	Appendix to Tender
1.1.3.1	Base Date
1.1.3.2	Commencement Date
1.1.4.1	Accepted Contract Amount
1.1.5.2	Goods
1.1.5.4	Permanent Works
1.1.6.2	Country
1.1.6.5	Laws.

1.1 Definitions

In the Conditions of Contract ('these Conditions'), which include Particular Conditions and these General Conditions, the following words and expressions shall have the meanings stated. Words indicating persons or parties include corporations and other legal entities, except where the context requires otherwise.

1.1.1 The Contract

1.1.1.1 **'Contract'** means the Contract Agreement, the Letter of Acceptance, the Letter of Tender, these Conditions, the Specification, the Drawings, the Schedules, and the further documents (if any) which are listed in the Contract Agreement or in the Letter of Acceptance.

1.1.1.2 **'Contract Agreement'** means the contract agreement (if any) referred to in Sub-Clause 1.6 [*Contract Agreement*].

1.1.1.3 **'Letter of Acceptance'** means the letter of formal acceptance, signed by the Employer, of the Letter of Tender, including any annexed memoranda comprising agreements between and signed by both Parties. If there is no such letter of acceptance, the expression 'Letter of Acceptance' means the Contract Agreement and the date of issuing or receiving the Letter of Acceptance means the date of signing the Contract Agreement.

1.1.1.4 **'Letter of Tender'** means the document entitled letter of tender, which was completed by the Contractor and includes the signed offer to the Employer for the Works.

1.1.1.5 **'Specification'** means the document entitled specification, as included in the Contract, and any additions and modifications to the specification in accordance with the Contract. Such document specifies the Works.

1.1.1.6 **'Drawings'** means the drawings of the Works, as included in the Contract, and any additional and modified drawings issued by (or on behalf of) the Employer in accordance with the Contract.

1.1.1.7 **'Schedules'** means the document(s) entitled schedules, completed by the Contractor and submitted with the Letter of Tender, as included in the Contract. Such document may include the Bill of Quantities, data, lists, and schedules of rates and/or prices.

1.1.1.8 **'Tender'** means the Letter of Tender and all other documents which the Contractor submitted with the Letter of Tender, as included in the Contract.

1.1.1.9 **'Appendix to Tender'** means the completed pages entitled appendix to tender which are appended to and form part of the Letter of Tender.

1.1.1.10 **'Bill of Quantities'** and **'Daywork Schedule'** mean the documents so named (if any) which are comprised in the Schedules.

1.1.2 Parties and Persons

1.1.2.1 **'Party'** means the Employer or the Contractor, as the context requires.

1.1.2.2 **'Employer'** means the person named as Employer in the Appendix to Tender and the legal successors in title to this person.

1.1.2.3 **'Contractor'** means the person(s) named as Contractor in the Letter of Tender accepted by the Employer and the legal successors in title to this person(s).

1.1.2.4 **'Engineer'** means the person appointed by the Employer to act as the Engineer for the purposes of the Contract and named in the Appendix to Tender, or other person appointed from time to time by the Employer and notified to the Contractor under Sub-Clause 3.4 [*Replacement of the Engineer*].

1.1.2.5 **'Contractor's Representative'** means the person named by the Contractor in the Contract or appointed from time to time by the Contractor under Sub-Clause 4.3 [*Contractor's Representative*], who acts on behalf of the Contractor.

1.1.2.6 **'Employer's Personnel'** means the Engineer, the assistants referred to in Sub-Clause 3.2 [*Delegation by the Engineer*] and all other staff, labour and other employees of the Engineer and of the Employer; and any other personnel notified to the Contractor, by the Employer or the Engineer, as Employer's Personnel.

1.1.2.7 **'Contractor's Personnel'** means the Contractor's Representative and all personnel whom the Contractor utilises on Site, who may include the staff, labour and other employees of the Contractor and of each Subcontractor; and any other personnel assisting the Contractor in the execution of the Works.

1.1.2.8 **'Subcontractor'** means any person named in the Contract as a subcontractor, or any person appointed as a subcontractor, for a part of the Works; and the legal successors in title to each of these persons.

1.1.2.9 **'DAB'** means the person or three persons so named in the Contract, or other person(s) appointed under Sub-Clause 20.2 [*Appointment of the Dispute Adjudication Board*] or under Sub-Clause 20.3 [*Failure to Agree Dispute Adjudication Board*].

1.1.2.10 **'FIDIC'** means the Federation Internationale des Ingenieurs-Conseils, the international federation of consulting engineers.

1.1.3 Dates, Tests, Periods and Completion
1.1.3.1 **'Base Date'** means the date 28 days prior to the latest date for submission of the Tender.

1.1.3.2 **'Commencement Date'** means the date notified under Sub-Clause 8.1 [*Commencement of Works*].

1.1.3.3 **'Time for Completion'** means the time for completing the Works or a Section (as the case may be) under Sub-Clause 8.2 [*Time* *for Completion*], as stated in the Appendix to Tender (with any extension under Sub-Clause 8.4 [*Extension of Time for Completion*]), calculated from the Commencement Date.

1.1.3.4 'Tests on Completion' means the tests which are specified in the Contract or agreed by both Parties or instructed as a Variation, and which are carried out under Clause 9 [*Tests on Completion*] before the Works or a Section (as the case may be) are taken over by the Employer.

1.1.3.5 'Taking-Over Certificate' means a certificate issued under Clause 10 [*Employer's Taking Over*].

1.1.3.6 'Tests after Completion' means the tests (if any) which are specified in the Contract and which are carried out in accordance with the provisions of the Particular Conditions after the Works or a Section (as the case may be) are taken over by the Employer.

1.1.3.7 'Defects Notification Period' means the period for notifying defects in the Works or a Section (as the case may be) under Sub-Clause 11.1 [*Completion of Outstanding Work and Remedying Defects*], as stated in the Appendix to Tender (with any extension under Sub-Clause 11.3 [*Extension of Defects Notification Period*]), calculated from the date on which the Works or Section is completed as certified under Sub-Clause 10.1 [*Taking Over of the Works and Sections*].

1.1.3.8 'Performance Certificate' means the certificate issued under Sub-Clause 11.9 [*Performance Certificate*].

1.1.3.9 'Day' means a calendar day and 'year' means 365 days.

1.1.4 Money and Payments
1.1.4.1 'Accepted Contract Amount' means the amount accepted in the Letter of Acceptance for the execution and completion of the Works and the remedying of any defects.

1.1.4.2 'Contract Price' means the price defined in Sub-Clause 14.1 [*The Contract Price*], and includes adjustments in accordance with the Contract.

1.1.4.3 'Cost' means all expenditure reasonably incurred (or to be incurred) by the Contractor, whether on or off the Site, including overhead and similar charges, but does not include profit.

1.1.4.4 'Final Payment Certificate' means the payment certificate issued under Sub-Clause 14.13 [*Issue of Final Payment Certificate*].

1.1.4.5 'Final statement' means the statement defined in Sub-Clause 14.11 [*Application for Final Payment Certificate*].

1.1.4.6 **'Foreign Currency'** means a currency in which part (or all) of the Contract Price is payable, but not the Local Currency.

1.1.4.7 **'Interim Payment Certificate'** means a payment certificate issued under Clause 14 [*Contract Price and Payment*], other than the Final Payment Certificate.

1.1.4.8 **'Local Currency'** means the currency of the Country.

1.1.4.9 **'Payment Certificate'** means a payment certificate issued under Clause 14 [*Contract Price and Payment*].

1.1.4.10 **'Provisional Sum'** means a sum (if any) which is specified in the Contract as a provisional sum, for the execution of any part of the Works or for the supply of Plant, Materials or services under Sub-Clause 13.5 [*Provisional Sums*].

1.1.4.11 **'Retention Money'** means the accumulated retention moneys which the Employer retains under Sub-Clause 14.3 [*Application for Interim Payment Certificates*] and pays under Sub-Clause 14.9 [*Payment of Retention Money*].

1.1.4.12 **'Statement'** means a statement submitted by the Contractor as part of an application, under Clause 14 [*Contract Price and Payment*], for a payment certificate.

1.1.5 Works and Goods

1.1.5.1 **'Contractor's Equipment'** means all apparatus, machinery, vehicles and other things required for the execution and completion of the Works and the remedying of any defects. However, Contractor's Equipment excludes Temporary Works, Employer's Equipment (if any), Plant, Materials and any other things intended to form or forming part of the Permanent Works.

1.1.5.2 **'Goods'** means Contractor's Equipment, Materials, Plant and Temporary Works, or any of them as appropriate.

1.1.5.3 **'Materials'** means things of all kinds (other than Plant) intended to form or forming part of the Permanent Works, including the supply-only materials (if any) to be supplied by the Contractor under the Contract.

1.1.5.4 **'Permanent Works'** means the permanent works to be executed by the Contractor under the Contract.

1.1.5.5 **'Plant'** means the apparatus, machinery and vehicles intended to form or forming part of the Permanent Works.

1.1.5.6 **'Section'** means a part of the Works specified in the Appendix to Tender as a Section (if any).

1.1.5.7 **'Temporary Works'** means all temporary works of every kind (other than Contractor's Equipment) required on Site for the execution and completion of the Permanent Works and the remedying of any defects.

1.1.5.8 **'Works'** mean the Permanent Works and the Temporary Works, or either of them as appropriate.

1.1.6 Other Definitions

1.1.6.1 **'Contractor's Documents'** means the calculations, computer programs and other software, drawings, manuals, models and other documents of a technical nature (if any) supplied by the Contractor under the Contract.

1.1.6.2 **'Country'** means the country in which the Site (or most of it) is located, where the Permanent Works are to be executed.

1.1.6.3 **'Employer's Equipment'** means the apparatus, machinery and vehicles (if any) made available by the Employer for the use of the Contractor in the execution of the Works, as stated in the Specification; but does not include Plant which has not been taken over by the Employer.

1.1.6.4 **'Force Majeure'** is defined in Clause 19 [*Force Majeure*].

1.1.6.5 **'Laws'** means all national (or state) legislation, statutes, ordinances and other laws, and regulations and by-laws of any legally constituted public authority.

1.1.6.6 **'Performance Security'** means the security (or securities, if any) under Sub-Clause 4.2 [*Performance Security*].

1.1.6.7 **'Site'** means the places where the Permanent Works are to be executed and to which Plant and Materials are to be delivered, and any other places as may be specified in the Contract as forming part of the Site.

1.1.6.8 **'Unforeseeable'** means not reasonably foreseeable by an experienced contractor by the date for submission of the Tender.

1.1.6.9 **'Variation'** means any change to the Works, which is instructed or approved as a variation under Clause 13 [*Variations and Adjustments*].

In the Yellow Book, the definitions 1.1.1.5, 1.1.1.6, 1.1.1.7, 1.1.1.10 and 1.1.6.9 have been changed and now read:

1.1.1.5 **'Employer's Requirements'** means the document entitled employer's requirements, as included in the Contract, and any additions and modifications to such document in accordance with the Contract.

Such document specifies the purpose, scope, and/or design and/or other technical criteria, for the Works.

1.1.1.6 **'Schedules'** means the document(s) entitled schedules, completed by the Contractor and submitted with the Letter of Tender, as included in the Contract. Such document may include data, lists and schedules of payments and/or prices.

1.1.1.7 **'Contractor's Proposal'** means the document entitled proposal, which the Contractor submitted with the Letter of Tender, as included in the Contract. Such document may include the Contractor's preliminary design.

1.1.1.10 **'Schedule of Guarantees'** and **'Schedule of Payments'** mean the documents so named (if any) which are comprised in the Schedules.

1.1.6.9 **'Variation'** means any change to the Employer's Requirements or the Works, which is instructed or approved as a variation under Clause 13 [*Variations and Adjustments*].

Sub-Clause 1.1 defines the meaning of 60 words and expressions used in the Conditions of Contract. These are listed alphabetically on page vi (also reproduced in this book in Chapter 8) and are then defined in separate Sub-Clauses under six subheadings:

1.1.1 The Contract
1.1.2 Parties and Persons
1.1.3 Dates, Tests, Periods and Completion
1.1.4 Money and Payments
1.1.5 Works and Goods
1.1.6 Other Definitions.

The definitions include technical and contractual terms, such as 'Final Payment Certificate' and words which are in everyday use, such as 'Cost' and 'Unforeseeable'. Many of the words which are defined are wellknown or were defined in previous FIDIC Contracts. However, some words are new to FIDIC, or are given definitions which are not the obvious meaning of the word. For example 'Employer's Personnel' covers not only staff directly employed by the Employer, but includes the Engineer and any other person who has been notified to the Contractor as being Employer's Personnel. Also, the equipment which is used by the Contractor for the construction of the Works is referred to as 'Contractor's Equipment', and the word 'Plant' is used for apparatus, machinery and vehicles which will be incorporated into the Permanent Works.

In general, words that are defined are printed with capital letters in the text. Exceptions are 'day' and 'year'. When a word in the FIDIC

Conditions has a capital letter, but is not at the beginning of a sentence, it is advisable to check at Sub-Clause 1.1 to establish the meaning of the word in the context of FIDIC.

Several of the terms defined at Sub-Clause 1.1 require further information, which must be given in the *Appendix to Tender*:

1.1.2.2   The name of the Employer
1.1.2.3   The name of the Contractor
1.1.2.4   The name of the Engineer
1.1.3.3   The number of days for completing the Works
          The number of days for the completion of Sections
1.1.3.7   The number of days in the period for notifying defects
1.1.5.6   Any part of the Works which is specified as a Section.

Other definitions refer to information which must be given elsewhere in the Contract documents.

Definitions that depend on the date for the submission of the Tender

1.1.3.1   The Base Date is fixed as 28 days before the latest date for the submission of the Tender.
1.1.6.8   Things which are Unforeseeable means unforeseeable by the date for submission of the Tender.

A potential problem is that the Invitation to Tender is not intended to be a Contract document under FIDIC procedures. It is therefore necessary to ensure that the date for submission of the Tender is recorded somewhere in the Contract. The FIDIC Guidance for the Preparation of Particular Conditions suggests at Sub-Clause 1.1 that the Base Date could be stated as a calendar date. The FIDIC Guidance also suggests at Sub-Clause 1.6 that the Base Date could be stated in the Contract Agreement. This has the advantage that, if the date for submission of the Tender was delayed, then the Base Date should change and the actual date is known by the time that the Contract Agreement is signed. Alternatively, the Appendix to Tender could be amended so as to allow the Contractor to insert the actual Tender date or Base Date.

Definition in the Letter of Tender which was accepted by the Employer

1.1.2.3   The name of the Contractor is given in the Letter of Tender which was accepted by the Employer.

The Letter of Tender is one of the documents which form the Contract and will be referred to in the Letter of Acceptance and Contract Agreement. The Contractor's name and address must also be added to the

Appendix to Tender and will be stated in the Contract Agreement. It is obvious, but not always achieved in practice, that the same name and address should appear in all these documents.

Definitions that depend on the Letter of Acceptance or the Contract Agreement

1.1.1.1 The list of documents which make up the Contract must be given in the letter of Acceptance and in the Contract Agreement.

1.1.2.5 The name of the Contractor's Representative is stated to be given in the Contract and could be in a memorandum annexed to the Letter of Acceptance. Sub-Clause 4.3 states that if the name is not stated in the Contract it must be submitted for the Engineer's approval before the Commencement Date.

1.1.2.9 Members of the DAB may be named in the Contract or appointed later, as discussed at Sub-Clause 20.2.

1.1.3.2 The Commencement Date must be notified to the Contractor by the Engineer within 42 days after the Contractor receives the Letter of Acceptance, unless a different number of days is stated in the Particular Conditions.

1.1.4.1 The Accepted Contract Amount must be given in the Letter of Acceptance and may be repeated in the Contract Agreement.

The definition of the Letter of Acceptance, at Sub-Clause 1.1.1.3, allow it to include annexed memoranda, which should include the agreed confirmation of negotiations and letters from the Contractor covering matters such as the name of the Contractor's Representative. Insurance arrangements should also have been discussed at this stage and any agreements annexed to the Letter of Acceptance, as reviewed at Clause 18.

Definitions that depend on the Contract documents, the Specification or Schedules

1.1.2.8 Subcontractors may be either named in the Contract, or appointed as a Subcontractor.

1.1.3.4 Tests on Completion may be specified in the Contract or agreed or instructed later.

1.1.3.6 Tests after Completion must be specified in the Contract with the procedures given in the Particular Conditions.

1.1.4.10 Any Provisional Sums must be specified in the Contract.

1.1.6.2 The Country in which most of the Site is located, should be apparent from the drawings.

1.1.6.3	Any Employer's Equipment must be stated in the Specification.
1.1.6.7	The Site must be defined in the Contract.

The names of Subcontractors and the details of Tests on Completion may be given during the construction. However, Tests after Completion are not considered to be a routine requirement for a project which is designed by the Employer and the procedures are not given in the FIDIC Conditions. The procedures must be given in the Particular Conditions with the technical details in the Specification. Guidance on these procedures can be obtained from Clause 12 of the FIDIC Conditions of Contract for Plant and Design-Build.

The details of Provisional Sums and any Equipment which the Employer intends to provide for the Contractor's use must be given in the Specification or Schedules in order that the Contractor can plan his work.

The precise location and extent of the Site must obviously be given in the Contract. This may include areas that are not to be occupied by the Permanent Works but which the Employer intends to make available for the Contractor's use. If the Site crosses the border and is located in more than one country, for example a bridge spanning a river which forms the national boundary, then the identity of the country in which most of it is located will be critical for the definition of 'Country' as Sub-Clause 1.1.6.2. To avoid any confusion the name of the Country could be stated in the Particular Conditions.

The FIDIC Guidance for the Preparation of Particular Conditions suggests that definitions of Foreign Currency at 1.1.4.6 and Local Currency at 1.1.4.8 may need to be amended if the Employer intends to specify a particular currency for payment.

An additional definition which would be useful and could be included in the Particular Conditions would be the 'Resident Engineer'. Previous FIDIC Contracts included a specific provision for the Engineer to appoint an Engineer's Representative, who was normally resident on the Site. This role has now disappeared although a Resident Engineer is mentioned at Sub-Clause 3.2 as a possible assistant to the Engineer. In practice, for any project which is large enough to justify the use of a FIDIC Contract, it is essential that the Employer or the Engineer has a member of his staff permanently on Site, so the position should be officially acknowledged in the Contract. Suitable wording for the definition might be:

1.1.2.11	*'Resident Engineer'* means an assistant to the Engineer who will be resident on the Site and is appointed from time to time by the Engineer under Sub-Clause 3.2 and notified to the Contractor.

In the review of Clause 3, in Chapter 11 of this book, it is suggested that an additional Sub-Clause 3.6 [*Management Meetings*] could be added in the Particular Conditions. This would require an additional definition:

> 1.1.6.10 *'Management Meeting'* means a meeting called by either the Engineer or the Contractor's Representative in accordance with Sub-Clause 3.6.

1.2 Interpretation

In the Contract, except where the context requires otherwise:

(a) words indicating one gender include all genders;

(b) words indicating the singular also include the plural and words indicating the plural also include the singular;

(c) provisions including the word 'agree', 'agreed' or 'agreement' require the agreement to be recorded in writing, and

(d) 'written' or 'in writing' means hand-written, type-written, printed or electronically made, and resulting in a permanent record.

The marginal words and other headings shall not be taken into consideration in the interpretation of these Conditions.

Sub-Clause 1.2 states that headings and marginal words must not be taken into consideration in the interpretation of the Conditions. This statement also applies in reverse. The reader cannot rely on the heading when searching for the Sub-Clause which covers a particular situation. Many sentences within a Sub-Clause refer to a completely different subject to the heading. One of the problems with the administration of a FIDIC Contract is the need to collect information on any subject from a variety of different, and sometimes unexpected, Sub-Clauses. The Index of Sub-Clauses, which is located after the Appendix and Annex which follow Clause 20, is helpful but cannot cover all the possible subjects and Sub-Clauses.

Sub-Clause 1.2 also confirms the usual conventions that one gender includes all genders, singular includes plural and vice versa. Other requirements which are important for efficient project management are that anything which is stated to be agreed must have been recorded in writing and 'written' means a record 'resulting in a permanent record'. The word 'permanent' must be interpreted in the context of the contract, in order to cover the examples which are quoted, such as 'hand-written' and 'electronically made'. The applicable law may also have some relevant provisions.

The FIDIC Guidance for the Preparation of Particular Conditions suggests that Sub-Clause 1.2 could be extended if a more precise explanation is required of the phrase 'Cost plus reasonable profit'. This phrase is included in Sub-Clauses such as 1.9, which refer to circumstances in which the Contractor may be entitled to additional payment. The FIDIC example states that reasonable profit would be one-twentieth (5%) of the Cost. The phrase 'reasonable profit' is certainly open to interpretation and argument, but it does not seem logical to stipulate a figure and then hide the figure at Sub-Clause 1.2. If a particular figure is imposed on the Contractor, it would be better if the figure was included in the Appendix to Tender. If the intention is to have a figure determined in the Contract, to avoid problems when claims are being valued, then it could be left open for completion by the Contractor.

1.3 Communications

Wherever these Conditions provide for the giving or issuing of approvals, certificates, consents, determinations, notices and requests, these communications shall be:

(a) in writing and delivered by hand (against receipt), sent by mail or courier, or transmitted using any of the agreed systems of electronic transmission as stated in the Appendix to Tender; and

(b) delivered, sent or transmitted to the address for the recipient's communications as stated in the Appendix to Tender. However:

　(i) if the recipient gives notice of another address, communications shall thereafter be delivered accordingly; and

　(ii) if the recipient has not stated otherwise when requesting an approval or consent, it may be sent to the address from which the request was issued.

Approvals, certificates, consents and determinations shall not be unreasonably withheld or delayed. When a certificate is issued to a Party, the certifier shall send a copy to the other Party. When a notice is issued to a Party, by the other Party or the Engineer, a copy shall be sent to the Engineer or the other Party, as the case may be.

Sub-Clause 1.3 requires that the formal communications provided for in the Conditions, which are listed as approvals, certificates, consents, determinations, notices and requests, must be in writing and delivered by hand, mail, courier or electronic means. The acceptable electronic means are stated in the Appendix to Tender under 'Electronic transmission systems'. The use of facsimile transmission is not listed but could be covered in the Appendix to Tender. The Sub-Clause requires hand delivery to be against a receipt, but does not require a receipt for the other means of delivery. Clearly it would often be prudent to use a system that requires the recipient to sign a receipt. Some actions, such as the payment provisions at Sub-Clauses 14.7 are required to be taken within a number of days following the receipt of another document so the date of receipt will be significant.

Communications must be sent to the address stated in the Appendix to Tender unless notice has been given of a different address. In practice, when the Parties and the Engineer have offices on Site they may wish to use these offices for most communications during the construction period and so must issue formal notices to this effect. Also, when a certificate or notice is issued to one Party it must be copied to the other Party and the Engineer. A particularly important statement is hidden within this Sub-Clause:

Approvals, certificates, consents and determinations shall not be unreasonably withheld or delayed.

In general, throughout the FIDIC Conditions of Contract, when the Contractor is required to take some action it must be carried out within a fixed time period. However, the same principle does not apply to many of the actions by the Engineer. The consequences or compensation for a document being unreasonably withheld or delayed are not stated but clearly it would be a breach of Contract. If the Contractor feels that he has suffered delay or additional cost then he could submit a claim using the procedures of Sub-Clause 20.1. The matter would be considered by the Engineer, who would make a determination under Sub-Clause 3.5, which could later be reviewed by the DAB or Arbitration Tribunal.

In previous FIDIC Contracts the Sub-Clauses which required the issue of a notice to the Engineer frequently stated that a copy must be sent to the Employer. In the 1999 Contracts this requirement has been omitted from most of the Sub-Clauses but a general requirement has been included at Sub-Clause 1.3. Certificates must be copied to the other Party and notices to a Party must be copied to the other Party or the Engineer. However, notices which are sent to the Engineer do not have to be copied to the other Party. This means that notices of claims do not have to be copied to the Employer, although these are the notices which the Employer will probably wish to receive.

This requirement only refers to certificates and notices. However, the use of the word notice, which is not a defined term, could cause confusion. In other Sub-Clauses the use of words such as notify, submit or instruct appears to be a matter of word selection rather than a deliberate intention to either require, or not to require, a copy to the other Party. The requirement for copies of particular notices should be reviewed during the preparation of the Particular Conditions.

Certificates and notices include the following.

(a) Certificates issued by the Engineer to the Employer, with a copy to the Contractor:
    (i) Payment Certificates as Sub-Clauses 14.2, 14.6, 14.13.
(b) Certificates issued by the Engineer to the Contractor, with a copy to the Employer:

(i) Taking-Over Certificate as Sub-Clause 10.1 or 10.2

(ii) Performance Certificate as Sub-Clause 11.9.

(c) Notices issued by either Party to the other Party, with a copy to the Engineer:

(i) an error or defect in a document as Sub-Clause 1.8

(ii) infringement of intellectual or industrial property rights as Sub-Clause 17.5

(iii) event or circumstances as Force Majeure as Sub-Clause 19.2

(iv) Force Majeure ceases to affect as Sub-Clause 19.3

(v) termination due to Force Majeure as Sub-Clause 19.6

(vi) dissatisfaction with a DAB decision as Sub-Clause 20.4.

(d) Notices issued by the Employer to the Contractor, with a copy to the Engineer:

(i) a change to his financial arrangements as Sub-Clause 2.4

(ii) claim particulars as Sub-Clause 2.5

(iii) details of a replacement Engineer as Sub-Clause 3.4

(iv) defects during the Defects Notification Period as Sub-Clause 11.1

(v) defects not at Contractor's Cost as Sub-Clause 11.2

(vi) date by which a defect is to be remedied as Sub-Clause 11.4

(vii) termination by Employer as Sub-Clause 15.2

(viii) release equipment after termination as Sub-Clause 15.2

(ix) termination for convenience as Sub-Clause 15.5.

(e) Notices issued by the Contractor to the Employer, with a copy to the Engineer:

(i) suspend or reduce work as Sub-Clause 16.1

(ii) termination as Sub-Clause 16.2

(iii) insurance cover ceases to be available as Sub-Clause 18.2.

(f) Notices issued by the Engineer to both Parties:

(i) agreement or Engineer's determination as Sub-Clause 3.5.

(g) Notices issued by the Engineer to the Contractor, with a copy to the Employer:

(i) does not require to inspect as Sub-Clause 7.3

(ii) intention to attend tests as Sub-Clause 7.4

(iii) rejection as Sub-Clause 7.5

(iv) Commencement Date as Sub-Clause 8.1

(v) programme does not comply with the Contract as Sub-Clause 8.3

(vi) programme not consistent with actual progress as Sub-Clause 8.3

(vii) instruction to carry out delayed tests as Sub-Clause 9.2

(viii) Tests on Completion after delay by the Employer as Sub-Clause 10.3

(ix) further tests as Sub-Clause 11.5

         (x) that part of the Works is to be measured as Sub-Clause 12.1

        (xi) payment is to be withheld as Sub-Clause 14.6

       (xii) correct a failure to carry out an obligation as Sub-Clause 15.1.

(h) Notices issued by the Contractor to the Engineer:

         (i) claims as Sub-Clauses 1.9, 4.12, 4.24, 16.1, 17.4, 19.4

        (ii) requiring a drawing or instruction as Sub-Clause 1.9

       (iii) Date of Commencement of Subcontractor's Work as Sub-Clause 4.4

       (iv) delivery to Site of Plant or other major items as Sub-Clause 4.16

        (v) shortage or defect in free-issue materials as Sub-Clause 4.20

       (vi) objection to a Nominated Subcontractor as Sub-Clause 5.2 (RB) and Sub-Clause 4.5 (YB)

      (vii) inspection before cover up as Sub-Clause 7.3

     (viii) circumstances which may have an adverse effect as Sub-Clause 8.3

      (ix) prolonged suspension as Sub-Clause 8.11

       (x) date for delayed Tests on Completion as Sub-Clause 9.1

      (xi) delayed Tests on Completion as Sub-Clause 9.2

     (xii) application for a Taking-Over Certificate as Sub-Clause 10.1

     (xiii) records are inaccurate as Sub-Clause 12.1

     (xiv) damage due to Employer's risks as Sub-Clause 17.4.

(i) Notices issued by both Parties to each Member of a DAB:

         (i) Dispute Adjudication Agreement takes effect as Appendix paragraph 2

        (ii) termination of Dispute Adjudication Agreement as Appendix paragraph 7.

(j) Notices issued by a DAB Member to both Parties:

         (i) resignation as Appendix paragraph 2

        (ii) termination of Dispute Adjudication Agreement as Appendix paragraph 7

      (iii) notice of its decision, as Annex paragraph 5

      (iv) notice of a hearing, as Annex paragraph 7.

There is no requirement for other correspondence or reports to be copied to a Party or to the Engineer although this may be done, by agreement or at the option of the Party concerned.

1.4 Law and Language

The Contract shall be governed by the law of the country (or other jurisdiction) stated in the Appendix to Tender.

If there are versions of any part of the Contract which are written in more than one language, the version which is in the ruling language stated in the Appendix to Tender shall prevail.

The language for communications shall be that stated in the Appendix to Tender. If no language is stated there, the language for communications shall be the language in which the Contract (or most of it) is written.

The Contractor, quite apart from any provisions in the Contract, is obliged to comply with the Laws of the Country in which he is working and Sub-Clause 1.13 states that 'the Contractor shall, in performing the Contract, comply with applicable laws'. If the Site is located in more than one Country, as discussed under Sub-Clause 1.1, then the Contractor may have to comply with the Laws of more than one Country. Work such as the manufacture of items of Plant in a different Country will be subject to the Laws and regulations of that Country.

Several other clauses, such as Sub-Clause 13.7, refer to the 'Laws of the Country', with 'Laws' and 'Country' as defined at Sub-Clause 1.1. Sub-Clause 13.7 refers to changes in the Laws of the Country. The 'governing law' as stated in the Appendix to Tender is the law which governs the Contract and is not necessarily the Law of the Country in which the Site is located. However, if the governing law is not the Laws of the Country then there is likely to be confusion and problems due to any difference between the different legal requirements.

The 'ruling language' is designated in the Appendix to Tender and is the language which has priority if any part of the Contract is written in more than one language. For example, the Contract Agreement is sometimes written in more than one language and technical documents such as manu-facturers' brochures may have been written in a different language.

The 'language for communications' should also be stated in the Appendix to Tender, but if it is not stated then it is the language in which most of the Contract is written. The separation of language for communications from the ruling language recognises that many FIDIC Contracts have English as the language for daily use on the project, even when it is not the language of the Country of the project. English will then be the official language for documents and meetings, although internal documents and meetings may use a different language. Any assistants to whom the Engineer has delegated authority under Sub-Clause 3.2, together with the Contractor's Representative and any assistants to whom powers have been delegated under Sub-Clause 4.3, are required to be fluent in the language for communications.

If the original of any document was written in a different language and a translation takes priority then care is necessary to ensure that the trans-lation truly gives the intended meaning of the document. It is not unknown for different translations of a document to exist which have different, or even opposite, meanings.

A problem sometimes arises in relation to the FIDIC General Condi-tions of Contract, which are available in several different languages, although it is stated in the Foreword that the English language version is the official and authentic text. If the FIDIC General Conditions are included in the Contract by reference it is important to state in the Particular Conditions exactly which language version is applicable. When a version of the General Conditions in the language for communications has been published by FIDIC then this version should be used for communications during the project. However, when FIDIC has not published an official translation it is possible that several different translations are available, which will inevitably differ in the translations of some words.

1.5   Priority of Documents
The documents forming the Contract are to be taken as mutually explanatory of one another. For the purposes of interpretation, the priority of the documents shall be in accordance with the following sequence:

(a)   the Contract Agreement (if any),
(b)   the Letter of Acceptance,
(c)   the Letter of Tender,
(d)   the Particular Conditions,
(e)   these General Conditions,
(f)   the Specification,
(g)   the Drawings, and
(h)   the Schedules and any other documents forming part of the Contract.

If an ambiguity or discrepancy is found in the documents, the Engineer shall issue any necessary clarification or instruction.

In the Yellow Book the documents (f), (g) and (h) are replaced by:

(f)   the Employer's requirements
(g)   the Schedules
(h)   the Contractor's Proposal and any other documents forming part of the Contract.

Sub-Clause 1.5 gives the order of priority of the Contract documents and must be read in conjunction with any requirements of the applicable law. The FIDIC Guidance for the Preparation of Particular Conditions includes an alternative for use when the Contract does not give an order of precedence, but it is to be governed by the applicable law.

Under Sub-Clause 1.5 the first priority document is the Contract Agreement, followed by the Letter of Acceptance and Letter of Tender. These are the documents, in reverse order, which constitute the Contractor's offer, the Employer's acceptance of that offer and the Agreement signed by both Parties. This is logical because the Letter of Acceptance may include documents which have been agreed and which change the original Tender. The definitions at Sub-Clauses 1.1.1.2 and 1.1.1.3 suggest that either the Contract Agreement or the Letter of Acceptance might be omitted for a particular project, with the other document serving both purposes and including all the information which is required in both documents.

The Engineer can clarify any ambiguity or discrepancy between documents, which gives him the opportunity to issue an instruction that a requirement of a lower priority document shall be obeyed. Any such instruction would be a Variation under Clause 13 and might entitle the Contractor to an additional payment.

Particular requirements in a high-priority document may be overruled by a lower priority document when the changed priority is stated in the higher priority document. For example Sub-Clause 7.1(c) of these Conditions includes the statement 'except as otherwise specified in the Contract'. This particular requirement in the specification would then take precedence over the requirements of Sub-Clause 7.1(c).

In the Yellow Book it is significant that, although the Contractor's Proposal was studied and approved before the Contract was awarded, it remains a lower priority than the Employer's Requirements. If the Contractor's Proposals include any details that are different to the Employer's Requirements, but the Employer decided he preferred the Contractor's details, then it must be incorporated in the Contract as an amendment to the Employer's Requirements.

Similarly, if there are any errors in the Employer's Requirements, or the Engineer approves a detail in the Contractor's design which is different to the Employer's requirements, then the change must be recorded as a variation. This situation will be discussed at Sub-Clauses 1.9, 13.1 and 13.2.

1.6 Contract Agreement
The Parties shall enter into a Contract Agreement within 28 days after the Contractor receives the Letter of Acceptance, unless they agree otherwise. The Contract Agreement shall be based upon the form annexed to the Particular Conditions. The costs of stamp duties and similar charges (if any) imposed by law in connection with entry into the Contract Agreement shall be borne by the Employer.

Sub-Clause 1.6 requires the Contract Agreement to be entered into within 28 days from the date the Contractor receives the Letter of Acceptance, unless the Parties have agreed otherwise. The FIDIC Conditions of Contract do not include a Sub-Clause or standard form for the Letter of Acceptance although it is an essential part of the sequence of documents at the start of the Contract. The standard form for the Letter of Tender states that it will be open for acceptance until a stated date and it is clear that the Letter of Tender and the Letter of Acceptance of that Tender, together with attached documents, will form an agreement between the Parties.

The Letter of Acceptance is defined at Sub-Clause 1.1.1.3 and is also referred to at Sub-Clauses:

- 1.5 as having priority only after the Contract Agreement (if any)
- 1.6 as starting the 28 day period for the Contract Agreement
- 4.2 as starting a 28 day period for the Contractor to deliver the Performance Security to the Employer
- 8.1 as starting a 42 day period for the Commencement Date
- 18.1 as the end of a period for the Parties to agree terms for insurances.

The definition at Sub-Clause 1.1.1.2 and the reference at Sub-Clause 1.5(a) confirm that there may not be a Contract Agreement document for a particular project. The Letter of Acceptance then becomes the formal, as well as the initial, acceptance by the Employer. However, there may be a legal requirement for a Contract Agreement document, particularly for government Contracts.

The FIDIC documents include a standard form for a Contract Agreement. If the Employer has his own standard form it should be checked to make sure that it includes all the details in the FIDIC Contract Agreement. The Yellow Book form is the same as the Red Book form except that it includes a reference to the Contractor's obligation for the design.

Sub-Clause 1.6 requires the Employer to bear the cost of any charges imposed by law in connection with entry into the Contract Agreement. The Agreement must be 'based' on the FIDIC form which is annexed to the Particular Conditions. The Employer may wish to use his own standard form, which must then be checked to ensure that it is consistent with the FIDIC Conditions, includes the information which is given in the FIDIC form and complies with any requirements of the applicable law. The form which the Employer intends to use must be included with the Tender documents, although agreed modifications may be necessary following any Tender negotiations.

The FIDIC Guidance for the Preparation of Particular Conditions suggests that the Contract Agreement may record the Accepted Contract Amount, Base Date and/or Commencement Date. If this is intended then the various definitions, together with Sub-Clause 8.1, should be amended in the Particular Conditions.

1.7 Assignment

Neither Party shall assign the whole or any part of the Contract or any benefit or interest in or under the Contract. However, either Party:

(a) may assign the whole or any part with the prior agreement of the other Party, at the sole discretion of such other Party, and
(b) may, as security in favour of a bank or financial institution, assign its right to any moneys due, or to become due, under the Contract.

Neither Party is permitted to assign the whole or any part of the Contract except with the agreement of the other Party, or for its limited use for financial security.

1.8 Care and Supply of Documents

The Specification and Drawings shall be in the custody and care of the Employer. Unless otherwise stated in the Contract, two copies of the Contract and of each subsequent Drawing shall be supplied to the Contractor, who may make or request further copies at the cost of the Contractor.

Each of the Contractor's Documents shall be in the custody and care of the Contractor, unless and until taken over by the Employer. Unless otherwise stated in the Contract, the Contractor shall supply to the Engineer six copies of each of the Contractor's Documents.

The Contractor shall keep, on the Site, a copy of the Contract, publications named in the Specification, the Contractor's Documents (if any), the Drawings and Variations and other communications given under the Contract. The Employer's Personnel shall have the right of access to all these documents at all reasonable times.

If a Party becomes aware of an error or defect of a technical nature in a document which was prepared for use in executing the Works, the Party shall promptly give notice to the other Party of such error or defect.

In the Yellow Book the first paragraph has been deleted. A Specification and Drawings provided by the Employer are not relevant to construction with Contractor's design and so this first paragraph is not required.

Under Sub-Clause 1.8 either Party must give prompt notice to the other if they become aware of any error or defect of a technical nature in a document. Whilst the Party who prepared a document must be responsible for its content, the other Party has an obligation to co-operate in minimising the consequences of any mistake. If there is a mistake on a Drawing then an experienced Contractor may notice the mistake when using the Drawing for planning or ordering materials. He can then ask for a corrected Drawing to be issued before the item of work is constructed. It may be difficult to prove that the Contractor failed to report a mistake immediately he became aware of the mistake, but any breach of the requirement could result in a claim by the Employer for the consequences of the failure to give notice, or a reduction in the value of the Contractor's claim for the consequences of the error or defect.

In the Yellow Book the requirement to give prompt notice of any technical error or defect in a document 'which was prepared for use in executing the Works' imposes an obligation on the Employer, or the Engineer acting as Employer's Personnel, to inform the Contractor promptly of any error or defect which he becomes aware of in the Contractor's Documents.

The problem which arises is that, although the Party which prepared a document should be able to identify an error, the other Party may believe that the wording used is correct to express what was intended.

1.9 (RB)   Delayed Drawings or Instructions

The Contractor shall give notice to the Engineer whenever the Works are likely to be delayed or disrupted if any necessary drawing or instruction is not issued to the Contractor within a particular time, which shall be reasonable. The notice shall include details of the necessary drawing or instruction, details of why and by when it should be issued, and details of the nature and amount of the delay or disruption likely to be suffered if it is late. If the Contractor suffers delay and/or incurs Cost as a result of a failure of the Engineer to issue the notified drawing or instruction within a time which is reasonable and is specified in the notice with supporting details, the Contractor shall give a further notice to the Engineer and shall be entitled subject to Sub-Clause 20.1 [*Contractor's Claims*] to:

(a) an extension of time for any such delay, if completion is or will be delayed, under Sub-Clause 8.4 [*Extension of Time for Completion*], and

(b) payment of any such Cost plus reasonable profit, which shall be included in the Contract Price.

After receiving this further notice, the Engineer shall proceed in accordance with Sub-Clause 3.5 [*Determinations*] to agree or determine these matters.

However, if and to the extent that the Engineer's failure was caused by any error or delay by the Contractor, including an error in, or delay in the submission of, any of the Contractor's Documents, the Contractor shall not be entitled to such extension of time, Cost or profit.

1.9 (YB)   Errors in the Employer's Requirements

If the Contractor suffers delay and/or incurs Cost as a result of an error in the Employer's Requirements, and an experienced contractor exercising due care would not have discovered the error when scrutinising the

Employer's Requirements under Sub-Clause 5.1 [*General Design Obligations*], the Contractor shall give notice to the Engineer and shall be entitled subject to Sub-Clause 20.1 [*Contractor's Claims*] to:

(a) an extension of time for any such delay, if completion is or will be delayed, under Sub-Clause 8.4 [*Extension of Time for Completion*], and

(b) payment of any such Cost plus reasonable profit, which shall be included in the Contract Price.

After receiving this notice, the Engineer shall proceed in accordance with Sub-Clause 3.5 [*Determinations*] to agree or determine (i) whether and (if so) to what extent the error could not reasonably have been so discovered, and (ii) the matters described in sub-paragraphs (a) and (b) above related to this extent.

Under Sub-Clause 1.9 (RB) the Contractor is required to give notice if he requires an additional Drawing or instruction, the lack of which could delay the Works. The timing of this notice should give the Engineer reasonable time to prepare and issue the Drawing or instruction. However, the Contractor needs to know that the Engineer does not intend to issue the Drawing or instruction without being asked, so some discussion may precede the formal notice. The Engineer should have informed the Contractor of his intentions for the issue of further Drawings and instructions which he intends to issue under Sub-Clause 3.3.

The same circumstances might also require the Contractor to issue a notice under Sub-Clause 8.3. This notice must be issued 'promptly', to notify the Engineer of circumstances which may adversely affect the project. Whilst this would be a duplication of the Sub-Clause 1.9 notice, it would enable the Engineer to ask the Contractor for a Variation proposal under Sub-Clause 13.3 in order to overcome the problem. The existence of a potential problem and the measures being taken to overcome the problem would be included in the Contractor's monthly progress report under Sub-Clause 4.21(h).

Failure to issue the Drawing or instruction in a reasonable time might result in delay or additional Cost to the Contractor and require a further notice under Sub-Clause 1.9 and also under Sub-Clause 20.1. This notice would be included in the monthly progress report under Sub-Clause 4.21(f). The Contractor would claim additional time and Cost plus reasonable profit. The claim would be considered by the Engineer under Sub-Clause 3.5. The Engineer would consider whether the delay in issuing the information would delay completion, as required by Sub-Clause 8.4, as distinct from any immediate delay to a particular part of the Works. The Engineer would also consider whether the Contractor was responsible for the delay, for example by failing to provide some information which was required in order to complete the Drawings.

Under a Contractor's design Contract the Employer's Requirements are fixed when the Contract is agreed, subject only to Variations under Clause 13. The Engineer can issue instructions, 'which may be necessary for the execution of the Works', under Sub-Clause 3.3, but he cannot issue additional Drawings to develop the basic information which was contained in the Tender Drawings.

The Red Book Sub-Clause 1.9 [*Delayed Drawings or Instructions*] is not therefore required. If an instruction under Sub-Clause 3.3 is delayed and the Contractor suffers additional Cost or delay then the Contractor would probably claim that the instruction constituted a Variation.

The Yellow Book Sub-Clause 1.9 enables the Contractor to claim for any delay or additional Cost as a result of an error in the Employer's Requirements. The Employer must give notice to the Engineer and then follow the same procedures as in the Red Book. The error must be such that it would not have been discovered by an experienced Contractor during the initial check of the Employer's requirements under the second paragraph of Sub-Clause 5.1.

1.10   Employer's Use of Contractor's Documents

As between the Parties, the Contractor shall retain the copyright and other intellectual property rights in the Contractor's Documents and other design documents made by (or on behalf of) the Contractor.

The Contractor shall be deemed (by signing the Contract) to give to the Employer a non-terminable transferable non-exclusive royalty-free licence to copy, use and communicate the Contractor's Documents, including making and using modifications of them. This licence shall:

(a)   apply throughout the actual or intended working life (whichever is longer) of the relevant parts of the Works;

(b)   entitle any person in proper possession of the relevant part of the Works to copy, use and communicate the Contractor's Documents for the purposes of completing, operating, maintaining, altering, adjusting, repairing and demolishing the Works; and

(c)   in the case of Contractor's Documents which are in the form of computer programs and other software, permit their use on any computer on the Site and other places as envisaged by the Contract, including replacements of any computers supplied by the Contractor.

The Contractor's Documents and other design documents made by (or on behalf of) the Contractor shall not, without the Contractor's consent, be used, copied or communicated to a third party by (or on behalf of) the Employer for purposes other than those permitted under this Sub-Clause.

This Sub-Clause enables the Employer to make use of documents which are the Contractor's copyright, for the purposes of the Contract.

1.11 Contractor's Use of Employer's Documents

As between the Parties, the Employer shall retain the copyright and other intellectual property rights in the Specification, the Drawings and other documents made by (or on behalf of) the Employer. The Contractor may, at his cost, copy, use, and obtain communication of these documents for the purposes of the Contract. They shall not, without the Employer's consent, be copied, used or communicated to a third party by the Contractor, except as necessary for the purposes of the Contract.

This Sub-Clause in the Yellow Book is the same as RB except that 'Specification, the Drawings' is replaced by 'Employer's Requirements'. The Contractor may copy and use the Employer's documents, but only for the purposes of the Contract.

1.12 Confidential Details

The Contractor shall disclose all such confidential and other information as the Engineer may reasonably require in order to verify the Contractor's compliance with the Contract.

The Engineer has a duty to check that the Contractor is complying with the requirements of the Contract. If, in order to carry out this duty, he requires information that would normally be confidential to the Contractor then the Contractor must provide this information. The extent of this information and any requirement for copies of documents will be limited by the Engineer's need to satisfy himself and he is not permitted to use the information for any other purpose. However, particularly under the Yellow Book, there may be information which the Contractor, or a Subcontractor, may wish to keep confidential. This would then be the subject of negotiation as to how the Engineer can comply with his obligations but permit sensitive information to remain confidential. The Employer should consider including in the Particular Conditions the Silver Book provision that the Contractor may state in his Tender that certain information is confidential.

The FIDIC Guidance for the Preparation of Particular Conditions includes an example Sub-Clause for use when the Employer requires the Contractor to keep the details of the Contract confidential and obtain the Employer's agreement before publishing any technical paper or other information concerning the Works.

1.13   Compliance with Laws

The Contractor shall, in performing the Contract, comply with applicable Laws. Unless otherwise stated in the Particular Conditions:

(a)   the Employer shall have obtained (or shall obtain) the planning, zoning or similar permission for the Permanent Works, and any other permissions described in the Specification as having been (or being) obtained by the Employer; and the Employer shall indemnify and hold the Contractor harmless against and from the consequences of any failure to do so; and

(b)   the Contractor shall give all notices, pay all taxes, duties and fees, and obtain all permits, licences and approvals, as required by the Laws in relation to the execution and completion of the Works and the remedying of any defects; and the Contractor shall indemnify and hold the Employer harmless against and from the consequences of any failure to do so.

The YB Sub-Clause is the same as that in the RB except that 'Specification' is replaced by 'Employer's Requirements' in paragraph (a) and 'design' is added before 'execution' in paragraph (b).

An overall requirement is given at Sub-Clause 1.13 that the Contractor shall comply with the applicable Laws, which includes giving notices and obtaining permits as required by the regulations. However, some permits should be obtained before the Employer calls for Tenders and the Contractor is not required to obtain planning permission, or any other permits which the Specification states will be obtained by the Employer. The phrase 'similar permission' in subparagraph (a) could be ambiguous and should be clarified in the Particular Conditions. Each Party is required to indemnify and hold harmless the other Party against any failure to comply with this requirement.

The requirement that each Party shall indemnify and hold the other Party harmless against any failure to obtain permissions, etc. is a severe sanction. The sums of money would be much larger than for a claim for Costs and reasonable profit. It is therefore essential that the responsibilities of the Parties are clearly stated. FIDIC provides that changes in principle must be given in the Particular Conditions. Planning and similar permissions for the Permanent Works must be obtained by the Employer and, if the Employer intends to obtain other permissions then they will be described in the Specification or Employer's Requirements. All other permissions, approvals, etc. will be obtained by the Contractor. However, if there is a change in the Laws which, as defined at Sub-Clause 1.1.6.5, includes regulation and by-laws, or 'in the judicial or official governmental interpretation of such laws' then the Contractor will be entitled to time and costs under Sub-Clause 13.7. If any authority causes disruption or a delay then the Contractor may be entitled to an extension of time under Sub-Clause 8.5.

The addition of the word 'design' at paragraph (b) of the Yellow Book confirms that the Contractor must obtain the necessary design approvals. This is in addition to the consent or approval by the Engineer under YB Sub-Clause 5.1. The Contractor must include a suitable allowance in the Sub-Clause 8.3 programme. If the Contractor is required to carry out any design under RB Sub-Clause 4.1 then the matter of obtaining approvals must be clarified in the Particular Conditions.

The FIDIC guidance for the Particular Conditions also raises the point that the Employer may need to obtain import licences and various consents for Goods for a plant Contract, but will first require information from the Contractor.

1.14   Joint and Several Liability

If the Contractor constitutes (under applicable Laws) a joint venture, consortium or other unincorporated grouping of two or more persons:

(a)   these persons shall be deemed to be jointly and severally liable to the Employer for the performance of the Contract;

(b)   these persons shall notify the Employer of their leader who shall have authority to bind the Contractor and each of these persons; and

(c)   the Contractor shall not alter its composition or legal status without the prior consent of the Employer.

If the Contractor is a joint venture, or other grouping of two or more persons, then Sub-Clause 1.14 requires that the separate persons are jointly and severally liable, but one of them must have the authority to bind them all and have been designated as the leader. The approval of the Employer is necessary if the persons in the joint venture wish to alter the composition or legal status of the Contractor.

The applicable law may also include requirements for joint ventures and the Employer may have other requirements, which should be included in the Instructions to Tenderers. For example, a parent company guarantee may be required from each member. FIDIC includes an example form as Annex A to the Guidance for the Preparation of Particular Conditions.

These requirements must have been considered by tenderers before they decide to tender for the Contract. The details of the joint venture or grouping will also have been checked by the Employer at pre-tender or tender stage, preferably during a pre-qualification procedure. The arrangements must be in place before the Employer accepts the Tender.

Chapter 10

Clause 2: The Employer

The FIDIC standard form for the Contract Agreement includes the statement that the Employer covenants to pay the Contractor the Contract Price in consideration of the execution and completion of the Works and the remedying of defects therein. However, this does not mean that the Employer is only required to appoint an Engineer to administer the project and then sign the payment cheques. The development of Conditions of Contract over the years has imposed additional tasks on the Employer, involving both rights and obligations. In some countries the law also imposes duties on the Employer in a construction Contract.

The Conditions of Contract require the Employer, as distinct from the Engineer, to take certain actions during the construction period. Even though the Engineer is now classed as 'Employer's Personnel' there are some tasks that are allocated to the Employer. Whilst the Employer could delegate the paperwork to the Engineer, particularly if the designated Engineer is an employee of the Employer, the actual tasks require the Employer to be involved. It is important that the Employer designates a staff member, separate from the Engineer, to represent him whenever the Contract requires notice to, or action by, the Employer.

Clause 2 must be read in conjunction with other Clauses and covers:

- possession of the Site
- assistance with permits, etc.
- Employer's Personnel, financial arrangements and claims.

Definitions at Sub-Clause 1.1 which are relevant to this Clause include:

1.1.1.2	Contract Agreement
1.1.1.5 (RB)	Specification
1.1.1.5 (YB)	Employer's Requirements
1.1.1.9	Appendix to Tender
1.1.2.2	Employer
1.1.2.6	Employer's Personnel

1.1.6.6   Performance Security
1.1.6.7   Site.

2.1   Right of Access to the Site

The Employer shall give the Contractor right of access to, and possession of, all parts of the Site within the time (or times) stated in the Appendix to Tender. The right and possession may not be exclusive to the Contractor. If, under the Contract, the Employer is required to give (to the Contractor) possession of any foundation, structure, plant or means of access, the Employer shall do so in the time and manner stated in the Specification. However, the Employer may withhold any such right or possession until the Performance Security has been received.

If no such time is stated in the Appendix to Tender, the Employer shall give the Contractor right of access to, and possession of, the Site within such times as may be required to enable the Contractor to proceed in accordance with the programme submitted under Sub-Clause 8.3 [*Programme*].

If the Contractor suffers delay and/or incurs Cost as a result of a failure by the Employer to give any such right or possession within such time, the Contractor shall give notice to the Engineer and shall be entitled subject to Sub-Clause 20.1 [*Contractor's Claims*] to:

(a)   an extension of time for any such delay, if completion is or will be delayed, under Sub-Clause 8.4 [*Extension of Time for Completion*]; and

(b)   payment of any such Cost plus reasonable profit, which shall be included in the Contract Price.

After receiving this notice, the Engineer shall proceed in accordance with Sub-Clause 3.5 [*Determinations*] to agree or determine these matters.

However, if and to the extent that the Employer's failure was caused by any error or delay by the Contractor, including an error in, or delay in the submission of, any of the Contractor's Documents, the Contractor shall not be entitled to such extension of time, Cost or profit.

In the Yellow Book the reference to 'Specification' is changed to 'Employer's Requirements'. Sub-Clause 2.1 refers to 'right of access to' and 'possession of the Site', but these terms are qualified at other Sub-Clauses. 'Access' refers to the right to enter the Site and must not be confused with 'access routes' which are the Contractor's responsibility as stated at Sub-Clause 4.15. 'Possession' refers to the Contractor taking over control and responsibility for the Site. The Appendix to Tender states the number of days from the Commencement Date within which the Employer must give access to the Site. When the Employer issues the Letter of Acceptance he is fixing the latest calendar date for providing possession of the Site. If this access and possession is to be restricted to different parts of the Site at different times then the restrictions must be stated in the Particular Conditions, dates being given in the Appendix to Tender, with full details in the Specification.

Sub-Clause 2.1 states that possession does not necessarily mean exclusive possession, but shared possession requires clarification in the Particular Conditions. When the Contractor takes possession of the Site he assumes responsibility for matters such as safety, security and insurance. If the Contractor does not have full control of the Site and the activities on the Site, or if these powers are to be shared, then the extent of the Contractor's responsibilities must be clearly stated.

The 'Site' is defined at Sub-Clause 1.1.6.7 as including not just the area of land on which the Works are to be executed, but also any other places which are specified in the Contract. These may include areas that have been set aside for the Contractor to use for storage or for obtaining excavated materials or for any other purpose. It is important that the Site area is delineated clearly in the Contract Drawings or Specification.

If the Employer fails to give right of access to and possession of the Site within the stated period then the Contractor will be entitled to an extension of time, plus his Costs and a reasonable profit, subject to his following the correct procedures as detailed at Sub-Clauses 2.1 and 20.1 and the delay not being attributable to a failure on the part of the Contractor.

2.2 Permits, Licences or Approvals

The Employer shall (where he is in a position to do so) provide reasonable assistance to the Contractor at the request of the Contractor:

(a) by obtaining copies of the Laws of the Country which are relevant to the Contract but are not readily available; and
(b) for the Contractor's applications for any permits, licences or approvals required by the Laws of the Country:
  (i) which the Contractor is required to obtain under Sub-Clause 1.13 [Compliance with Laws], (ii) for the delivery of Goods, including clearance through customs, and (iii) for the export of Contractor's Equipment when it is removed from the Site.

Sub-Clause 2.2 obliges the Employer to assist the Contractor to obtain copies of the Laws of the Country and with applications for any permits, licences or approvals required by these Laws, in the circumstances which are listed in the Sub-Clause. This refers to the Laws of the Country, which are not necessarily the governing law as stated in the Appendix to Tender, but are documents to which the Employer can be assumed to have access.

The obligation is qualified as 'reasonable' and the Employer being in the position to give assistance. The Contractor will also rely on his local partner, agent or representative before calling on the assistance of the Employer. Co-operation and assistance should always be given when possible, but it must be doubtful whether, if the assistance fails to achieve the desired result, this would reduce the Contractor's obligations or give grounds for a claim. However, a delay in any of these operations could result in a claim under Sub-Clause 8.5 for Delays by Authorities.

The Sub-Clause does not refer to the Employer being able to charge the Contractor for providing this service. The provision of 'reasonable' assistance must be assumed to be free of any charge. However, if the Contractor is asking for excessive 'unreasonable' assistance then the Employer might give notice under Sub-Clause 2.5 that he intends to make a charge. The Contractor might then decide to withdraw his request and obtain the information elsewhere.

2.3   Employer's Personnel

The Employer shall be responsible for ensuring that the Employer's Personnel and the Employer's other contractors on the Site:

(a)   co-operate with the Contractor's efforts under Sub-Clause 4.6 [*Co-operation*]; and

(b)   take actions similar to those which the Contractor is required to take under subparagraphs (a), (b) and (c) of Sub-Clause 4.8 [*Safety Procedures*] and under Sub-Clause 4.18 [*Protection of the Environment*].

Employer's Personnel are defined at Sub-Clause 1.1.2.6 as being people so notified to the Contractor, including:

*   the Engineer and his assistants;
*   all staff, labour and employees of the Employer and the Engineer;
*   any other person who the Employer or the Engineer has decided to designate as Employer's Personnel.

The designation as Employer's Personnel must be used with discretion. Anyone so designated has rights under other Sub-Clauses including the Sub-Clause 17.1 indemnities. The Employer also indemnifies the Contractor for certain actions by Employer's Personnel, including Sub-Clause 17.1.

Sub-Clause 4.6 has a separate requirement for the Contractor to co-operate with other Contractors and public authority personnel. They are not normally Employer's Personnel, but presumably some individuals could be designated and notified to the Contractor as Employer's Personnel.

Sub-Clause 2.3 obliges the Employer to take responsibility for Employer's Personnel and for other Contractors' reciprocal co-operation under Sub-Clause 4.6, Safety Procedures similar to Sub-Clause 4.8(a), (b), (c) and Protection of the Environment as Sub-Clause 4.18. It is important that the Employer includes similar Clauses in his Contracts with all the Contractors who will be working on the Site.

When two or more Contractors are working on the same Site the possibilities of delays and Costs from failures of co-operation, or other problems, can have serious consequences. If the Contractor incurs Costs as a consequence of an action by another Contractor then he may wish to claim against the Employer, but the liability is not clear and may depend on the applicable law. The FIDIC Clauses may be adequate when this Contractor is carrying out a high percentage of the total work on the Site. However, if the work is more evenly divided between two or more Contractors it is necessary to review the provisions of the Contract.

2.4   Employer's Financial Arrangements

The Employer shall submit, within 28 days after receiving any request from the Contractor, reasonable evidence that financial arrangements have been made and are being maintained which will enable the Employer to pay the Contract Price (as estimated at that time) in accordance with Clause 14 [*Contract Price and Payment*]. If the Employer intends to make any material change to his financial arrangements, the Employer shall give notice to the Contractor with detailed particulars.

Sub-Clause 2.4 is a new provision which could be reassuring to Contractors. The Sub-Clause requires the Employer to provide evidence that he has the finance available to pay the Contractor in accordance with the Contract. The evidence must be provided within 42 days of a request by the Contractor. If the project is financed by an international development agency or similar organisation then it may be advisable to state this fact in the Particular Conditions to reassure tenderers and avoid the subsequent request. Any representative of the finance institution could then be declared as Employer's Personnel and visit the Site if necessary.

If the Employer fails to comply with this Sub-Clause then the Contractor can give 21 days' notice to suspend work, or reduce the rate of work, under Sub-Clause 16.1. If he does not receive reasonable evidence within 42 days of giving notice under Sub-Clause 16.1 then he is entitled to terminate the Contract under Sub-Clause 16.2. The procedures of Sub-Clauses 16.3 and 16.4 will then apply.

The protracted time periods are necessary to give the Employer a reasonable time to make arrangements and satisfy the Contractor.

However, they make a total period of 105 days or three and a half months from the initial request to the entitlement to terminate the Contract. During this period the Contractor may have spent substantial sums of money on the Contract, perhaps with little chance of recovery. Hence the value of giving the name of any financing body in the Particular Conditions.

The Sub-Clause is not clear as to who provides the estimate of the Contract Price and what would constitute reasonable evidence. If the Contractor has already submitted claims, which have been rejected by the Engineer, then they may have very different estimates of the figure which should be taken as the estimated Contract Price. The matter of what constitutes reasonable evidence will depend on the circumstances and could require a statement from the bank, financing authority, Ministry of Finance, or whoever is providing the finance for the project. A payment guarantee by the Employer, on the standard form at Annex G at the back of the FIDIC document, would presumably meet the requirement. The consequences that can arise if the Employer fails to comply with the request are so serious that this situation could result in a dispute, which could be referred to the DAB.

2.5 Employer's Claims

If the Employer considers himself to be entitled to any payment under any Clause of these Conditions or otherwise in connection with the Contract, and/or to any extension of the Defects Notification Period, the Employer or the Engineer shall give notice and particulars to the Contractor. However, notice is not required for payments due under Sub-Clause 4.19 [*Electricity, Water and Gas*], under Sub-Clause 4.20 [*Employer's Equipment and Free-Issue Material*], or for other services requested by the Contractor.

The notice shall be given as soon as practicable after the Employer became aware of the event or circumstances giving rise to the claim. A notice relating to any extension of the Defects Notification Period shall be given before the expiry of such period.

The particulars shall specify the Clause or other basis of the claim, and shall include substantiation of the amount and/or extension to which the Employer considers himself to be entitled in connection with the Contract. The Engineer shall then proceed in accordance with Sub-Clause 3.5 [*Determinations*] to agree or determine (i) the amount (if any) which the Employer is entitled to be paid by the Contractor, and/or (ii) the extension (if any) of the Defects Notification Period in accordance with Sub-Clause 11.3 [*Extension of Defects Notification Period*].

This amount may be included as a deduction in the Contract Price and Payment Certificates. The Employer shall only be entitled to set off against or make any deduction from an amount certified in a Payment Certificate, or to otherwise claim against the Contractor, in accordance with this Sub-Clause.

Sub-Clause 2.5 enables the Employer to give notice of any claim for an extension to the Defects Notification Period or for payments from the Contractor. This procedure must be followed for all deductions or claims for payment except payments for:

- electricity, water and gas under Sub-Clause 4.19;
- Employer's Equipment and free-issue material under Sub-Clause 4.20;
- other services requested by the Contractor, for which the payment has presumably been agreed in advance.

The procedure also applies to any other claims for payment, including claims for amounts not insured or not recovered from the insurers as the final paragraph of Sub-Clause 18.1. This procedure should prevent Employers from making unexpected deductions from payment certificates or raising unexpected claims or counterclaims.

The notice must be given 'as soon as practicable after the Employer became aware of the event or circumstances giving rise to the claim', which should normally be a shorter period than the 28 days from the event which the Contractor is allowed under Sub-Clause 20.1. However, the requirement omits the phrase 'or should have become aware', which would be more usual in these circumstances. Any notice for extension must be given before the expiry of the Defects Notification Period, but other notices may presumably be given before or after the issue of the Performance Certificate. A notice of claim given after the issue of the Performance Certificate would need to overcome the statement at Sub-Clause 11.9 that 'Only the Performance Certificate shall be deemed to constitute acceptance of the Works'.

The notice is not just a 'notice of claim', comparable to the Contractor's Sub-Clause 20.1 notice. It must also include the Clause or other basis of the claim and substantiation of the amount or time period which is claimed. The need to include this substantiation will obviously delay the issue of the notice. From a project management point of view it would be better to follow the Sub-Clause 20.1 procedure of giving an initial notice of claim, followed by the detailed substantiation as soon as this information is available.

Any such claim by the Employer is then dealt with by the Engineer under Sub-Clause 3.5 for Determinations. If the Engineer determines that the Employer is entitled to payment then the amount may be deducted from the Contract Price and from Payment Certificates. If either Party is not satisfied with the Engineer's determination then the resulting dispute could be referred to the Dispute Adjudication Board under Sub-Clause 20.4.

The actual procedure for recording the deduction will depend on the reason for the deduction. It is important that it is kept separate from the items of payments to the Contractor and the reasons for the deduction, or deductions, are clearly stated. A problem will arise if the Employer's claim occurs during the Defects Notification Period or when, for some reason, the Contractor is not asking for an Interim Payment Certificate. Even if the Contractor included the Engineer's determination in his monthly statement the time periods for payment, at Clause 14, could result in the Employer being entitled to claim against the Performance Security under Sub-Clause 4.2(b), which would obviously be unreasonable.

Chapter 11

Clause 3: The Engineer

The 'Engineer' is defined at Sub-Clause 1.1.2.4 as the person appointed by the Employer and named in the Appendix to Tender. Under the introductory paragraph to Sub-Clause 1.1 the word 'person' can mean a company, so the Engineer may be named as a firm of Consulting Engineers rather than an individual. If the Engineer is a company then the company should designate an individual to carry out the role of the Engineer. Alternatively, the Engineer may be an individual or a member of the Employer's own staff. If the Employer wishes to change the Engineer from the person named in the Appendix to Tender then he must follow the procedures of Sub-Clause 3.4.

One of the most important changes from the 1987 FIDIC Fourth Edition to the 1999 FIDIC Conditions of Contract is in the role of the Engineer. The 1987 FIDIC Edition required the Engineer to exercise his discretion 'impartially within the terms of the Contract and having regard to all the circumstances'. The 1999 Conditions state that the Engineer 'shall be deemed to act for the Employer' but, when he is making a decision under Sub-Clause 3.5, 'shall make a fair determination in accordance with the Contract, taking due regard of all relevant circumstances'. Whether this change means that the Engineer would make a different decision on any particular claim and the extent to which this change of role will influence the Engineer when he is making decisions will emerge in time. If the Engineer acts fairly in accordance with the Contract, then the change in the wording may be less significant than it would at first seem. The Engineer must also remember that any decision can be overruled by the DAB within a very short period of time. A series of adverse decisions by the DAB may cause an Employer to question the competence of the Engineer.

Furthermore, the previous FIDIC Contracts had a clear distinction between the tasks and procedures that are the duty of the Engineer and those that are matters for the Employer. The 1999 Conditions have omitted the requirement that some notices which are sent to the Engineer must be copied to the Employer. However, the distinction has been maintained in other provisions, although some of these are likely in practice to be carried out by the Engineer now that he is 'deemed to act for the Employer'.

Definitions at Sub-Clause 1.1 relevant to this Clause include:

1.1.2.2   Employer
1.1.2.3   Contractor
1.1.2.4   Engineer
1.1.2.5   Contractor's Representative
1.1.2.6   Employer's Personnel
1.1.2.9   DAB.

3.1   Engineer's Duties and Authority

The Employer shall appoint the Engineer who shall carry out the duties assigned to him in the Contract. The Engineer's staff shall include suitably qualified engineers and other professionals who are competent to carry out these duties.

The Engineer shall have no authority to amend the Contract.

The Engineer may exercise the authority attributable to the Engineer as specified in or necessarily to be implied from the Contract. If the Engineer is required to obtain the approval of the Employer before exercising a specified authority, the requirements shall be as stated in the Particular Conditions. The Employer undertakes not to impose further constraints on the Engineer's authority, except as agreed with the Contractor.

However, whenever the Engineer exercises a specified authority for which the Employer's approval is required, then (for the purposes of the Contract) the Employer shall be deemed to have given approval.

Except as otherwise stated in these Conditions:

(a)   whenever carrying out duties or exercising authority, specified in or implied by the Contract, the Engineer shall be deemed to act for the Employer;

(b)   the Engineer has no authority to relieve either Party of any duties, obligations or responsibilities under the Contract; and

(c)   any approval, check, certificate, consent, examination, inspection, instruction, notice, proposal, request, test, or similar act by the Engineer (including absence of disapproval) shall not relieve the Contractor from any responsibility he has under the Contract, including responsibility for errors, omissions, discrepancies and non-compliances.

The Engineer has an extremely important role in the administration of the Contract and the way in which he carries out his duties will have a major impact on the work of the Contractor and the success of the project. The

Contractor will have made an assumption concerning the likely performance of the Engineer (having been named in the Tender documents) and taken this into account when pricing his Tender.

The Particular Conditions must include details of any requirements for the Engineer to obtain the Employer's approval before exercising any authority which is given to him under the Contract. When writing the Particular Conditions it is important that the Employer considers the implications on the whole sequence of project management events and does not just consider isolated Sub-Clauses. This Sub-Clause recognises that having to obtain such approval is a constraint on the Engineer's authority and his freedom to make 'fair' decisions. Any additional constraint imposed on the Engineer after the Contract has been agreed would be a breach of Contract by the Employer, for which the Contractor would be entitled to claim damages.

The approvals that are required will vary dependent on whether the Engineer is an independent consultant or a member of the Employer's own staff. An Engineer who is a member of the Employer's staff may have limits on his authority such that additional expenditure, or certifying payment, requires approval from a senior person or a different department. If a named individual is the Engineer any limits on his authority must be stated. A consultant working for a private Employer may have been given the necessary authority, but a consultant working for a Government Employer will probably have limits placed on his authority. The Contractor does not see the contract between the Engineer and the Employer so a clear statement of his authority is essential. These limitations may differ if the Engineer is not the designer for a Red Book Contract.

Approval could reasonably be required before issuing variations under Clause 13 which would involve changes to the design or result in additional cost greater than a designated figure. Some Employers require the Engineer to obtain approval before certifying *any* additional cost or extension of time. However, under Sub-Clause 3.5, the Engineer is required to consult with the Employer before making 'a fair determination in accordance with the Contract' on a claim for time or money. To require approval of the action after this consultation would imply that the Employer may wish to prevent the Engineer from giving a determination based on his technical and contractual assessment of the claim.

In accordance with Sub-Clause 3.1(a) the Engineer is deemed to act for the Employer 'except as otherwise stated in these Conditions'. However, it is not clear which Sub-Clauses comply with this 'otherwise stated' exception. Several Sub-Clauses, such as Sub-Clause 3.5 and the payment provisions require the Engineer to be 'fair' and it must be assumed that he will always act in accordance with the requirements of the Contract. Furthermore, whether acting for the Employer or under

Sub-Clause 3.5 he will presumably discuss any approval, certificate or action with the Employer if he wishes to obtain the Employer's point of view before deciding what action to take.

A problem will arise if the Employer persuades the Engineer to take some action which is clearly against the provisions of the Contract. This situation would be exposed if a dispute is referred to the DAB and their decision so clearly contradicts the action of the Engineer that no reasonable Engineer could have been expected to act in that way.

3.2   Delegation by the Engineer

The Engineer may from time to time assign duties and delegate authority to assistants, and may also revoke such assignment or delegation. These assistants may include a resident engineer, and/or independent inspectors appointed to inspect and/or test items of Plant and/or Materials. The assignment, delegation or revocation shall be in writing and shall not take effect until copies have been received by both Parties. However, unless otherwise agreed by both Parties, the Engineer shall not delegate the authority to determine any matter in accordance with Sub-Clause 3.5 [*Determinations*].

Assistants shall be suitably qualified persons, who are competent to carry out these duties and exercise this authority, and who are fluent in the language for communications defined in Sub-Clause 1.4 [*Law and Language*].

Each assistant, to whom duties have been assigned or authority has been delegated, shall only be authorised to issue instructions to the Contractor to the extent defined by the delegation. Any approval, check, certificate, consent, examination, inspection, instruction, notice, proposal, request, test, or similar act by an assistant, in accordance with the delegation, shall have the same effect as though the act had been an act of the Engineer. However:

(a)   any failure to disapprove any work, Plant or Materials shall not constitute approval, and shall therefore not prejudice the right of the Engineer to reject the work, Plant or Materials;

(b)   if the Contractor questions any determination or instruction of an assistant, the Contractor may refer the matter to the Engineer, who shall promptly confirm, reverse or vary the determination or instruction.

The Engineer, either as an individual or a designated member of a company, will require assistance to carry out all the duties assigned to him under the Contract. Details of the delegation must be sent in writing to both Parties. If a company is designated as Engineer then all the individuals who will be exercising authority by checking or instructing the Contractor, as Engineer or as assistants to the Engineer, should be named and their authority confirmed.

Previous FIDIC Contracts included specific reference to the 'Engineer's Representative', who was normally resident on the Site, acted as the representative of the Engineer and to whom most of the daily administration was delegated. Reference to this position has now been deleted and seems to be replaced by the phrase 'These assistants may include a resident engineer'. The implication is that the Engineer no longer needs a deputy who is permanently on the Site. Possibly the Engineer himself is expected to spend more time on the Site and so be able to supervise the work of a number of assistants to whom particular duties have been delegated. This would mean that the Engineer would be a less senior person within his organisation. Sub-Clause 4.3 requires the Contractor to designate a 'Contractor's Representative' who will be employed full time on the Contract, so it would be logical for the Engineer to designate someone to act as resident engineer on the Site.

The Engineer is not permitted to delegate his authority under Sub-Clause 3.5, except with the agreement of both Parties. However, the duties under numerous other Sub-Clauses require immediate action on the Site. It is therefore convenient for the Engineer to delegate all authority to a deputy, except for specified Sub-Clauses.

In practice, for a major project, the Engineer will need a large team of engineers, inspectors and other specialists. A detailed organisation chart should be issued to the Contractor at the start of the project and updated whenever there are changes in personnel. All such people are designated by definition as Employer's Personnel.

3.3 Instructions of the Engineer

The Engineer may issue to the Contractor (at any time) instructions and additional or modified Drawings which may be necessary for the execution of the Works and the remedying of any defects, all in accordance with the Contract. The Contractor shall only take instructions from the Engineer, or from an assistant to whom the appropriate authority has been delegated under this Clause. If an instruction constitutes a Variation, Clause 13 [*Variations and Adjustments*] shall apply.

The Contractor shall comply with the instructions given by the Engineer or delegated assistant, on any matter related to the Contract. Whenever practicable, their instructions shall be given in writing. If the Engineer or a delegated assistant:

(a) gives an oral instruction,
(b) receives a written confirmation of the instruction, from (or on behalf of) the Contractor, within two working days after giving the instruction, and

(c)   does not reply by issuing a written rejection and/or instruction within two working days after receiving the confirmation;

then the confirmation shall constitute the written instruction of the Engineer or delegated assistant (as the case may be).

In the Yellow Book the provisions for the Engineer to issue additional or modified Drawings and to give oral instructions have been deleted. When the Contractor is responsible for the design any instructions or additional Drawings from the Engineer will be Variations, as Clause 13.

Sub-Clause 3.3 requires the Contractor to comply with any instruction from the Engineer, or an assistant to whom authority has been delegated under Sub-Clause 3.2, with a procedure for the confirmation of oral instructions. If the Contractor considers that an instruction will result in additional Costs or delay to completion then he should confirm receipt as a Variation, in accordance with Sub-Clause 13.3.

The Sub-Clause gives the Engineer the power to issue additional or modified Drawings. This is an important power because many Contracts under the FIDIC Conditions of Contract rely on a very small number of Drawings in the Tender documents. The majority of the detailed Drawings are issued as and when required during construction. It is for the Engineer to ensure that the Drawings are issued to suit the progress requirements and he will rely on the Contractor's programme as Sub-Clause 8.3, the monthly progress reports as Sub-Clause 4.21, information on any design which is the responsibility of the Contractor as Sub-Clauses 4.1(a) and (b) and any requests from the Contractor as Sub-Clause 1.9.

3.4   Replacement of the Engineer

If the Employer intends to replace the Engineer, the Employer shall, not less than 42 days before the intended date of replacement, give notice to the Contractor of the name, address and relevant experience of the intended replacement Engineer. The Employer shall not replace the Engineer with a person against whom the Contractor raises reasonable objection by notice to the Employer, with supporting particulars.

The Employer is entitled to change the Engineer provided he gives 42 days' notice with details of the proposed replacement. However, a change to the named individual, when the Engineer is a company, does not require this notification, although reasonable notice and discussion would assist in efficient administration. The Employer does not have to give any reason for the change, but should take into account that to change the Engineer will have serious consequences for the administration of the Contract, whether the change is made at the start or during the progress of the Works.

The 42 day notice period must be considered in relation to the other time periods stated in the Conditions of Contract. For example, at the start of the project, if the Employer gave notice in the Letter of Acceptance, the Engineer named in the Appendix to Tender would still be obliged to give the notice of the Commencement Date, unless the 42 days stated at Sub-Clause 8.1 had been changed in the Particular Conditions. Similarly, whenever the notice is given, the original Engineer will issue at least one monthly Interim Payment Certificate under Sub-Clause 14.6 during the notice period. A change of Engineer could also mean changes to the resident engineer and other assistants appointed under Sub-Clause 3.2. The Contractor should indicate as quickly as possible whether he intends to object to the replacement Engineer so that the 42 day period can be used as a changeover period as well as a notice period. If the Engineer should die, or otherwise cease to be available, then the notice period should be waived, by agreement between the Parties.

3.5 Determinations

Whenever these Conditions provide that the Engineer shall proceed in accordance with this Sub-Clause 3.5 to agree or determine any matter, the Engineer shall consult with each Party in an endeavour to reach agreement. If agreement is not achieved, the Engineer shall make a fair determination in accordance with the Contract, taking due regard of all relevant circumstances.

The Engineer shall give notice to both Parties of each agreement or determination, with supporting particulars. Each Party shall give effect to each agreement or determination unless and until revised under Clause 20 [*Claims, Disputes and Arbitration*].

Throughout the Conditions of Contract, whenever the Contractor submits a claim for an extension of time or reimbursement of costs, the Engineer is required to proceed in accordance with Sub-Clause 3.5. This Sub-Clause requires the Engineer to consult with each Party in an endeavour to reach agreement. To comply with this requirement the Engineer must act as a mediator and try to help the Parties towards agreement.

If agreement is not achieved the Engineer must make 'a fair determination in accordance with the Contract, taking due regard of all relevant circumstances'. The key phrase here is 'in accordance with the Contract'. The determination must express the rights and obligations of the Parties, in accordance with the Contract and the applicable law, regardless of the preferences of either Party. Under Sub-Clause 3.2 the Engineer cannot delegate this task without the agreement of both Parties.

This Sub-Clause does not impose a time limit on the Engineer for making his determination, but the situation would be covered by the requirement of Sub-Clause 1.3 that a determination 'shall not be unreasonably withheld'. The timing of this determination is discussed further in Chapter 30 of this book, under Sub-Clause 20.1.

Additional Sub-Clause 3.6 [*Management Meetings*]

The FIDIC Guidance for the Preparation of Particular Conditions includes an example Sub-Clause for either the Engineer or the Contractor's representative to call a management meeting. This is a very useful provision and should be included in any FIDIC Contract. A definition of 'Management Meeting' should be added to Sub-Clause 1.1.6. FIDIC procedures rely on the exchange of notices and written information whereas from a practical project management point of view a meeting to discuss a problem is far more effective than an exchange of paperwork. Whilst most Contractors and Engineers arrange meetings when necessary without any provision in the Contract there may be occasions when a contractual provision is required. The FIDIC suggested wording is as follows.

> The Engineer or the Contractor's Representative may require the other to attend a management meeting in order to review the arrangements for future work. The Engineer shall record the business of management meetings and supply copies of the record to those attending the meeting and to the Employer. In the record, responsibilities for any actions to be taken shall be in accordance with the Contract.

The purpose of the Sub-Clause is presumably to encourage good management procedures and enable the Contractor to demand a meeting to discuss an important problem or proposal. Management meetings would be particularly useful in a claim situation or to prevent a claim developing into a serious conflict. When the Contractor gives an initial notice of a potential claim situation, as discussed in Chapter 4 of this book, a management meeting could serve as an early warning meeting at which the Engineer and the Contractor could discuss alternative ways to avoid or overcome a problem.

If the Engineer wants the Contractor to attend a meeting, for any purpose, then he has always been able simply to tell the Contractor to do so. The significance of this provision is that it enables the Contractor to require the Engineer to attend a meeting. The right for the Contractor to demand a meeting is an extremely useful provision and could help to solve potential problems. For a management meeting to serve its purpose, it will need to be held immediately the need arises so the Engineer should delegate the duty of attending any such meeting to his Resident Engineer.

The most likely reason for the Contractor to wish to discuss the arrangements for future work is that he is aware of some potential problem and wants to discuss the options available to avoid or minimise delay or additional cost. For example, if the Contractor gives notice under Sub-Clause 8.3 of 'specific probable future events or circumstances which may adversely affect the work, increase the Contract Price or delay the execution of the Works', then it is likely that to avoid or reduce the effect of the problem will require action from the Engineer as well as from the Contractor. Similarly, many of the situations which lead to a reference to the Engineer under Sub-Clause 3.5 might be avoided or the consequences reduced by a meeting held when the problem was first reported.

The final sentence of this additional FIDIC Sub-Clause, referring to responsibilities for any actions to be taken, is confusing and difficult to understand, and could be omitted. Sub-Clause 3.1 is clear that the Engineer has no authority to amend the Contract so it is difficult to see how the minutes of a meeting could impose responsibilities that are not in accordance with the Contract.

Chapter 12

Clause 4: The Contractor

In the Red Book the Contract Agreement confirms that the Contractor will 'execute and complete the Works and remedy any defects therein, in conformity with the provisions of the Contract'. In the Yellow Book the Contract Agreement includes that the Contractor will also design the Works. In order to meet this primary obligation the Contractor accepts a large number of secondary obligations. Clause 4 defines and confirms details of many of these obligations. However, this is not the only Clause which imposes detailed obligations on the Contractor and it must be read in conjunction with the other Clauses in the Conditions of Contract. When unexpected problems and costs occur during the construction of a project the Contractor may submit claims in order to recover Costs. The detailed requirements in Clause 4 are often used to support or respond to these claims.

Clause 4 is the longest and one of the most important clauses in the Contract. Clause 4 Sub-Clauses cover a wide range of subjects and frequently include topics which would not be anticipated from the headings.

Definitions at Sub-Clause 1.1 relevant to this Clause include:

1.1.2.3   Contractor
1.1.2.5   Contractor's Representative
1.1.2.7   Contractor's Personnel
1.1.2.8   Subcontractor
1.1.3.1   Base Date
1.1.4.1   Accepted Contract Amount
1.1.5.1   Contractor's Equipment
1.1.5.2   Goods
1.1.5.8   Works
1.1.6.2   Country
1.1.6.3   Employer's Equipment
1.1.6.5   Laws
1.1.6.6   Performance Security

1.1.6.7   Site
1.1.6.8   Unforeseeable
1.1.6.9   Variation.

4.1   Contractor's General Obligations

The Contractor shall design (to the extent specified in the Contract), execute and complete the Works in accordance with the Contract and with the Engineer's instructions, and shall remedy any defects in the Works.

The Contractor shall provide the Plant and Contractor's Documents specified in the Contract, and all Contractor's Personnel, Goods, consumables and other things and services, whether of a temporary or permanent nature, required in and for this design, execution, completion and remedying of defects.

The Contractor shall be responsible for the adequacy, stability and safety of all Site operations and of all methods of construction. Except to the extent specified in the Contract, the Contractor (i) shall be responsible for all Contractor's Documents, Temporary Works, and such design of each item of Plant and Materials as is required for the item to be in accordance with the Contract, and (ii) shall not otherwise be responsible for the design or specification of the Permanent Works.

The Contractor shall, whenever required by the Engineer, submit details of the arrangements and methods which the Contractor proposes to adopt for the execution of the Works. No significant alteration to these arrangements and methods shall be made without this having previously been notified to the Engineer.

If the Contract specifies that the Contractor shall design any part of the Permanent Works, then unless otherwise stated in the Particular Conditions:

(a)   the Contractor shall submit to the Engineer the Contractor's Documents for this part in accordance with the procedures specified in the Contract;

(b)   these Contractor's Documents shall be in accordance with the Specification and Drawings, shall be written in the language for communications defined in Sub-Clause 1.4 [*Law and Language*], and shall include additional information required by the Engineer to add to the Drawings for co-ordination of each Party's designs;

(c)   the Contractor shall be responsible for this part and it shall, when the Works are completed, be fit for such purposes for which the part is intended as are specified in the Contract; and

(d)   prior to the commencement of the Tests on Completion, the Contractor shall submit to the Engineer the ''as-built'' documents

121

and operation and maintenance manuals in accordance with the Specification and in sufficient detail for the Employer to operate, maintain, dismantle, reassemble, adjust and repair this part of the Works. Such part shall not be considered to be completed for the purposes of taking-over under Sub-Clause 10.1 [*Taking Over of the Works and Sections*] until these documents and manuals have been submitted to the Engineer.

In the Yellow Book the references to limited design and the requirements in the final paragraph have been deleted and are replaced by Clause 5.

The FIDIC Conditions of Contract for Construction are intended to be used for projects with the design provided by the Employer. The Contractor's obligation is to 'execute and complete the Works' and 'remedy any defects'. These overall obligations must be read in conjunction with the requirements of other Clauses, such as to 'proceed with the Works with due expedition and without delay' at Sub-Clause 8.1 and 'take full responsibility for the care of the Works' at Sub-Clause 17.2.

The phrase 'execute and complete' may seem to be repetitive, but it draws attention to the importance of the procedures at Completion, such as those given at Clauses 8, 9 and 10. The requirement to execute and complete can also give an obligation to complete any item of work which is necessary for total completion of the Works, but which may not have been shown in detail on the Drawings. However, this is an obligation to carry out and complete the Works and the question of whether payment is included in the Accepted Contract Amount is a separate issue.

If the Employer requires the Contractor to carry out the design of part of the Permanent Works then the requirement must be specified in the Contract. The obligations and procedures given at subparagraphs (a) to (d) will apply and must be read in conjunction with other Clauses which refer to the same subjects.

Care must be taken to co-ordinate the various documents that make up the Contract. Problems often arise when different documents are prepared by different consultants and information on the requirements for the Contractor's design is scattered throughout different technical specifications and other documents.

The standard of design performance is stated at subparagraph (c) as 'be fit for such purposes for which the part is intended as are specified in the Contract'. The details of this requirement must be clearly stated and compliance will often be checked by the Tests on Completion, which are carried out under Clause 9, or Tests after Completion, which are specified separately. This is a much more rigorous standard than the 'reasonable skill, care and diligence' obligation which governs most Consultants' Contracts. This difference in design standards would lead to serious problems in the event of a dispute as to whether a failure was caused by defective design by either the Employer's designer or the Contractor.

4.2   Performance Security

The Contractor shall obtain (at his cost) a Performance Security for proper performance, in the amount and currencies stated in the Appendix to Tender. If an amount is not stated in the Appendix to Tender, this Sub-Clause shall not apply.

The Contractor shall deliver the Performance Security to the Employer within 28 days after receiving the Letter of Acceptance, and shall send a copy to the Engineer. The Performance Security shall be issued by an entity and from within a country (or other jurisdiction) approved by the Employer, and shall be in the form annexed to the Particular Conditions or in another form approved by the Employer.

The Contractor shall ensure that the Performance Security is valid and enforceable until the Contractor has executed and completed the Works and remedied any defects. If the terms of the Performance Security specify its expiry date, and the Contractor has not become entitled to receive the Performance Certificate by the date 28 days prior to the expiry date, the Contractor shall extend the validity of the Performance Security until the Works have been completed and any defects have been remedied.

The Employer shall not make a claim under the Performance Security, except for amounts to which the Employer is entitled under the Contract in the event of:

(a)   failure by the Contractor to extend the validity of the Performance Security as described in the preceding paragraph, in which event the Employer may claim the full amount of the Performance Security;

(b)   failure by the Contractor to pay the Employer an amount due, as either agreed by the Contractor or determined under Sub-Clause 2.5 [*Employer's Claims*] or Clause 20 [*Claims, Disputes and Arbitration*], within 42 days after this agreement or determination;

(c)   failure by the Contractor to remedy a default within 42 days after receiving the Employer's notice requiring the default to be remedied; or

(d)   circumstances which entitle the Employer to termination under Sub-Clause 15.2 [*Termination by Employer*], irrespective of whether notice of termination has been given.

The Employer shall indemnify and hold the Contractor harmless against and from all damages, losses and expenses (including legal fees and expenses) resulting from a claim under the Performance Security to the extent to which the Employer was not entitled to make the claim.

123

The Employer shall return the Performance Security to the Contractor within 21 days after receiving a copy of the Performance Certificate.

The requirements for the Performance Security will only apply when the amount of the Security is stated in the Appendix to Tender.

The FIDIC Annexes to the Guidance for the Preparation of Particular Conditions include example forms C and D for Performance Securities as a Demand Guarantee or as a Surety Bond. Reference is made to guides published by the International Chamber of Commerce (38 Cours Albert ler, 75008 Paris, France). The form which is to be used should be included in the Particular Conditions.

The Performance Security must be delivered to the Employer within 28 days from receipt of the Letter of Acceptance and must be approved by the Employer. The receipt and approval of the Performance Security is critical for the start of the project. It is desirable that this is completed before the issue of the notice of commencement as Sub-Clause 8.1. Sub-Clause 2.1 allows the Employer to refuse access to the Site if the Performance Security has not been received. Sub-Clause 14.6 states that the Engineer will not issue an Interim Payment Certificate, for the advance payment or any other payment, until the Employer has received and approved the Performance Security.

Any claim by the Employer under the Performance Security must follow the procedures of Sub-Clause 2.5. The Employer should proceed with caution before making a claim because Sub-Clause 4.2 includes an indemnity to the Contractor if the Employer was not entitled to make the claim. The Employer must also be aware that the 42 day time periods at (b) and (c) are very short by comparison with other time periods for actions by the Contractor. It is possible that the Contractor might have already started a procedure to rectify these situations, in which case the Performance Security should not be invoked.

4.3   Contractor's Representative

The Contractor shall appoint the Contractor's Representative and shall give him all authority necessary to act on the Contractor's behalf under the Contract.

Unless the Contractor's Representative is named in the Contract, the Contractor shall, prior to the Commencement Date, submit to the Engineer for consent the name and particulars of the person the Contractor proposes to appoint as Contractor's Representative. If consent is withheld or subsequently revoked, or if the appointed person fails to act as Contractor's Representative, the Contractor shall similarly submit the name and particulars of another suitable person for such appointment.

The Contractor shall not, without the prior consent of the Engineer, revoke the appointment of the Contractor's Representative or appoint a replacement.

The whole time of the Contractor's Representative shall be given to directing the Contractor's performance of the Contract. If the Contractor's Representative is to be temporarily absent from the Site during the execution of the Works, a suitable replacement person shall be appointed, subject to the Engineer's prior consent, and the Engineer shall be notified accordingly.

The Contractor's Representative shall, on behalf of the Contractor, receive instructions under Sub-Clause 3.3 [*Instructions of the Engineer*].

The Contractor's Representative may delegate any powers, functions and authority to any competent person, and may at any time revoke the delegation. Any delegation or revocation shall not take effect until the Engineer has received prior notice signed by the Contractor's Representative, naming the person and specifying the powers, functions and authority being delegated or revoked.

The Contractor's Representative and all these persons shall be fluent in the language for communications defined in Sub-Clause 1.4 [*Law and Language*].

The Contract gives onerous requirements for the Contractor's Representative. He must:

- have either been named in the Contract or had his name and particulars submitted to the Engineer before the Commencement Date;
- have received the consent of the Engineer, which can subsequently be revoked;
- not be removed or replaced without the prior consent of the Engineer;
- have the authority to act on the Contractor's behalf under the Contract;
- spend the whole of his time directing the Contractor's performance of the Contract;
- be on the Site whenever work is in progress, or be replaced by an approved substitute;
- be fluent in the language for communications stated in the Appendix to Tender;
- ensure that any delegation is to a competent person, fluent in the language for communications and that the Engineer is notified of any delegation.

The FIDIC Guidance for the Preparation of Particular Conditions includes additional paragraphs for the situation when the Contractor's

Representative is required to be fluent in more than one language, or when it would be acceptable to use an interpreter.

The Contractor's Representative is, in effect, the Contractor's equivalent to the Engineer. Some Tender documents specify the required qualifications and experience and that the Contractor's Representative must be named in the Tender. This causes problems when the named person is no longer available at the Commencement Date. However, Sub-Clause 4.3 allows for a named person to be replaced, subject to the Engineer's consent to the replacement.

4.4   Subcontractors

The Contractor shall not subcontract the whole of the Works.

The Contractor shall be responsible for the acts or defaults of any Subcontractor, his agents or employees, as if they were the acts or defaults of the Contractor. Unless otherwise stated in the Particular Conditions:

(a)   the Contractor shall not be required to obtain consent to suppliers of Materials, or to a subcontract for which the Subcontractor is named in the Contract;

(b)   the prior consent of the Engineer shall be obtained to other proposed Subcontractors;

(c)   the Contractor shall give the Engineer not less than 28 days' notice of the intended date of the commencement of each Subcontractor's work, and of the commencement of such work on the Site; and

(d)   each subcontract shall include provisions which would entitle the Employer to require the subcontract to be assigned to the Employer under Sub-Clause 4.5 [*Assignment of Benefit of Subcontract*] (if or when applicable) or in the event of termination under Sub-Clause 15.2 [*Termination by Employer*].

In the Yellow Book paragraph (d) has been deleted. The provision at paragraph (d) may cause problems under the governing law and may be difficult to apply.

4.5 (RB)   Assignment of Benefit of Subcontract

If a Subcontractor's obligations extend beyond the expiry date of the relevant Defects Notification Period and the Engineer, prior to this date, instructs the Contractor to assign the benefit of such obligations to the Employer, then the Contractor shall do so. Unless otherwise stated in the assignment, the Contractor shall have no liability to the Employer for the work carried out by the Subcontractor after the assignment takes effect.

In the Yellow Book Sub-Clause 4.5 has been replaced by the following.

4.5 (YB)   Nominated Subcontractors

In this Sub-Clause, "nominated Subcontractor" means a Subcontractor whom the Engineer, under Clause 13 [*Variations and Adjustments*], instructs the Contractor to employ as a Subcontractor. The Contractor shall not be under any obligation to employ a nominated Subcontractor against whom the Contractor raises reasonable objection by notice to the Engineer as soon as practicable, with supporting particulars.

The Yellow Book does not include provision for a Nominated Subcontractor to be named in the Contract but the Engineer can issue instructions nominating a Subcontractor as a Variation. However, the Contractor is not obliged to use a Subcontractor against which he raises a reasonable objection. A Yellow Book Nominated Subcontractor does not enjoy the benefits of the same payment provisions as a Nominated Subcontractor under the Red Book.

The provisions concerning the Contractor's liability for the actions of Subcontractors apply to Subcontractors that have been designated by the Employer, as well as to Subcontractors that have been selected by the Contractor.

The FIDIC Subcontract 'Conditions of Subcontract for Works of Civil Engineering Construction' (first edition 1994) was published for use in conjunction with the FIDIC fourth edition. Whilst the principles and many of the clauses would still be appropriate for use with the 1999 FIDIC Conditions of Contract, a careful check would be necessary and some changes would be required. For example, the requirement concerning assignment in the event of termination, at subparagraph 4.4(d) (RB) was not a specific requirement in the previous FIDIC Contract. No doubt FIDIC will publish a revised edition of the Subcontract to suit the new Contracts.

It is also essential to check the provisions of the applicable law concerning the rights and obligations of Subcontractors. Under some legal systems the Subcontractor may have the right of direct access to the Employer in order to obtain payment of sums that have been withheld by the Contractor.

4.6   Co-operation

The Contractor shall, as specified in the Contract or as instructed by the Engineer, allow appropriate opportunities for carrying out work to:

(a)   the Employer's Personnel,
(b)   any other contractors employed by the Employer, and
(c)   the personnel of any legally constituted public authorities,

who may be employed in the execution on or near the Site of any work not included in the Contract.

Any such instruction shall constitute a Variation if and to the extent that it causes the Contractor to incur Unforeseeable Cost. Services for these personnel and other contractors may include the use of Contractor's Equipment, Temporary Works or access arrangements which are the responsibility of the Contractor.

If, under the Contract, the Employer is required to give to the Contractor possession of any foundation, structure, plant or means of access in accordance with Contractor's Documents, the Contractor shall submit such documents to the Engineer in the time and manner stated in the Specification.

In the Yellow Book the final word 'Specification' is changed to 'Employer's Requirements' and a paragraph is added, as the penultimate paragraph of the Sub-Clause.

The Contractor shall be responsible for his construction activities on the Site, and shall co-ordinate his own activities with those of other contractors to the extent (if any) specified in the Employer's Requirements.

The heading 'Co-operation' implies that the Sub-Clause deals with mutual co-operation between the Employer and the Contractor. In fact, the co-operation is one sided and refers to the provision of facilities by the Contractor, and by Subcontractors, to anyone who has been instructed by the Employer to carry out work on the Site. The reciprocal requirement, at Sub-Clause 2.3(a), is that the Employer's Personnel and other contractors on the Site shall co-operate with the Contractor's efforts.

The Sub-Clause requires the Contractor to provide the use of his Equipment, Temporary Works and access arrangements, but allows for all Unforeseeable Costs to be claimed and paid as a Variation. Any delays as a consequence of the application of this Sub-Clause would qualify for an extension of time under Sub-Clause 8.4(e). Alternatively, if the other Contractor is a legally constituted public authority then the delay might be covered by Sub-Clause 8.5. This compensation would be important in the event of misuse or damage caused by the other Contractor.

The final paragraph of Sub-Clause 4.6 refers to a more complex situation. A 'foundation, structure, plant or means of access' is occupied by the Employer and the Contractor requires possession in order to execute his work. The Contractor is required to submit the relevant Contractor's Documents in the time and manner stated in the Specification. The reference to Contractor's Documents implies that the situation relates to work that was designed by the Contractor. The Employer's obligation is given at the first paragraph of Sub-Clause 2.1.

The additional paragraph in the Yellow Book depends on the inclusion in the Employer's Requirements of any co-ordination which is required from the Contractor. Any such requirements would need to be shown in the Sub-Clause 8.3 programme.

4.7   Setting Out

The Contractor shall set out the Works in relation to original points, lines and levels of reference specified in the Contract or notified by the Engineer. The Contractor shall be responsible for the correct positioning of all parts of the Works, and shall rectify any error in the positions, levels, dimensions or alignment of the Works.

The Employer shall be responsible for any errors in these specified or notified items of reference, but the Contractor shall use reasonable efforts to verify their accuracy before they are used.

If the Contractor suffers delay and/or incurs Cost from executing work which was necessitated by an error in these items of reference, and an experienced contractor could not reasonably have discovered such error and avoided this delay and/or Cost, the Contractor shall give notice to the Engineer and shall be entitled, subject to Sub-Clause 20.1 [*Contractor's Claims*] to:

(a)   an extension of time for any such delay, if completion is or will be delayed, under Sub-Clause 8.4 [*Extension of Time for Completion*]; and

(b)   payment of any such Cost plus reasonable profit, which shall be included in the Contract Price.

After receiving this notice, the Engineer shall proceed in accordance with Sub-Clause 3.5 [*Determinations*] to agree or determine (i) whether and (if so) to what extent the error could not reasonably have been discovered, and (ii) the matters described in subparagraphs (a) and (b) above related to this extent.

The Employer and the Contractor are each responsible for their own work. If setting out information from the Employer, or the Engineer on his behalf, is not accurate then the Contractor can give notice and follow the usual claims procedure for a determination by the Engineer. However, the Contractor is obliged to use reasonable efforts to check the accuracy of the reference items. To what extent this is feasible will depend on the circumstances. If the Contractor finds an error then he would be required to give notice under the final paragraph of Sub-Clause Clause 1.8. Under the Yellow Book the Contractor is also required, by Sub-Clause 5.1, to check the items of reference and report any errors within the period stated in the Appendix to Tender.

4.8   Safety Procedures

The Contractor shall:

(a)   comply with all applicable safety regulations;
(b)   take care for the safety of all persons entitled to be on the Site;
(c)   use reasonable efforts to keep the Site and Works clear of unnecessary obstruction so as to avoid danger to these persons;
(d)   provide fencing, lighting, guarding and watching of the Works until completion and taking over under Clause 10 [*Employer's Taking Over*]; and
(e)   provide any Temporary Works (including roadways, footways, guards and fences) which may be necessary, because of the execution of the Works, for the use and protection of the public and of owners and occupiers of adjacent land.

Most countries have their own health and safety regulations although the details vary considerably. Paragraph (a) of Sub-Clause 4.8 requires the Contractor to comply with the local regulations. The Sub-Clause includes safety requirements which may be less onerous, or more onerous, than the local regulations. The requirements for safety may be expanded in the Particular Conditions.

If the Contractor does not have exclusive possession of the Site, as permitted by Sub-Clause 2.1, then the Particular Conditions should clarify the responsibility for site safety.

4.9   Quality Assurance

The Contractor shall institute a quality assurance system to demonstrate compliance with the requirements of the Contract. The system shall be in accordance with the details stated in the Contract. The Engineer shall be entitled to audit any aspect of the system.

Details of all procedures and compliance documents shall be submitted to the Engineer for information before each design and execution stage is commenced. When any document of a technical nature is issued to the Engineer, evidence of the prior approval by the Contractor himself shall be apparent on the document itself.

Compliance with the quality assurance system shall not relieve the Contractor of any of his duties, obligations or responsibilities under the Contract.

The requirements for a quality assurance system depend on the details of the system which is required being included in the Contract. If the Employer does not intend to include such details then the Sub-Clause should be deleted.

When considering whether to include a requirement for a Contractor's quality assurance system the Employer must consider whether the benefits will outweigh the cost. If the tenderers are experienced in the operation of their own quality control then the additional cost will probably be justified. However, with a Contractor who is not accustomed to operating his own quality control systems, the Employer may prefer to rely on the quality control exercised by the Engineer in accordance with the Contract. A good quality assurance system, operated by experienced personnel from both Parties and the Engineer, should avoid quality problems, benefit the project and justify the additional cost.

4.10   Site Data

The Employer shall have made available to the Contractor for his information, prior to the Base Date, all relevant data in the Employer's possession on sub-surface and hydrological conditions at the Site, including environmental aspects. The Employer shall similarly make available to the Contractor all such data which come into the Employer's possession after the Base Date. The Contractor shall be responsible for interpreting all such data.

To the extent which was practicable (taking account of cost and time), the Contractor shall be deemed to have obtained all necessary information as to risks, contingencies and other circumstances which may influence or affect the Tender or Works. To the same extent, the Contractor shall be deemed to have inspected and examined the Site, its surroundings, the above data and other available information, and to have been satisfied before submitting the Tender as to all relevant matters, including (without limitation):

(a)   the form and nature of the Site, including sub-surface conditions;
(b)   the hydrological and climatic conditions;
(c)   the extent and nature of the work and Goods necessary for the execution and completion of the Works and the remedying of any defects;
(d)   the Laws, procedures and labour practices of the Country; and
(e)   the Contractor's requirements for access, accommodation, facilities, personnel, power, transport, water and other services.

The heading and first sentence of this Sub-Clause do not give any indication of the wide scope of the Sub-Clause. Even the list of items about which the Contractor must have satisfied himself does not limit the scope of these matters.

For the Employer to 'make available to the Contractor for his information' the details of sub-surface and other conditions does not mean that copies of the data will have been provided in the Tender documents. The Employer may just have indicated that certain information is available for inspection. The phrase 'all relevant data in the Employer's possession' is a very wide requirement and must include all the information which the Employer has acquired concerning the Site. Although the Employer is only required to make available 'relevant' data, it is advisable for the Employer to disclose all data relating to the Site. Data that may seem not be relevant at Tender stage may become relevant if problems occur during construction. Information which appears to be inconsistent may be a clue to sub-surface problems and is important for prospective Contractors. The information must be made available at least 28 days before the latest date for the submission of Tenders, in order to give tenderers time to make their own studies and enquiries. If the Employer obtains further information after the Base Date this must also be made available to the Contractor.

For a Yellow Book Contract each tenderer must make his own preliminary design in order to prepare his Tender. Different tenderers will locate foundations, and even structures, in different locations on the site. It is important that the data on sub-surface and hydrological conditions provided by the Employer covers all possible foundation locations. In order that the Employer can compare Tenders on an equal basis they must be prepared based on the same information. If one Tender was prepared based on boreholes and another was based only on trial pits then the borehole Tender might be based on the expectation of softer material at a greater depth than was checked by the trial pits, and so result in a more expensive Tender. The cheaper tenderer might then be awarded the contract only to encounter problems later and submit claims for unforeseeable physical conditions under Sub-Clause 4.12.

The Contractor is responsible for interpreting the Site data and making his own enquiries in order to satisfy himself that his Tender is adequate, as required by Sub-Clause 4.11. The extent and detail of the Contractor's enquiries can be restricted as stated at the second paragraph of Sub-Clause 4.10. The interpretation of the phrase 'which was practicable (taking account of cost and time)' must be subjective. If the Contractor submits a claim, perhaps under Sub-Clause 4.12, the Engineer may respond that the Contractor should have made further enquiries and investigations before submitting his Tender.

The second paragraph of Sub-Clause 4.10 requires tenderers to have examined the surroundings to the Site, as well as the Site itself. The extent and detail of this examination is not clear. If the project involves deep excavation close to the site boundary then the tenderer will have to consider the support necessary to avoid causing problems for the adjoining site, particularly under a Yellow Book Contract. However, if there is a potential for a problem to originate from the adjoining or nearby area, at no fault of the Contractor, then it would be unreasonable to expect a tenderer to allow for the cost of protecting his Works against that problem. If a tenderer is expected to include any such allowance in his Tender then the potential problem should have been identified in the Tender documents so that all Tenders are prepared on the same basis. This is an important consideration because claims against the Employer which result from activities or events on an adjoining area will be difficult to substantiate. They may be a matter of Employer's Risks as Sub-Clause 17.3(h), Insurance as Clause 18, Force Majeure as Sub-Clause 19.1, or a claim against a third party.

The Contractor should keep records of any studies and investigations which he has made in compliance with this Sub-Clause. Records to show that he has taken reasonable action in all the circumstances may be useful to support any claim for unforeseeable physical conditions, in accordance with the final paragraph of Sub-Clause 4.12.

The second part of Sub-Clause 4.10 covers a much wider range of subjects than is indicated by the heading 'Site Data'. Subparagraph (c) requires the Contractor to have studied his proposed method of construction and considered his requirements and the availability of the Materials, Equipment and Temporary Works which will be required. Subparagraph (d) requires a review of 'the Laws, procedures and labour practices of the Country'. This is a very wide subject and includes many subjects mentioned elsewhere in the Contract, such as health and safety regulations, normally accepted practices for local labour, restrictions on imported labour and equipment and the local tax regulations. A lack of knowledge on any of these subjects will not be accepted as justification for a claim.

4.11   Sufficiency of the Accepted Contract Amount

The Contractor shall be deemed to:

(a)   have satisfied himself as to the correctness and sufficiency of the Accepted Contract Amount; and

(b)   have based the Accepted Contract Amount on the data, interpretations, necessary information, inspections, examinations and satisfaction as to all relevant matters referred to in Sub-Clause 4.10 [*Site Data*].

Unless otherwise stated in the Contract, the Accepted Contract Amount covers all the Contractor's obligations under the Contract (including those under Provisional Sums, if any) and all things necessary for the proper execution and completion of the Works and the remedying of any defects.

In the Yellow Book paragraph (b) is extended to include 'any further data relevant to the contractor's design'.

This is another Sub-Clause which refers to actions by the Contractor during the preparation of his Tender. The Contractor is deemed to have based his Tender submission on the requirements of Sub-Clause 4.10. Hence, if there is an error in any of the information which was provided by the Employer under Sub-Clause 4.10 then the Contractor may have the basis for a claim for additional payment.

If the Contractor discovered any errors or omissions in the information which was provided in the Tender documents then he should have raised the problem before becoming committed to the Accepted Contract Amount.

4.12   Unforeseeable Physical Conditions

In this Sub-Clause, "physical conditions" means natural physical conditions and man-made and other physical obstructions and pollutants, which the Contractor encounters at the Site when executing the Works, including sub-surface and hydrological conditions but excluding climatic conditions.

If the Contractor encounters adverse physical conditions which he considers to have been Unforeseeable, the Contractor shall give notice to the Engineer as soon as practicable.

This notice shall describe the physical conditions, so that they can be inspected by the Engineer, and shall set out the reasons why the Contractor considers them to be Unforeseeable. The Contractor shall continue executing the Works, using such proper and reasonable measures as are appropriate for the physical conditions, and shall comply with any instructions which the Engineer may give. If an instruction constitutes a Variation, Clause 13 [*Variations and Adjustments*] shall apply.

If and to the extent that the Contractor encounters physical conditions which are Unforeseeable, gives such a notice, and suffers delay and/or incurs Cost due to these conditions, the Contractor shall be entitled subject to Sub-Clause 20.1 [*Contractor's Claims*] to:

(a)   an extension of time for any such delay, if completion is or will be delayed, under Sub-Clause 8.4 [*Extension of Time for Completion*]; and

(b)   payment of any such Cost, which shall be included in the Contract Price.

After receiving such notice and inspecting and/or investigating these physical conditions, the Engineer shall proceed in accordance with Sub-Clause 3.5 [*Determinations*] to agree or determine (i) whether and (if so) to what extent these physical conditions were Unforeseeable, and (ii) the matters described in subparagraphs (a) and (b) above related to this extent.

However, before additional Cost is finally agreed or determined under subparagraph (ii), the Engineer may also review whether other physical conditions in similar parts of the Works (if any) were more favourable than could reasonably have been foreseen when the Contractor submitted the Tender. If and to the extent that these more favourable conditions were encountered, the Engineer may proceed in accordance with Sub-Clause 3.5 [*Determinations*] to agree or determine the reductions in Cost which were due to these conditions, which may be included (as deductions) in the Contract Price and Payment Certificates. However, the net effect of all adjustments under sub-paragraph (b) and all these reductions, for all the physical conditions encountered in similar parts of the Works, shall not result in a net reduction in the Contract Price.

The Engineer may take account of any evidence of the physical conditions foreseen by the Contractor when submitting the Tender, which may be made available by the Contractor, but shall not be bound by any such evidence.

Unforeseeable physical conditions are probably the most common source of claims and disputes in construction projects. The definition of 'physical conditions' is wider than might be expected and will include many of the unexpected situations which the Contractor 'encounters at the Site when executing the Works'. It was the Employer who decided to construct the project on this particular Site and designed the project to suit the Site; in principle, the Employer should take responsibility for the consequences of any problems present on his Site. The difficult question is whether a particular problem should have been anticipated and allowed for in the Accepted Contract Amount, or whether the situation could not have been foreseen by an experienced Contractor. The restraints of cost and time referred to at Sub-Clause 14.10 must be considered in making this assessment.

When a problem arises the Contractor must give a notice 'as soon as practicable' describing the physical conditions. This initial notice may result in the Engineer deciding to issue an instruction for a variation under Clause 13 so the delay and additional costs would be covered by the variation procedures. However, the Contractor may also need to consider notices under other clauses, such as the final two paragraphs of Sub-Clause 8.3, Sub-Clause 8.4 for an extension of time, Sub-Clause 13.2 if he has a Value Engineering proposal, Sub-Clause 19.2 for Force Majeure, and the notice under Sub-Clause 20.1 which is essential for any claims.

The Contractor will need to comply with the appropriate time periods for any notices. The Contractor may also have a claim under an unforeseeable circumstances provision in the governing law.

Physical conditions situations frequently require a change to the design or method of working. Under the Yellow Book it may be necessary for the Contractor to change his design and this will be taken into account in any claim. Under the Red Book the Contractor is obliged to continue the Works, so an immediate notice followed by prompt action from the Engineer is essential. The Contractor can take 'such proper and reasonable measures as are appropriate for the physical conditions' but, if these measures constitute a Variation, an instruction is required from the Engineer. Clearly there is a potential for misunderstanding and claims, particularly if the Engineer fails to give instructions and the Contractor feels obliged to make decisions as to what action to take.

The situations that may be covered by this Sub-Clause give a clear example of the need for a meeting between the Engineer and the Contractor in order to discuss the problem and agree on the best technical solution. Whilst an immediate meeting would be normal practice on most projects it is unfortunate that the Contract fails to put a clear obligation on both the Contractor and the Engineer to call and attend such a meeting. This is another reason for introducing a provision for management meetings, as discussed at the proposed Sub-Clause 3.6.

Having received the Contractor's notices the Engineer will investigate the situation and proceed in accordance with the usual claims procedures at Sub-Clauses 20.1, 8.4 and 3.5.

Sub-Clause 4.12 also includes a provision to enable the Engineer to take into account physical conditions at other parts of the Site which were more favourable than could reasonably have been foreseen. This is a new provision for the FIDIC Red Book and will be controversial. Whilst it may seem reasonable that better than foreseeable should balance worse than foreseeable, in practice the situation is rarely straightforward. The Contractor has made assumptions, brought on Site the appropriate materials and equipment and made the appropriate assumptions in his programme. Any change to these initial assumptions, whether more or less favourable, can result in delay and additional cost. Analysis of actual time and cost, compared to the time and cost assumed in the Accepted Contract Amount, will be a lengthy and complex procedure. Evidence of the Contractor's Tender assumptions, as the final paragraph of Sub-Clause 4.12, could be crucial in the discussions. The situation may become even more complex under a Yellow Book Contract. The Contractor may claim either that his design took these conditions into account, or that he intends to change his design to take the unforeseeable better conditions into account and so claim an extension of time.

This provision is worded as a plus and minus review and calculation by the Engineer in his valuation of the Contractor's claim, rather than as a separate claim by the Employer under Sub-Clause 2.5.

The FIDIC Particular Conditions include a suggested provision for the risk of sub-surface conditions being shared between the Parties. The percentage of the cost which is to be borne by the Contractor would be stated in the Particular Conditions. For this provision to be both fair and workable in practice the Contractor must be given the time and opportunity to carry out investigations at Tender stage.

The potential for technical problems, claims and disputes due to unforeseeable physical conditions, enhanced by any uncertainty at Tender stage, demonstrates the importance of the Employer carrying out a proper investigation before calling Tenders. The value of Site investigation is not just in order to prepare the design, but also to enable the Contractor to prepare a realistic Tender.

4.13   Rights of Way and Facilities
The Contractor shall bear all costs and charges for special and/or temporary rights-of-way which he may require, including those for access to the Site. The Contractor shall also obtain, at his risk and cost, any additional facilities outside the Site which he may require for the purposes of the Works.

This Sub-Clause recognises that the Contractor may require additional facilities outside the Site. The location and boundaries of the Site are defined in the Contract. The use of these additional facilities would require the Engineer's agreement under Sub-Clause 4.23.

Under Sub-Clause 7.3 the Contractor must provide access and facilities for inspection of work in these additional areas, as required by the Employer's Personnel. Matters of insurance and payment for work done must also be considered for all off-site facilities.

4.14   Avoidance of Interference
The Contractor shall not interfere unnecessarily or improperly with:

(a)   the convenience of the public; or
(b)   the access to and use and occupation of all roads and footpaths, irrespective of whether they are public or in the possession of the Employer or of others.

The Contractor shall indemnify and hold the Employer harmless against and from all damages, losses and expenses (including legal fees and expenses) resulting from any such unnecessary or improper interference.

The indemnity under this Sub-Clause only covers cost resulting from interference which is 'unnecessary or improper'. This does not imply that there is some form of necessary or proper interference that is not the Contractor's responsibility. Presumably the necessary and proper interference was anticipated and allowed for in the Contract, for example in relation to Sub-Clause 4.15. However, the indemnity could have wider implications, possible including a breach of the Sub-Clause 4.23 requirement to keep Contractor's Equipment and Personnel within the Site and off adjacent land.

4.15   Access Route

The Contractor shall be deemed to have been satisfied as to the suitability and availability of access routes to the Site. The Contractor shall use reasonable efforts to prevent any road or bridge from being damaged by the Contractor's traffic or by the Contractor's Personnel. These efforts shall include the proper use of appropriate vehicles and routes. Except as otherwise stated in these Conditions:

(a)   the Contractor shall (as between the Parties) be responsible for any maintenance which may be required for his use of access routes;

(b)   the Contractor shall provide all necessary signs or directions along access routes, and shall obtain any permission which may be required from the relevant authorities for his use of routes, signs and directions;

(c)   the Employer shall not be responsible for any claims which may arise from the use or otherwise of any access route;

(d)   the Employer does not guarantee the suitability or availability of particular access routes; and

(e)   Costs due to non-suitability or non-availability, for the use required by the Contractor, of access routes shall be borne by the Contractor.

The first sentence of this Sub-Clause repeats the requirement of Sub-Clause 4.10(e) with regard to access routes to the Site. If access for heavy Contractor's Equipment or Plant is impossible because of the lack of suitable roads or bridges then the problem should have been raised by the Contractor before he submitted his Tender.

The obligations and responsibilities imposed by this Sub-Clause are between the Contractor and the Employer. If the Contractor causes damage to any roads or bridges, or fails to comply with any regulation, then he will also have a problem with the relevant authority and a liability under the governing law.

4.16   Transport of Goods

Unless otherwise stated in the Particular Conditions:

(a)   the Contractor shall give the Engineer not less than 21 days' notice of the date on which any Plant or a major item of other Goods will be delivered to the Site;

(b) the Contractor shall be responsible for packing, loading, transporting, receiving, unloading, storing and protecting all Goods and other things required for the Works; and

(c) the Contractor shall indemnify and hold the Employer harmless against and from all damages, losses and expenses (including legal fees and expenses) resulting from the transport of Goods, and shall negotiate and pay all claims arising from their transport.

The definition of Goods covers virtually everything that will be delivered to the Site and this Sub-Clause repeats the Contractor's general obligations under the Contract. The requirement for 21 days' notice of delivery only applies to Plant or major items. The reason for this notice is not stated. The arrangements for access, delivery and storage are the Contractor's responsibility and so the Engineer will only be interested from his usual concerns for progress, payment and supervision. The notice should confirm the dates that have already been given in the Contractor's programme and monthly progress reports.

The indemnity for costs arising from the transport of Goods includes an additional requirement that the Contractor shall negotiate any claims from third persons that rise from the transport of Goods.

4.17 Contractor's Equipment

The Contractor shall be responsible for all Contractor's Equipment. When brought on to the Site, Contractor's Equipment shall be deemed to be exclusively intended for the execution of the Works. The Contractor shall not remove from the Site any major items of Contractor's Equipment without the consent of the Engineer. However, consent shall not be required for vehicles transporting Goods or Contractor's Personnel off Site.

By definition, Contractor's Equipment includes any workshop or manufacturing equipment which is used to manufacture items for the Works. Any such Equipment which is installed on the Site cannot be used to manufacture items for sale to other projects.

When the Contractor has completed the work for which a particular item of Contractor's Equipment was brought to the Site then that item will obviously be removed. If the Engineer, for whatever reason, does not give prompt consent, then the Contractor will probably claim for the cost of keeping the equipment on the Site.

The FIDIC Guidance for the Preparation of Particular Conditions includes an additional paragraph with provision that the Contractor's Equipment would be deemed to be the property of the Employer when it is on the Site. This provision could lead to other problems and may not be recognised by the governing law.

4.18 Protection of the Environment

The Contractor shall take all reasonable steps to protect the environment (both on and off the Site) and to limit damage and nuisance to people and property resulting from pollution, noise and other results of his operations. The Contractor shall ensure that emissions, surface discharges and effluent from the Contractor's activities shall not exceed the values indicated in the Specification, and shall not exceed the values prescribed by applicable Laws.

In the Yellow Book, references to the 'Specification' are replaced by the 'Employer's Requirements'.

Under Sub-Clause 4.10(d) the Contractor is deemed to have obtained information on the Laws and procedures of the Country and, under Sub-Clause 1.13, is required to comply with applicable Laws.

Sub-Clause 4.18 also states that maximum values for emissions, surface discharges and effluent from the Contractor's activities will be given in the Specification. These values may be higher or lower than the figures in local regulations.

Sub-Clause 4.18 does not require an indemnity from the Contractor if anyone should claim against the Employer, but the general indemnity at Sub-Clause 17.1 would probably cover breaches of this Sub-Clause.

4.19 Electricity, Water and Gas

The Contractor shall, except as stated below, be responsible for the provision of all power, water and other services he may require.

The Contractor shall be entitled to use for the purposes of the Works such supplies of electricity, water, gas and other services as may be available on the Site and of which details and prices are given in the Specification. The Contractor shall, at his risk and cost, provide any apparatus necessary for his use of these services and for measuring the quantities consumed.

The quantities consumed and the amounts due (at these prices) for such services shall be agreed or determined by the Engineer in accordance with Sub-Clause 2.5 [*Employer's Claims*] and Sub-Clause 3.5 [*Determinations*]. The Contractor shall pay these amounts to the Employer.

In the Yellow Book, references to the 'Specification' are replaced by the 'Employer's Requirements'. Sub-Clause 4.19 is reviewed together with Sub-Clause 4.20.

4.20 Employer's Equipment and Free-Issue Material

The Employer shall make the Employer's Equipment (if any) available for the use of the Contractor in the execution of the Works in accordance with the details, arrangements and prices stated in the Specification. Unless otherwise stated in the Specification:

(a) the Employer shall be responsible for the Employer's Equipment, except that

(b) the Contractor shall be responsible for each item of Employer's Equipment whilst any of the Contractor's Personnel is operating it, driving it, directing it or in possession or control of it.

The appropriate quantities and the amounts due (at such stated prices) for the use of Employer's Equipment shall be agreed or determined by the Engineer in accordance with Sub-Clause 2.5 [*Employer's Claims*] and Sub-Clause 3.5 [*Determinations*]. The Contractor shall pay these amounts to the Employer.

The Employer shall supply, free of charge, the "free-issue materials" (if any) in accordance with the details stated in the Specification. The Employer shall, at his risk and cost, provide these materials at the time and place specified in the Contract. The Contractor shall then visually inspect them, and shall promptly give notice to the Engineer of any shortage, defect or default in these materials. Unless otherwise agreed by both Parties, the Employer shall immediately rectify the notified shortage, defect or default.

After this visual inspection, the free-issue materials shall come under the care, custody and control of the Contractor. The Contractor's obligations of inspection, care, custody and control shall not relieve the Employer of liability for any shortage, defect or default not apparent from a visual inspection.

In the Yellow Book, references to the 'Specification' are replaced by the 'Employer's Requirements'.

If the Contractor wishes to use services that are available on the Site, or equipment that is made available by the Employer, he must pay at the prices stated in the Specification or Employer's Requirements. Under Sub-Clause 2.5 the Employer does not have to give notice of a claim for this payment. However, the quantity or time for each item must be recorded and agreed. If there is any disagreement then the Engineer will act under Sub-Clauses 2.5 and 3.5. Payment can then be made as a deduction in the Contractor's monthly statement under Sub-Clause 14.3(f).

Whilst it may be convenient for the Employer to provide free-issue material or the use of equipment, the procedure can cause problems. If, for example, the Contractor is relying on this supply and the materials do not comply with the Specification or Employer's Requirements then the Employer must find an alternative. Any such division of responsibility which changes the Contractor's general obligations is difficult to control. The costs to the Employer of any problems will be more than might be expected.

4.21 Progress Reports

Unless otherwise stated in the Particular Conditions, monthly progress reports shall be prepared by the Contractor and submitted to the Engineer in six copies. The first report shall cover the period up to the end of the first calendar month following the Commencement Date. Reports shall be submitted monthly thereafter, each within 7 days after the last day of the period to which it relates.

Reporting shall continue until the Contractor has completed all work which is known to be outstanding at the completion date stated in the Taking-Over Certificate for the Works.

Each report shall include:

(a) charts and detailed descriptions of progress, including each stage of design (if any), Contractor's Documents, procurement, manufacture, delivery to Site, construction, erection and testing; and including these stages for work by each nominated Subcontractor (as defined in Clause 5 [*Nominated Subcontractors*]);

(b) photographs showing the status of manufacture and of progress on the Site;

(c) for the manufacture of each main item of Plant and Materials, the name of the manufacturer, manufacture location, percentage progress, and the actual or expected dates of:
  (i)   commencement of manufacture,
  (ii) Contractor's inspections,
  (iii) tests, and
  (iv) shipment and arrival at the Site;

(d) the details described in Sub-Clause 6.10 [*Records of Contractor's Personnel and Equipment*];

(e) copies of quality assurance documents, test results and certificates of Materials;

(f) list of notices given under Sub-Clause 2.5 [*Employer's Claims*] and notices given under Sub-Clause 20.1 [*Contractor's Claims*];

(g) safety statistics, including details of any hazardous incidents and activities relating to environmental aspects and public relations; and

(h) comparisons of actual and planned progress, with details of any events or circumstances which may jeopardise the completion in accordance with the Contract, and the measures being (or to be) adopted to overcome delays.

In the Yellow Book the material which is to be included in the progress report has been changed to suit the requirements for a Contract with

Contractor design. In paragraph (a) '(if any)' after design and the reference to Nominated Subcontractors have been omitted. A reference to commissioning and trial operation has been added and paragraph (f) requires a list of Variations in addition to the lists of claim notices. Both these additional requirements may be relevant to Contracts under the Red Book and could be added to the Particular Conditions.

The requirement for the Contractor to provide monthly progress reports is a new requirement in the FIDIC Red Book, although it has sometimes been included by Employers in the Particular Conditions or Specification. The detailed requirements are onerous and are not just a matter of reporting progress on the Site and elsewhere but include safety statistics, lists of claims and other matters. The Particular Conditions may include further requirements, such as submitting the progress report for discussion at a meeting or replacing the six copies by an electronic submission. However, some of the requirements may not be relevant to a particular project and the format of the report should be agreed at the start of the project.

The report will be a substantial document and must be submitted within seven days from the last day of the relevant month, which means five working days. To meet this requirement the Contractor must record and collect the information during the month, including information from Subcontractors. Most of the information will probably have been recorded by the Contractor as part of his own internal procedures and records to monitor the project so the aim must be to keep records in a form that will meet the requirements of Sub-Clause 4.21 as well as to satisfy the Contractor's internal procedures. The collection and collation of information from Subcontractors may cause problems for the Contractor.

Some Employers and the building laws of some countries also require Contractors to keep progress and other records; these records should be combined wherever possible. The format of the monthly progress report does not have to be agreed with the Engineer, but some discussion is desirable in order to minimise the work and co-ordinate the format and avoid duplication with other submissions such as the Clause 20.1 claims records.

The progress report is submitted to the Engineer, but does not have to be approved or agreed by the Engineer. However, the information in the progress reports will undoubtedly be used in support of claims. For example, if figures have not been disputed at the time it may be difficult for the Employer to reject them at a later date. A regular progress meeting to discuss the report would enable the Engineer to raise any points which he wishes to query.

Under Sub-Clause 14.3 a copy of the progress report must be included with the Contractor's Statement for interim payments. However,

Sub-Clause 14.6 is clear that the Engineer cannot withhold the issue of an Interim Payment Certificate because the report has not been submitted. The Engineer could only withhold the value of the report, as Sub-Clause 14.6(b).

4.22 Security of the Site
Unless otherwise stated in the Particular Conditions:

(a) the Contractor shall be responsible for keeping unauthorised persons off the Site; and

(b) authorised persons shall be limited to the Contractor's Personnel and the Employer's Personnel; and to any other personnel notified to the Contractor, by the Employer or the Engineer, as authorised personnel of the Employer's other contractors on the Site.

The procedure which the Contractor will adopt to control access to the Site will depend on the circumstances. Any special requirements should be stated in the Particular Conditions and detailed in the Specification.

The FIDIC Guidance for the Preparation of Particular Conditions draws attention to the potential problems that may arise when the Employer has more than one Contractor working on the Site. The Contractor can identify his own employees and the employees of his Subcontractors. To identify and check the Employer's Personnel may be more difficult but only requires co-operation from the Engineer. To identify and check the employees of another Contractor will be extremely difficult and requires a rigorous identification procedure. However, the Contractor is responsible for Site security and for keeping unauthorised persons out of the Site.

The Contractor's responsibility for Site security must be considered in relation to other Sub-Clauses, including Sub-Clause 4.6 concerning co-operation with other Contractors, Sub-Clause 4.8 concerning Site fencing and other temporary Works, Sub-Clause 17.2 concerning the Contractor's responsibility for the care of the Works and the Clause 18 insurance requirements. If the Contractor does not have total control over Site access there will be implications for his other responsibilities.

Where more than one Contractor is working on the Site it is important that Site security procedures are described in detail in the Particular Conditions and Specifications. Sub-Clause 4.6 would enable the Contractor to claim any additional costs that he incurs as a consequence of the work involved in controlling Site access by other Contractors.

If the Site is part of a larger Site or existing operation, or the project involves work which the Employer considers to be particularly sensitive or confidential, then the Particular Conditions should include additional requirements for controlling access to the Site.

4.23   Contractor's Operations on Site

The Contractor shall confine his operations to the Site, and to any additional areas which may be obtained by the Contractor and agreed by the Engineer as working areas. The Contractor shall take all necessary precautions to keep Contractor's Equipment and Contractor's Personnel within the Site and these additional areas, and to keep them off adjacent land.

During the execution of the Works, the Contractor shall keep the Site free from all unnecessary obstruction, and shall store or dispose of any Contractor's Equipment or surplus materials. The Contractor shall clear away and remove from the Site any wreckage, rubbish and Temporary Works which are no longer required.

Upon the issue of a Taking-Over Certificate, the Contractor shall clear away and remove, from that part of the Site and Works to which the Taking-Over Certificate refers, all Contractor's Equipment, surplus material, wreckage, rubbish and Temporary Works. The Contractor shall leave that part of the Site and the Works in a clean and safe condition. However, the Contractor may retain on Site, during the Defects Notification Period, such Goods as are required for the Contractor to fulfil obligations under the Contract.

The requirements of Sub-Clause 4.23 are related to the requirements of other Sub-Clauses. The requirement that work can only be carried out on the Site, or locations 'which have been agreed by the Engineer as working areas', will apply to Subcontractors and staff or consultants who are carrying out any design work. Whilst total compliance may be impractical, the requirement is important in relation to the Engineer's right to inspect materials, workmanship and work in progress, as Sub-Clause 7.3. The requirement is presumably not intended to apply to the manufacture of mechanical and electrical items which will then be incorporated into Plant for the Works. The extent of off-site work and the requirements for notification and inspection should be discussed between the Contractor and the Engineer.

The requirement to keep the Contractor's Personnel off adjacent land relates to the Sub-Clause 4.14 requirement not to interfere with the convenience of the public and the Sub-Clause 4.8(e) requirement to provide Temporary Works for the protection of owners and occupiers of adjacent land. The requirement to keep the Site free from rubbish and other obstructions also relates to the safety provisions at Sub-Clause 4.8.

The requirements for clearing the Site on completion must be read in conjunction with Clause 10 Employer's Taking Over and Clause 11 Defects Liability. Sub-Clause 11.7 gives the Contractor the right of access during the Defects Notification Period and the final sentence of Sub-Clause 4.23 gives him the right to retain on the Site such Goods, that is Equipment, Material and Temporary Works, as are required to fulfil his obligations. An area of the Site will need to be agreed for his use.

4.24 Fossils

All fossils, coins, articles of value or antiquity, and structures and other remains or items of geological or archaeological interest found on the Site shall be placed under the care and authority of the Employer. The Contractor shall take reasonable precautions to prevent Contractor's Personnel or other persons from removing or damaging any of these findings.

The Contractor shall, upon discovery of any such finding, promptly give notice to the Engineer, who shall issue instructions for dealing with it. If the Contractor suffers delay and/or incurs Cost from complying with the instructions, the Contractor shall give a further notice to the Engineer and shall be entitled subject to Sub-Clause 20.1 [*Contractor's Claims*] to:

(a) an extension of time for any such delay, if completion is or will be delayed, under Sub-Clause 8.4 [*Extension of Time for Completion*]; and

(b) payment of any such Cost, which shall be included in the Contract Price.

After receiving this further notice, the Engineer shall proceed in accordance with Sub-Clause 3.5 [*Determinations*] to agree or determine these matters.

The procedure when fossils or similar objects are found on the Site follows the typical notice and claims procedures and Sub-Clause 20.1. However, the Contractor is required to give an initial notice when the fossils are discovered, in order that the Engineer can examine the situation and issue any appropriate instructions. These instructions may constitute a Variation under Clause 13. The Contractor will also be obliged to comply with the governing law and any local regulations. It may also have been necessary to permit archaeological investigation of the Site before work commenced, which may be covered by Sub-Clause 1.13 and included as Site data under Sub-Clause 4.10.

Chapter 13

Clause 5 (RB): Nominated Subcontractors

Clause 5 gives a procedure whereby the Employer can impose a particular Subcontractor on the Contractor, either by the nominated Subcontractor being stated as such in the Contract, or by an instruction from the Engineer as a Variation under Clause 13. Whilst there may be good reasons why the Employer would like a particular Subcontractor to be used for certain work, there are considerable potential problems from imposing a Subcontractor on the Contractor. The procedure should be used with caution and a full appreciation of the potential problems, including indemnities that may be required by the Contractor, is necessary.

Attempts to impose a particular Subcontractor but to avoid the nomination route, perhaps by a Plant specification which can only be achieved by one supplier, could result in the Subcontractor being deemed to have been nominated.

Under these procedures, Sub-Clause 4.4(a) is clear that the Contractor does not need to obtain the Engineer's consent to the nominated Subcontractor. Sub-Clause 4.4 requires that the Contractor 'shall be responsible for the acts or defaults of any Subcontractor, his agents or employees, as if they were the acts or defaults of the Contractor'. The use of the phrase 'any Subcontractor' must include a nominated Subcontractor. Sub-Clauses 5.2(b) and (c) enable the Contractor to object to the nomination if the subcontract does not indemnify the Contractor against failures by the Subcontractor, but indemnities do not lessen the Contractor's obligations to the Employer. The extension of time provisions at Sub-Clause 8.4 do not provide for an extension in the event of delay caused by a nominated Subcontractor.

The Contract is silent on the procedures for the replacement of a nominated Subcontractor, in the event of default by the Subcontractor. The Engineer might argue that he is entitled to issue a Variation to nominate a different Subcontractor. Alternatively, the Engineer might argue that, under Sub-Clause 4.4, it is the Contractor's problem and, under Sub-Clause 8.1, the Contractor must 'proceed with the Works with due expedition and without delay'. The consequences in cost and delay could be considerable and the Contractor would no doubt wish to claim for reimbursement of his loss, possibly under a provision of the local law. Alternatively, the Contractor may have sought an indemnity by the Employer against such an eventuality under the provisions of Sub-Clause 5.2.

Definitions at Sub-Clause 1.1 that are relevant to this Clause include:

1.1.2.8	Subcontractor
1.1.4.10	Provisional Sum
1.1.5.3	Materials
1.1.5.4	Permanent Works.

5.1 (RB)   Definition of 'nominated Subcontractor'

In the Contract, 'nominated Subcontractor' means a Subcontractor:

(a)   who is stated in the Contract as being a nominated Subcontractor; or

(b)   whom the Engineer, under Clause 13 [*Variations and Adjustments*], instructs the Contractor to employ as a Subcontractor.

Previous FIDIC Contracts had a definition of nominated Subcontractors which included anyone who supplied Goods for which a Provisional Sum had been included in the Contract, as well as those who executed work. Sub-Clause 5.1 now refers only to Subcontractors who are either named in the Contract or are the subject of a Variation under Clause 13. Subcontractors are defined at Sub-Clause 1.1.2.8 to include a person who is appointed as a Subcontractor for a part of the Works and 'Materials' are defined at Sub-Clause 1.1.5.3 as forming part of the Permanent Works. Hence, under FIDIC, a material supplier who is nominated would appear to be a nominated Subcontractor and be covered by the provisions of Clause 5.

Instructions for the purchase of Plant, Materials or services are also covered at Sub-Clause 13.5 concerning Provisional Sums. Paragraph (b) refers to Plant, Materials or services to be purchased from a nominated Subcontractor or otherwise.

5.2 (RB)   Objection to Nomination

The Contractor shall not be under any obligation to employ a nominated Subcontractor against whom the Contractor raises reasonable objection by notice to the Engineer as soon as practicable, with supporting particulars. An objection shall be deemed reasonable if it arises from (among other things) any of the following matters, unless the Employer agrees to indemnify the Contractor against and from the consequences of the matter:

(a) there are reasons to believe that the Subcontractor does not have sufficient competence, resources or financial strength;
(b) the subcontract does not specify that the nominated Subcontractor shall indemnify the Contractor against and from any negligence or misuse of Goods by the nominated Subcontractor, his agents and employees; or
(c) the subcontract does not specify that, for the subcontracted work (including design, if any), the nominated Subcontractor shall:
  (i) undertake to the Contractor such obligations and liabilities as will enable the Contractor to discharge his obligations and liabilities under the Contract, and
  (ii) indemnify the Contractor against and from all obligations and liabilities arising under or in connection with the Contract and from the consequences of any failure by the Subcontractor to perform these obligations or to fulfil these liabilities.

If the Contractor does not wish to employ a particular nominated Subcontractor he must raise an objection 'as soon as practicable'. If the nominated Subcontractor was named in the Tender documents then the Contractor had the opportunity to object before signing the Contract. The causes for an objection are not limited to the matters stated at paragraphs (a) to (c), but must be 'reasonable'. Any dispute about whether an objection is reasonable could result in considerable problems and delays. If the Contractor does not wish to employ a particular Subcontractor then for the Employer to insist could result in problems later if there is a query concerning the Subcontractor's performance. Some queries as to whether a Subcontractor should be imposed on a Contractor might be overcome by an indemnity from the Employer as provided for at Sub-Clause 5.2.

The provisions whereby either the Employer or the Subcontractor may be required to indemnify the Contractor against the consequences of failure by the Subcontractor are indicative of the potential problems that can arise from the use of nominated Subcontractors.

5.3 (RB) Payments to nominated Subcontractors

The Contractor shall pay to the nominated Subcontractor the amounts which the Engineer certifies to be due in accordance with the subcontract. These amounts plus other charges shall be included in the Contract Price in accordance with subparagraph (b) of Sub-Clause 13.5 [*Provisional Sums*], except as stated in Sub-Clause 5.4 [*Evidence of Payments*].

Payments to a nominated Subcontractor are certified by the Engineer as being due under the particular subcontract. These payments are certified by the Engineer in the Clause 14 Payment Certificates and are included in the Contract Price as Provisional Sums under Sub-Clause 13.5(b). The Contractor is also paid for overheads and profit at the percentage stated either in an appropriate Schedule or in the Appendix to Tender.

5.4 (RB)   Evidence of Payments

Before issuing a Payment Certificate which includes an amount payable to a nominated Subcontractor, the Engineer may request the Contractor to supply reasonable evidence that the nominated Subcontractor has received all amounts due in accordance with previous Payment Certificates, less applicable deductions for retention or otherwise. Unless the Contractor:

(a)   submits this reasonable evidence to the Engineer; or

(b)   (i) satisfies the Engineer in writing that the Contractor is reasonably entitled to withhold or refuse to pay these amounts, and (ii) submits to the Engineer reasonable evidence that the nominated Subcontractor has been notified of the Contractor's entitlement;

then the Employer may (at his sole discretion) pay, direct to the nominated Subcontractor, part or all of such amounts previously certified (less applicable deductions) as are due to the nominated Subcontractor and for which the Contractor has failed to submit the evidence described in sub-paragraphs (a) or (b) above. The Contractor shall then repay, to the Employer, the amount which the nominated Subcontractor was directly paid by the Employer.

The Engineer is entitled to check that the Contractor has passed on the payments to the nominated Subcontractor and, in certain circumstances, to make payments direct to the Subcontractor. Any payment that has been made to the nominated Subcontractor, after having been paid to the Contractor, will be recovered from the Contractor.

Before making any direct payment the Engineer will need to check *why* the money has not been paid to the nominated Subcontractor, following the procedure of paragraph (b) (i). Any subsequent deduction from the Contractor will need to follow the procedures of Sub-Clause 2.5. Any action for direct payments to a Subcontractor must also be considered in conjunction with any relevant provisions in the governing law.

Chapter 14

Clause 5 (YB): Design

Clause 5 in the Yellow Book covers the procedures for design carried out by the Contractor. The design must comply with the Employer's Requirements, must comply with any applicable regulations and must satisfy the Engineer that it complies with the Contract. Whether the Engineer's satisfaction can be achieved by a review, or requires detailed study and approval, must be stated in the Employer's Requirements. The Engineer must recognise that the design is the Contractor's responsibility and the Engineer's task is to check that it complies with the Contract, not to impose his personal preferences for design methods and details. If the Engineer requires any changes to the design or Contractor's Documents then the Contractor will check whether the change is a Variation.

This chapter reviews the procedures and requirements for the Contractor to prepare the design and Contractor's Documents which relate to the design, construction, installation and operation of the Works which have been designed. If, under a Yellow Book Contract, part of the Works is required to be constructed in accordance with design prepared by the Employer then this must be clearly stated in the Employer's Requirements. The extent of the Contractor's obligations and liability must be defined and it will probably be necessary to import some Clauses from the FIDIC Red Book.

The Contract procedures for design must be linked to the procedures for obtaining the necessary permissions and approvals from the relevant authorities. Under some legal systems it is necessary to obtain design approval before the Employer can obtain approval to proceed with the project. The compliance with Laws is also referred to at Sub-Clause 1.13, which is reviewed in Chapter 9 of this book. The sequence of the events described in this chapter is given in Fig. 4 in Chapter 5. Although this Clause is headed 'Design', many of the requirements, such as the undertaking at Sub-Clause 5.3, also refer to the execution and the completed Works.

Definitions at Sub-Clause 1.1 relevant to this Clause include:

1.1.1.5 (YB)	Employer's Requirements
1.1.1.7 (YB)	Contractor's Proposal
1.1.1.8	Tender
1.1.2.6	Employer's Personnel
1.1.2.8	Subcontractor
1.1.3.1	Base Date
1.1.3.5	Taking-Over Certificate
1.1.3.7	Defects Notification Period
1.1.3.8	Performance Certificate
1.1.5.8	Works
1.1.6.1	Contractor's Documents
1.1.6.2	Country
1.1.6.5	Laws
1.1.6.9	Variation.

5.1 (YB) General Design Obligations

The Contractor shall carry out, and be responsible for, the design of the Works. Design shall be prepared by qualified designers who are engineers or other professionals who comply with the criteria (if any) stated in the Employer's Requirements. Unless otherwise stated in the Contract, the Contractor shall submit to the Engineer for consent the name and particulars of each proposed designer and design Subcontractor.

The Contractor warrants that he, his designers and design Subcontractors have the experience and capability necessary for the design. The Contractor undertakes that the designers shall be available to attend discussions with the Engineer at all reasonable times, until the expiry date of the relevant Defects Notification Period.

Upon receiving notice under Sub-Clause 8.1 [*Commencement of Works*], the Contractor shall scrutinise the Employer's Requirements (including design criteria and calculations, if any) and the items of reference mentioned in Sub-Clause 4.7 [*Setting Out*]. Within the period stated in the Appendix to Tender, calculated from the Commencement Date, the Contractor shall give notice to the Engineer of any error, fault or other defect found in the Employer's Requirements or these items of reference.

After receiving this notice, the Engineer shall determine whether Clause 13 [*Variations and Adjustments*] shall be applied, and shall give notice to the Contractor accordingly. If and to the extent that (taking account of cost and time) an experienced contractor exercising due care would have discovered the error, fault or other defect when examining the Site and the Employer's Requirements before submitting the Tender, the Time for Completion shall not be extended and the Contract Price shall not be adjusted.

Sub-Clause 5.1 requires the Contractor to submit the names and details of each proposed designer and design Subcontractor for the Engineer's consent. All the designers must be qualified professionals who meet any criteria in the Employer's Requirements. The Laws may also require them to be qualified in the Country. However, if they were named in the Tender and so were accepted by the Employer, then consent has already been given. The designers must be available to attend discussions with the Engineer, right up to the end of the Defects Notification Period.

The third paragraph of Sub-Clause 5.1 requires the Contractor to carry out a detailed study of the Employer's Requirements and the setting out information which has been provided under Sub-Clause 4.7. Any errors, faults or other defects must be reported to the Engineer within the period stated in the Appendix to Tender. The Appendix to Tender refers to these as being 'unforeseeable', which presumably means that they were unforeseeable when the Contractor prepared his Tender. The problem for the Contractor is that he does not know the details of exactly what the Employer requires. He only knows what is stated in the Employer's Requirements, which has formed the basis of his calculations in preparing his Tender. The Contractor will probably raise questions and ask for instructions. The Engineer will then decide whether the Contractor should have noticed the problem when preparing his Tender. The Contractor will, of course, know whether any other tenderer raised the matter, all questions raised having been answered to *all* tenderers. The Engineer will inform the Contractor whether he intends to issue a Variation order. If the Contractor is not satisfied with the Engineer's reply then he must give notice of a claim, under Sub-Clause 20.1, and the claim procedures will apply.

The requirements for this review are wider than just a simple design check. The review must cover everything in the Employer's Requirements, including the requirements for obtaining permissions from authorities, as described at Sub-Clause 1.13.

If the Contractor suffers delay and/or incurs cost due to an error in the Employer's Requirements which was not noticed under Sub-Clause 5.1 then he must give notice under Sub-Clause 1.9, reviewed in Chapter 9 of this book. If there is a problem with the setting out information, which was not noticed under Sub-Clause 5.1, then the Contractor can give notice under Sub-Clause 4.7, reviewed in Chapter 12 of this book. In both cases he must also comply with the requirements of Sub-Clause 20.1.

When a query is raised under any of these Sub-Clauses it is essential that the Engineer gives clear instructions as to what is required for the Works. This is necessary so that the work can proceed in the design office or on Site whilst any liability is decided.

5.2 (YB)   Contractor's Documents

The Contractor's Documents shall comprise the technical documents specified in the Employer's Requirements, documents required to satisfy all regulatory approvals, and the documents described in Sub-Clause 5.6 [*As-Built Documents*] and Sub-Clause 5.7 [*Operation and Maintenance Manuals*]. Unless otherwise stated in the Employer's Requirements, the Contractor's Documents shall be written in the language for communications defined in Sub-Clause 1.4 [*Law and Language*].

The Contractor shall prepare all Contractor's Documents, and shall also prepare any other documents necessary to instruct the Contractor's Personnel. The Employer's Personnel shall have the right to inspect the preparation of all these documents, wherever they are being prepared.

If the Employer's Requirements describe the Contractor's Documents which are to be submitted to the Engineer for review and/or for approval, they shall be submitted accordingly, together with a notice as described below. In the following provisions of this Sub-Clause, (i) 'review period' means the period required by the Engineer for review and (if so specified) for approval, and (ii) 'Contractor's Documents' exclude any documents which are not specified as being required to be submitted for review and/or for approval.

Unless otherwise stated in the Employer's Requirements, each review period shall not exceed 21 days, calculated from the date on which the Engineer receives a Contractor's Document and the Contractor's notice. This notice shall state that the Contractor's Document is considered ready, both for review (and approval, if so specified) in accordance with this Sub-Clause and for use. The notice shall also state that the Contractor's Document complies with the Contract, or the extent to which it does not comply.

The Engineer may, within the review period, give notice to the Contractor that a Contractor's Document fails (to the extent stated) to comply with the Contract. If a Contractor's Document so fails to comply, it shall be rectified, resubmitted and reviewed (and, if specified, approved) in accordance with this Sub-Clause, at the Contractor's cost.

For each part of the Works, and except to the extent that the prior approval or consent of the Engineer shall have been obtained:

(a)   in the case of a Contractor's Document which has (as specified) been submitted for the Engineer's approval:
 (i)   the Engineer shall give notice to the Contractor that the Contractor's Document is approved, with or without comments, or that it fails (to the extent stated) to comply with the Contract;
 (ii)   execution of such part of the Works shall not commence until the Engineer has approved the Contractor's Document; and

(iii) the Engineer shall be deemed to have approved the Contractor's Document upon the expiry of the review periods for all the Contractor's Documents which are relevant to the design and execution of such part, unless the Engineer has previously notified otherwise in accordance with sub-paragraph (i);

(b) execution of such part of the Works shall not commence prior to the expiry of the review periods for all the Contractor's Documents which are relevant to its design and execution;

(c) execution of such part of the Works shall be in accordance with these reviewed (and, if specified, approved) Contractor's Documents; and

(d) if the Contractor wishes to modify any design or document which has previously been submitted for review (and, if specified, approval), the Contractor shall immediately give notice to the Engineer. Thereafter, the Contractor shall submit revised documents to the Engineer in accordance with the above procedure.

If the Engineer instructs that further Contractor's Documents are required, the Contractor shall prepare them promptly.

Any such approval or consent, or any review (under this Sub-Clause or otherwise), shall not relieve the Contractor from any obligation or responsibility.

Sub-Clause 5.2 gives the procedures and requirements for the production of the Contractor's Documents. This refers to documents which the Contract requires the Contractor to prepare, either in the Employer's Requirements, elsewhere in the Contract, or to satisfy a statutory requirement. Documents which the Contractor prepares as instructions to his personnel, or for other internal purposes, do not have to follow these procedures. The Employer's Requirements must describe the documents that the Contractor is required to submit to the Engineer, whether they are to be submitted for review and/or for approval and whether the review period will exceed 21 days.

The procedures and notices are described in detail in the Sub-Clause and the sequence of events is summarised in Fig. 4 (Design procedures (YB only)) of Chapter 5. The periods for reviews and other submissions, approvals and consents must be included in the Contractor's programme as Sub-Clause 8.3. It is the Contractor's responsibility to ensure that his documents are accurate and in accordance with the Employer's Requirements. Sub-Clause 1.5 is clear that the Employer's Requirements have priority over any document prepared by the Contractor. If the Engineer has agreed to, or instructed, anything which differs from the Employer's Requirements then the Contractor must ensure that this is properly recorded, in accordance with Sub-Clause 3.3. The Yellow Book, unlike the Red Book, does *not* permit oral instructions. If the Contractor receives an oral instruction he must immediately confirm the instruction in writing and ask for a written instruction. Failure to obtain a written instruction could lead to the instruction being denied, with serious possible problems and disputes at a later stage of the project.

The potential problem from the review procedures is that the Engineer has the power to ask for the resubmission of documents and to delay the construction until he is satisfied. Whilst the Engineer can only object that the document fails to comply with the Contract, to the extent stated, most design is a subjective process, subject to the preferences of the particular designer. The Contractor is ultimately responsible for the performance of his design and the Engineer must not try to impose his own design preferences on to the Contractor's design.

5.3 (YB) Contractor's Undertaking

The Contractor undertakes that the design, the Contractor's Documents, the execution and the completed Works will be in accordance with:

(a) the Laws in the Country; and
(b) the documents forming the Contract, as altered or modified by Variations.

This is a clear statement to confirm that the Contractor will meet his obligations.

5.4 (YB) Technical Standards and Regulations

The design, the Contractor's Documents, the execution and the completed Works shall comply with the Country's technical standards, building, construction and environmental Laws, Laws applicable to the product being produced from the Works, and other standards specified in the Employer's Requirements, applicable to the Works, or defined by the applicable Laws.

All these Laws shall, in respect of the Works and each Section, be those prevailing when the Works or Section are taken over by the Employer under Clause 10 [*Employer's Taking Over*]. References in the Contract to published standards shall be understood to be references to the edition applicable on the Base Date, unless stated otherwise.

If changed or new applicable standards come into force in the Country after the Base Date, the Contractor shall give notice to the Engineer and (if appropriate) submit proposals for compliance. In the event that:

(a) the Engineer determines that compliance is required, and
(b) the proposals for compliance constitute a variation,

then the Engineer shall initiate a Variation in accordance with Clause 13 [*Variations and Adjustments*].

This Sub-Clause highlights a difference in procedure between changes in the Laws and changes in technical standards, during the period from the Base Date to the date of the Taking-Over Certificate. If there is a change in the Laws, which include regulations, then the Contractor must be aware of the change and can claim under Sub-Clause 13.7. However, if there is a change to an applicable standard the Contractor must give notice and submit proposals to the Engineer. The Engineer then decides whether he requires compliance with the new standard and whether the proposals require a Variation order. If the Contractor is not satisfied with the actions by the Engineer then he must initiate claims procedures.

5.5 (YB)   Training

The Contractor shall carry out the training of Employer's Personnel in the operation and maintenance of the Works to the extent specified in the Employer's Requirements. If the Contract specifies training which is to be carried out before taking-over, the Works shall not be considered to be completed for the purposes of taking-over under Sub-Clause 10.1 [*Taking Over of the Works and Sections*] until this training has been completed.

Training of Employer's Personnel is an important part of any plant or design-build Contract. The Employer's Requirements must specify the extent and timing of the required training. The Contractor's Proposal will add further details. If the training is to be carried out before taking-over then it must be included in the Contractor's programme as Sub-Clause 8.3 and in the lists of work to be completed at Sub-Clauses 8.2 and 10.1. The period for trial operation may be co-ordinated with the training requirement, although the Contractor will not want compliance with the performance requirements to be compromised by the use of inexperienced personnel undergoing training.

5.6 (YB)   As-Built Documents

The Contractor shall prepare, and keep up-to-date, a complete set of 'as-built' records of the execution of the Works, showing the exact as-built built locations, sizes and details of the work as executed. These records shall be kept on the Site and shall be used exclusively for the purposes of this Sub-Clause. Two copies shall be supplied to the Engineer prior to the commencement of the Tests on Completion.

In addition, the Contractor shall supply to the Engineer as-built drawings of the Works, showing all Works as executed, and submit them to the Engineer for review under Sub-Clause 5.2 [*Contractor's Documents*]. The Contractor shall obtain the consent of the Engineer as to their size, the referencing system, and other relevant details.

Prior to the issue of any Taking-Over Certificate, the Contractor shall supply to the Engineer the specified numbers and types of copies of the relevant as-built drawings, in accordance with the Employer's Requirements. The Works shall not be considered to be completed for the purposes of taking-over under Sub-Clause 10.1 [*Taking Over of the Works and Sections*] until the Engineer has received these documents.

The as-built records must be submitted to the Engineer for review before the issue of the Taking-Over Certificate. They will probably be required before training, commissioning and trial operation.

5.7 (YB)   Operation and Maintenance Manuals

Prior to commencement of the Tests on Completion, the Contractor shall supply to the Engineer provisional operation and maintenance manuals in sufficient detail for the Employer to operate, maintain, dismantle, reassemble, adjust and repair the Plant.

The Works shall not be considered to be completed for the purposes of taking-over under Sub-Clause 10.1 [*Taking Over of the Works and Sections*] until the Engineer has received final operation and maintenance manuals in such detail, and any other manuals specified in the Employer's Requirements for these purposes.

The details and timing of the operation and maintenance manuals should be given in the Employer's Requirements and included in the Contractor's Sub-Clause 8.3 programme.

5.8 (YB)   Design Error

If errors, omissions, ambiguities, inconsistencies, inadequacies or other defects are found in the Contractor's Documents, they and the Works shall be corrected at the Contractor's cost, notwithstanding any consent or approval under this Clause.

This Sub-Clause confirms and repeats other statements that the Contractor's work is his own responsibility, regardless of any consents or approvals. Sub-Clause 11.9 is also relevant and includes the statement that 'Only the Performance Certificate shall be deemed to constitute acceptance of the Works'.

Chapter 15

Clause 6: Staff and Labour

Under Sub-Clause 4.1 the Contractor is required to provide 'all Contractor's Personnel'. Clause 6 covers requirements for the recruitment, employment and behaviour of the Contractor's staff and labour, together with specific requirements for superintendence and records.

The description 'staff and labour' appears to refer to personnel who are employed by the Contractor, whereas 'Contractor's Personnel', as defined at Sub-Clause 1.1.2.7, includes the employees of Subcontractors and 'any other personnel assisting the Contractor in the execution of the Works'. Many of the requirements of Clause 6 include Subcontractors and the conditions of Subcontracts should include similar provisions.

Additional requirements to suit local conditions may be included in the Particular Conditions. Example clauses are included in the FIDIC Guidance for the Preparation of Particular Conditions for Foreign Staff and Labour; Measures against Insect and Pest Nuisance; Alcohol Liquor or Drugs; Arms and Ammunition; Festivals and Religious Customs. When it is considered necessary to include these matters they are likely to be the subject of local Laws or regulations.

Although the Clause is headed Staff and Labour, the records required under Sub-Clause 6.10 include Contractor's Equipment.

Definitions at Sub-Clause 1.1 relevant to this Clause include:

1.1.1.5 (RB)	Specification
1.1.1.5 (YB)	Employer's Requirements
1.1.2.6	Employer's Personnel
1.1.2.7	Contractor's Personnel
1.1.5.1	Contractor's Equipment.

6.1 Engagement of Staff and Labour

Except as otherwise stated in the Specification, the Contractor shall make arrangements for the engagement of all staff and labour, local or otherwise, and for their payment, housing, feeding and transport.

In the Yellow Book the reference to 'Specification' is replaced by 'Employer's Requirements'. Sub-Clause 6.1 requires the Contractor to make all the necessary arrangements for his staff and labour, but allows for this to be overruled by the Specification or Employer's Requirements. The Specification or Employer's Requirements could state that some aspect of recruitment, payment, housing, feeding or transport would be provided by the Employer, either direct or through some other agency. This exception is important because, without a specific exception, if there is any difference between the Contract Clause and the Specification or Employer's Requirements, the requirement of the Contract Clause would take priority under Sub-Clause 1.5.

6.2 Rates of Wages and Conditions of Labour

The Contractor shall pay rates of wages, and observe conditions of labour, which are not lower than those established for the trade or industry where the work is carried out. If no established rates or conditions are applicable, the Contractor shall pay rates of wages and observe conditions which are not lower than the general level of wages and conditions observed locally by employers whose trade or industry is similar to that of the Contractor.

The Particular Conditions may include additional requirements to conform to local requirements. The Contractor will also need to comply with any local Laws and regulations that apply to wages and working conditions, in accordance with Sub-Clauses 1.13 and 6.4.

6.3 Persons in the Service of Employer

The Contractor shall not recruit, or attempt to recruit, staff and labour from amongst the Employer's Personnel.

Employees of the Employer will have knowledge of local conditions which may be valuable for the Contractor. However, the Employer will not want to lose the services of valuable staff. At pre-qualification stage the Contractor may have been asked how he proposes to recruit staff for the project, either by local recruitment or by bringing in expatriate staff and labour.

Sub-Clause 6.3 attempts to prevent the Contractor from recruiting, or attempting to recruit, staff and labour from amongst the Employer's Personnel. The subtitle refers to 'Persons in the Service of the Employer's Personnel' and the Sub-Clause, by referring to 'Employer's Personnel', covers a wider range than people who are directly employed by the Employer, as defined at Sub-Clause 1.1.2.6.

Whilst the intention of this Sub-Clause is clear, experience of similar Clauses in practice suggests its application may be more difficult. If the person concerned decided that he wanted to change his employment then it is difficult for the Employer to prevent his departure. If he has already left the employment of the Employer before he is recruited by the Contractor, then the requirement may not be applicable. However, it would be a breach of Contract for the Contractor, or a Subcontractor, to take the initiative and persuade someone to leave the employment of the Employer.

6.4 Labour Laws

The Contractor shall comply with all the relevant labour Laws applicable to the Contractor's Personnel, including Laws relating to their employment, health, safety, welfare, immigration and emigration, and shall allow them all their legal rights.

The Contractor shall require his employees to obey all applicable Laws, including those concerning safety at work.

Sub-Clause 6.4 is reviewed together with Sub-Clause 6.5.

6.5 Working Hours

No work shall be carried out on the Site on locally recognised days of rest, or outside the normal working hours stated in the Appendix to Tender, unless:

(a) otherwise stated in the Contract;
(b) the Engineer gives consent; or
(c) the work is unavoidable, or necessary for the protection of life or property or for the safety of the Works, in which case the Contractor shall immediately advise the Engineer.

The normal working hours may be restricted by the Employer, due to security or other local requirements, or may be left open for the Appendix to Tender to be completed by the Contractor.

The Contractor's normal working hours will also depend on whether he is bringing workers from outside the Country. Expatriate workers will often expect to work long hours, with fewer than normal days for weekends. Workers from the Country, or nearby countries, may have a tradition of long weekends after pay day. The Contractor will be deemed to have made enquiries and taken local custom into account when preparing his Tender, as required by Sub-Clauses 4.10 and 4.11.

Work outside the normal working hours requires the consent of the Engineer. The additional work will presumably benefit the project so consent should not normally be refused. Exceptions to the normal working hours may be necessary for particular operations, when the Contractor wishes to overcome delays, or when the Engineer has invoked the procedures of Sub-Clause 8.6 and required the Contractor to adopt measures to expedite progress. Sub-Clause 8.6 enables the Employer to claim from the Contractor any additional supervision Costs and similar provisions may be instructed as a condition of the Engineer's consent to work out of normal hours.

6.6   Facilities for Staff and Labour

Except as otherwise stated in the Specification, the Contractor shall provide and maintain all necessary accommodation and welfare facilities for the Contractor's Personnel. The Contractor shall also provide facilities for the Employer's Personnel as stated in the Specification.

The Contractor shall not permit any of the Contractor's Personnel to maintain any temporary or permanent living quarters within the structures forming part of the Permanent Works.

In the Yellow Book the reference to 'Specification' is replaced by 'Employer's Requirements'. Sub-Clause 6.6 repeats the same requirement and exclusion as Sub-Clause 6.1, specifically for the provision of accommodation and welfare facilities. The Contractor is also required to provide the facilities for the Employer's Personnel, including the Engineer's Site staff as stated at Sub-Clause 1.1.2.6, which are stated in the Specification or Employer's Requirements.

6.7   Health and Safety

The Contractor shall at all times take all reasonable precautions to maintain the health and safety of the Contractor's Personnel. In collaboration with local health authorities, the Contractor shall ensure that medical staff, first aid facilities, sick bay and ambulance service are available at all times at the Site and at any accommodation for Contractor's and Employer's Personnel, and that suitable arrangements are made for all necessary welfare and hygiene requirements and for the prevention of epidemics.

The Contractor shall appoint an accident prevention officer at the Site, responsible for maintaining safety and protection against accidents. This person shall be qualified for this responsibility, and shall have the authority to issue instructions and take protective measures to prevent accidents. Throughout the execution of the Works, the Contractor shall provide whatever is required by this person to exercise this responsibility and authority.

The Contractor shall send, to the Engineer, details of any accident as soon as practicable after its occurrence. The Contractor shall maintain records and make reports concerning health, safety and welfare of persons, and damage to property, as the Engineer may reasonably require.

This Sub-Clause must be considered together with the health and safety regulations which apply under the applicable Laws. The Contractor is also required to appoint an accident prevention officer, who is suitably qualified and is responsible for ensuring that these requirements are followed. The requirement to ensure that medical facilities are available at the Site could be an onerous requirement for a project that is located a long way away from any centre of population. If the project is intended to encourage further development in the area, the Employer should consider including the provision of a permanent medical facility as a part of the project.

The Contractor must keep records of safety matters as required by the Engineer and these records will form a basis for the safety statistics which are necessary for the monthly progress reports under Sub-Clause 4.21(g).

6.8   Contractor's Superintendence

Throughout the execution of the Works, and as long thereafter as is necessary to fulfil the Contractor's obligations, the Contractor shall provide all necessary superintendence to plan, arrange, direct, manage, inspect and test the work.

Superintendence shall be given by a sufficient number of persons having adequate knowledge of the language for communications (defined in Sub-Clause 1.4 [*Law and Language*]) and of the operations to be carried out (including the methods and techniques required, the hazards likely to be encountered and methods of preventing accidents), for the satisfactory and safe execution of the Works.

In the Yellow Book the words 'design and' are added before 'execution'. Sub-Clause 6.8 imposes an all-embracing obligation on the Contractor to provide 'all necessary superintendence', which is described as the people who will 'plan, arrange, direct, manage, inspect and test the work' and to comply with the detailed requirements. This requirement may seem to be obvious, but it gives the Engineer the opportunity to raise the matter, as a breach of this Sub-Clause, if he considers that the progress or quality of the work has suffered due to the lack of a suitable person to fulfil one of these functions.

6.9   Contractor's Personnel

The Contractor's Personnel shall be appropriately qualified, skilled and experienced in their respective trades or occupations. The Engineer may require the Contractor to remove (or cause to be removed) any person employed on the Site or Works, including the Contractor's Representative if applicable, who:

(a)   persists in any misconduct or lack of care;
(b)   carries out duties incompetently or negligently;
(c)   fails to conform with any provisions of the Contract; or
(d)   persists in any conduct which is prejudicial to safety, health, or the protection of the environment.

If appropriate, the Contractor shall then appoint (or cause to be appointed) a suitable replacement person.

This provision applies, by the definition at Sub-Clause 1.1.2.7, to personnel employed by Subcontractors as well the Contractor's own personnel. If the person concerned is in a supervisory position then Sub-Clause 6.8 could also be relevant.

6.10   Records of Contractor's Personnel and Equipment

The Contractor shall submit, to the Engineer, details showing the number of each class of Contractor's Personnel and of each type of Contractor's Equipment on the Site. Details shall be submitted each calendar month, in a form approved by the Engineer, until the Contractor has completed all work which is known to be outstanding at the completion date stated in the Taking-Over Certificate for the Works.

The records and monthly reports under Sub-Clause 6.10 must include Contractor's Equipment and Personnel, as well as 'staff and labour'. The Contractor's Equipment and Personnel includes those provided by Subcontractors. The report is included in the monthly progress report under Sub-Clause 4.21(d). For a large or complex project it may be useful for the Particular Conditions to require that the numbers are allocated to particular parts of the project. It is also essential that any contemporary records, which are submitted under Sub-Clause 20.1, are consistent with these records.

6.11   Disorderly Conduct

The Contractor shall at all times take all reasonable precautions to prevent any unlawful, riotous or disorderly conduct by or amongst the Contractor's Personnel, and to preserve peace and protection of persons and property on and near the Site.

Failure to comply with these requirements could result in a claim under the insurance provided to Sub-Clause 18.3 or the indemnity under Sub-Clause 17.1, as well as under the provisions of Sub-Clause 4.14. It could also affect any liability of the Employer under other clauses, exclude Force Majeure under Sub-Clause 19.1(iii) and liability as an Employer's risk under Sub-Clause 17.3(c).

Chapter 16

Clause 7: Plant, Materials and Workmanship

Clause 7 covers the Contractor's obligations concerning the quality of his work and the procedures to be followed for tests and in the event that an item of work fails the test. The matter of the time when an item of Plant or Materials becomes the property of the Employer is covered at Sub-Clause 7.7 and Royalties are dealt with at Sub-Clause 7.8.

If the Contract includes a requirement for a quality assurance system, as Sub-Clause 4.9, then the application of Clause 7 will need to be considered in relation to that system.

For a Yellow Book Contract the Contractor's Proposal may include proposals relating to the quality of Plant, Materials and workmanship which are different to the provisions in the Employer's Requirements. The Employer's Requirements will prevail, in accordance with the priority at Sub-Clause 1.5.

The FIDIC Guidance for the Preparation of Particular Conditions includes an additional Sub-Clause for use when the financing institution imposes restrictions on the use of its funds.

Definitions relevant to Clause 7 include:

1.1.1.5 (YB)	Employer's Requirements
1.1.1.7 (YB)	Contractor's Proposal
1.1.2.6	Employer's Personnel
1.1.3.4	Tests on Completion
1.1.3.6	Tests after Completion
1.1.5.2	Goods
1.1.5.3	Materials
1.1.5.5	Plant
1.1.6.2	Country
1.1.6.5	Laws
1.1.6.7	Site.

7.1 Manner of Execution
The Contractor shall carry out the manufacture of Plant, the production and manufacture of Materials, and all other execution of the Works:

(a) in the manner (if any) specified in the Contract;
(b) in a proper workmanlike and careful manner, in accordance with recognised good practice; and
(c) with properly equipped facilities and non-hazardous Materials, except as otherwise specified in the Contract.

The quality of Materials and standard of workmanship will be specified elsewhere in the Contract documents, and will normally refer to the national standard specifications of the Country of the project. Phrases such as 'proper workmanlike and careful manner', 'recognised good practice' and 'properly equipped facilities', which are used in this Sub-Clause are not precise. These requirements will be interpreted by the Engineer in relation to the actual Goods supplied and the work that is executed by the Contractor.

7.2   Samples

The Contractor shall submit the following samples of Materials, and relevant information, to the Engineer for consent prior to using the Materials in or for the Works:

(a) manufacturer's standard samples of Materials and samples specified in the Contract, all at the Contractor's cost; and
(b) additional samples instructed by the Engineer as a Variation.

Each sample shall be labelled as to origin and intended use in the Works.

In the Yellow Book the phrase 'for the Engineer's consent prior to using the Materials in or for the Works' is replaced by 'to the Engineer for review in accordance with the procedures for Contractor's Documents described in Sub-Clause 5.2' [*Contractor's Documents*].

When samples are specified or instructed then the requirement and details should be clear. The requirement for 'manufacturer's standard samples' is not always clear. However, the Sub-Clause refers only to samples of Materials which, by definition, excludes Plant. The samples are provided to the Engineer for consent which, under Sub-Clause 1.3, shall not be unreasonably withheld or delayed.

7.3   Inspection

The Employer's Personnel shall at all reasonable times:

(a) have full access to all parts of the Site and to all places from which natural Materials are being obtained; and
(b) during production, manufacture and construction (at the Site and elsewhere), be entitled to examine, inspect, measure and test the

167

materials and workmanship, and to check the progress of manufacture of Plant and production and manufacture of Materials.

The Contractor shall give the Employer's Personnel full opportunity to carry out these activities, including providing access, facilities, permissions and safety equipment. No such activity shall relieve the Contractor from any obligation or responsibility.

The Contractor shall give notice to the Engineer whenever any work is ready and before it is covered up, put out of sight, or packaged for storage or transport. The Engineer shall then either carry out the examination, inspection, measurement or testing without unreasonable delay, or promptly give notice to the Contractor that the Engineer does not require to do so. If the Contractor fails to give the notice, he shall, if and when required by the Engineer, uncover the work and thereafter reinstate and make good, all at the Contractor's cost.

Sub-Clause 7.3 requires the Contractor to allow the Employer's Personnel to enter the Site and any factories, quarries or other places where work is being carried out for the Works. The Contractor must provide 'access, facilities, permissions and safety equipment' to enable the person concerned to inspect and check the Materials, workmanship and progress.

Clearly, the Contractor can insist that anyone carrying out an inspection shall have proper authority to enter the Site and inspect the work. This is covered by the definition of 'Employer's Personnel' at Sub-Clause 1.1.2.6, which requires that all Employer's Personnel have been notified to the Contractor by the Employer or Engineer. The person concerned can inspect, but cannot give any instructions unless they have been given delegated authority under Sub-Clause 3.3. The Contractor will also insist that anyone entering the Site or other premises shall follow the appropriate safety regulations.

The Contractor is required to give notice when any work is ready for inspection and before it is concealed in any way. The Specification or Employer's Requirements will often include a more detailed procedure and standard Notice for Inspection, or the Contractor may introduce his own standard form. The notice should also state when the Contractor wishes to proceed with the work in order to comply with his programme. Standard notice forms often have space for the Inspector to sign that the work has passed or failed the inspection. Any such signature must have been authorised in accordance with Sub-Clause 3.3 and the Engineer may decide only to authorise an 'I have inspected' signature.

The Engineer will either inspect 'without unreasonable delay' or indicate that he does not need to do so. If the Contractor fails to give notice that work is ready then he can be required to uncover the work and reinstate at his own cost. This will be at the Contractor's cost, regardless of whether the work is found to be faulty.

If the Contractor gives notice but then, for whatever reason, the work is covered before it is inspected then the Contractor would appear to be in breach of Sub-Clause 7.3, unless the Engineer failed to inspect within a reasonable time.

The provisions of this Sub-Clause are typical of the provisions for the supervision of civil engineering work. If the Works include mechanical and electrical work then the application of the provisions may be difficult. Items of Plant may include items of standard manufacture which the Subcontractor purchases when they are required. The extent of detail which is required for compliance with paragraph (b) and with paragraph (c) of the monthly progress report under Sub-Clause 4.21, will need to be agreed to suit the actual procedures that are normally adopted. Items which are specified by performance and subject to Tests on, or after, Completion would not normally be subject to the same detailed inspection during manufacture as is required for civil engineering work.

7.4 Testing

This Sub-Clause shall apply to all tests specified in the Contract, other than the Tests after Completion (if any).

The Contractor shall provide all apparatus, assistance, documents and other information, electricity, equipment, fuel, consumables, instruments, labour, materials, and suitably qualified and experienced staff, as are necessary to carry out the specified tests efficiently. The Contractor shall agree, with the Engineer, the time and place for the specified testing of any Plant, Materials and other parts of the Works.

The Engineer may, under Clause 13 [*Variations and Adjustments*], vary the location or details of specified tests, or instruct the Contractor to carry out additional tests. If these varied or additional tests show that the tested Plant, Materials or workmanship is not in accordance with the Contract, the cost of carrying out this Variation shall be borne by the Contractor, notwithstanding other provisions of the Contract.

The Engineer shall give the Contractor not less than 24 hours' notice of the Engineer's intention to attend the tests. If the Engineer does not attend at the time and place agreed, the Contractor may proceed with the tests, unless otherwise instructed by the Engineer, and the tests shall then be deemed to have been made in the Engineer's presence.

If the Contractor suffers delay and/or incurs Cost from complying with these instructions or as a result of a delay for which the Employer is responsible, the Contractor shall give notice to the Engineer and shall be entitled subject to Sub-Clause 20.1 [*Contractor's Claims*] to:

(a) an extension of time for any such delay, if completion is or will be delayed, under Sub-Clause 8.4 [*Extension of Time for Completion*]; and

(b) payment of any such Cost plus reasonable profit, which shall be included in the Contract Price.

After receiving this notice, the Engineer shall proceed in accordance with Sub-Clause 3.5 [*Determinations*] to agree or determine these matters.

The Contractor shall promptly forward to the Engineer duly certified reports of the tests. When the specified tests have been passed, the Engineer shall endorse the Contractor's test certificate, or issue a certificate to him, to that effect. If the Engineer has not attended the tests, he shall be deemed to have accepted the readings as accurate.

Sub-Clause 7.4 gives the procedures for tests specified in the Contract and additional tests instructed under Clause 13. Tests on Completion are covered at Clause 9, which refers back to Sub-Clause 7.4. Tests after Completion, as Yellow Book Clause 12, require different procedures because, after completion, the project is occupied and controlled by the Employer. For a Red Book Contract, Tests after Completion must be required in the Particular Conditions, as referred to at Sub-Clause 1.1.3.6 (RB).

The Contractor will have given notice under Sub-Clause 7.3 that the item is ready to be tested. The Engineer will then give the Contractor not less than 24 hours' notice of his intention to attend the tests and the time and place will be agreed between Engineer and Contractor. The Contractor will provide all the facilities necessary for the test. If the Engineer wants to change any of the specified details then he must issue a Variation under Clause 13. If the Engineer fails to attend the test, without issuing an appropriate instruction, then the Contractor can proceed. The tests are deemed to have been made in the Engineer's presence and he will be deemed to have accepted the readings as accurate.

After the tests, the Contractor will send to the Engineer a certified report and, when the test has been successful, the Engineer will issue a Certificate. If an item fails a test then the Engineer can reject that item under Sub-Clause 7.5, but must give reasons for the rejection. The Contractor must then make good the item and ensure that it complies with the Contract. Alternatively the Employer may agree to accept the item under the procedures of Sub-Clause 9.4.

7.5 Rejection

If, as a result of an examination, inspection, measurement or testing, any Plant, Materials or workmanship is found to be defective or otherwise not in accordance with the Contract, the Engineer may reject the Plant, Materials or workmanship by giving notice to the Contractor, with reasons. The Contractor shall then promptly make good the defect and ensure that the rejected item complies with the Contract.

If the Engineer requires this Plant, Materials or workmanship to be retested, the tests shall be repeated under the same terms and conditions. If the rejection and retesting cause the Employer to incur additional costs, the Contractor shall subject to Sub-Clause 2.5 [*Employer's Claims*] pay these costs to the Employer.

The cost of tests is dealt with at Sub-Clauses 7.4 and 7.5:

- Tests that are specified are clearly included in the Accepted Contract Amount. If quantities are stated in the Bill of Quantities they would be remeasured in accordance with Clause 12. If the item fails the test then it is not clear whether the Contractor will be paid for the cost of the test. However, if the Engineer requires the test to be repeated, presumably either before or after remedial work and the Employer incurs additional costs, then these can be claimed from the Contractor using the procedures at Sub-Clause 2.5.
- The cost of tests that are instructed by the Engineer under Clause 13 is only paid if the test is successful.

7.6   Remedial Work

Notwithstanding any previous test or certification, the Engineer may instruct the Contractor to:

(a)   remove from the Site and replace any Plant or Materials which is not in accordance with the Contract;

(b)   remove and re-execute any other work which is not in accordance with the Contract; and

(c)   execute any work which is urgently required for the safety of the Works, whether because of an accident, unforeseeable event or otherwise.

The Contractor shall comply with the instruction within a reasonable time, which shall be the time (if any) specified in the instruction, or immediately if urgency is specified under sub-paragraph (c).

If the Contractor fails to comply with the instruction, the Employer shall be entitled to employ and pay other persons to carry out the work. Except to the extent that the Contractor would have been entitled to payment for the work, the Contractor shall subject to Sub-Clause 2.5 [*Employer's Claims*] pay to the Employer all costs arising from this failure.

Sub-Clause 7.6 gives powers to the Engineer to deal with items which, in his opinion, are not in accordance with the Contract. The Engineer may instruct that Plant, Materials or any other work is removed from the Site and the item replaced. The Contractor must comply with the instruction within a reasonable time, which may be stated in the instruction.

Under Sub-Clause 7.6(c) the Engineer may also issue instructions for any work which is required for the safety of the Works, which must be carried out immediately. If the Contractor fails, or is unable, to comply with this instruction then the Employer may employ others to carry out the work and claim the Costs arising from the failure to the Contractor under Sub-Clause 2.5.

7.7 Ownership of Plant and Materials

Each item of Plant and Materials shall, to the extent consistent with the Laws of the Country, become the property of the Employer at whichever is the earlier of the following times, free from liens and other encumbrances:

(a) when it is delivered to the Site;

(b) when the Contractor is entitled to payment of the value of the Plant and Materials under Sub-Clause 8.10 [*Payment for Plant and Materials in Event of Suspension*].

Sub-Clause 7.7 states that any item of Plant and Materials which has been delivered to the Site becomes the property of the Employer. The definition of 'Site' at Sub-Clause 1.1.6.7 includes places specified in the Contract as forming part of the Site. The Plant and Materials which become the property of the Employer should have been included in Interim Payment Certificates under Sub-Clause 14.5, if the Contractor has provided all the paperwork required by this Sub-Clause. This provision could be unfair on the Contractor in the event that the Employer went into liquidation before the payment had actually been made.

The reference to the Laws of the Country is extremely important and should also refer to the governing law at stated in the Appendix to Tender. Any conflict between the law and Sub-Clause 7.7 should have been checked by the Employer and clarified in the Particular Conditions.

7.8 Royalties

Unless otherwise stated in the Specification, the Contractor shall pay all royalties, rents and other payments for:

(a) natural Materials obtained from outside the Site; and

(b) the disposal of material from demolitions and excavations and of other surplus material (whether natural or man-made), except to the extent that disposal areas within the Site are specified in the Contract.

In the Yellow Book, 'Specification' is replaced by 'Employer's Requirements'. The cost of royalties for Materials and for the disposal of material can be anticipated and should be allowed in the Contractor's Tender.

Chapter 17

Clause 8: Commencement, Delays and Suspension

Clause 8 covers three very important subjects, all of which are related to the period during which the Contractor will construct the Works:

- the start and duration of the construction period, at Sub-Clauses 8.1–8.3;
- programme, delays and extension of time, at Sub-Clauses 8.4–8.7;
- suspension of work by the Engineer, at Sub-Clauses 8.8–8.12.

The procedures for the completion of the Works are given at Clause 10.

Although Clause 8 deals primarily with matters that are a function of time, the requirement for a notice under Sub-Clause 8.3 also applies to events or circumstances that may adversely affect the work or increase the Contract Price. Definitions at Clause 1.1 relevant to this Clause include:

1.1.1.2   Contract Agreement
1.1.1.3   Letter of Acceptance
1.1.1.9   Appendix to Tender
1.1.3.2   Commencement Date
1.1.3.3   Time for Completion
1.1.3.9   day and year
1.1.4.2   Contract Price
1.1.4.5   Final Statement
1.1.5.2   Goods
1.1.5.6   Section
1.1.6.2   Country
1.1.6.8   Unforeseeable
1.1.6.9   Variation.

8.1   Commencement of Work

The Engineer shall give the Contractor not less than 7 days' notice of the Commencement Date. Unless otherwise stated in the Particular Conditions, the Commencement Date shall be within 42 days after the Contractor receives the Letter of Acceptance.

The Contractor shall commence the execution of the Works as soon as is reasonably practicable after the Commencement Date, and shall then proceed with the Works with due expedition and without delay.

In the Yellow Book the words 'design and' have been added before 'execution'. The Contract starts with the Letter of Acceptance or, if required by the governing law or other regulation, the Contract Agreement as defined at Sub-Clause 1.1.1.6. Notification by the Letter of Acceptance constitutes the formation of the Contract, so any negotiations and discussions on bond or insurance arrangements must have been completed before it is issued. If the Employer decides, for whatever reason, to issue a letter that he intends to enter into a Contract, it is important that the letter of intent is worded so as to be clear that it is not a Letter of Acceptance. Even if the governing law requires a Contract Agreement in order to commence the formal contractual relationship, it is important that any letter from the Employer to the Contractor before the Contract Agreement is signed should be very carefully worded. The issue of the Letter of Acceptance creates obligations and starts a sequence of events and time periods which require the Employer to hand over the Site and the Contractor to start work on the project. The Employer is then liable to pay the Contractor for Costs incurred in order to comply with the Letter of Acceptance.

The 'Commencement Date' is the start of the 'Time for Completion' which is the period within which the Contractor has agreed to construct the Works. When the Commencement Date has been determined the Engineer should calculate the calendar date for completion. Potential arguments can be avoided by agreeing the calendar date at the start of the construction period. The number of days in the Time for Completion is given in the Appendix to Tender and may refer to the whole of the Works, or a designated Section of the Works. 'Day' is defined as a calendar day and not a working day and so the number of days includes weekends and holidays.

The Commencement Date is fixed by the Engineer, subject to the requirements of Sub-Clause 8.1:

- the Commencement Date shall be within 42 days after the Contractor receives the Letter of Acceptance, unless a different period is stated in the Particular Conditions;
- the Engineer shall give the Contractor not less than 7 days' notice of the Commencement Date.

The 7 day notice period is short, particularly for a design-build Contract which extends over a period of several years, and the Contractor must commence his preparation immediately he receives the Letter of Acceptance. Sub-Clause 2.1 then requires the Employer to give the Contractor

175

access to and possession of the Site within the number of days from the Commencement Date stated in the Appendix to Tender.

If, for any reason, it is not possible for the Engineer to meet these dates, or for the Employer to give possession of the Site, then a change to the Conditions of Contract must be agreed between the Contractor and the Employer. The Engineer does not have the authority to issue an instruction to change these requirements.

The Contractor is then required to start the execution of the Works 'as soon as is reasonably practicable' and proceed 'with due expedition and without delay'. The precise interpretation of due expedition and without delay will depend on the circumstances but the general requirement imposes an overall obligation on the Contractor to continue working, even when some problem has arisen.

8.2   Time for Completion

The Contractor shall complete the whole of the Works, and each Section (if any), within the Time for Completion for the Works or Section (as the case may be), including:

(a)   achieving the passing of the Tests on Completion; and
(b)   completing all work which is stated in the Contract as being required for the Works or Section to be considered to be completed for the purposes of taking-over under Sub-Clause 10.1 [*Taking Over of the Works and Sections*].

Under Sub-Clause 8.2 the Contractor is obliged to complete all the work which is required for taking over under Sub-Clause 10.1, including passing the Tests on Completion as Clause 9, before expiry of the Time for Completion.

If Sections of the Works are required to be completed before the overall Time for Completion then the Sections must be described in the Appendix to Tender, together with the Time for Completion and delay damages for each Section.

Sub-Clause 10.1 [*Taking Over of the Works and Sections*] just refers back to Sub-Clause 8.2, which is not very helpful. The Particular Conditions could include a more detailed list of the work which must be completed, in addition to the actual construction and tests. Under the Yellow Book this includes training, commissioning and trial operation.

8.3   Programme

The Contractor shall submit a detailed time programme to the Engineer within 28 days after receiving the notice under Sub-Clause 8.1

[*Commencement of Works*]. The Contractor shall also submit a revised programme whenever the previous programme is inconsistent with actual progress or with the Contractor's obligations. Each programme shall include:

(a) the order in which the Contractor intends to carry out the Works, including the anticipated timing of each stage of design (if any), Contractor's Documents, procurement, manufacture of Plant, delivery to Site, construction, erection and testing;

(b) each of these stages for work by each nominated Subcontractor (as defined in Clause 5 [*Nominated Subcontractors*]);

(c) the sequence and timing of inspections and tests specified in the Contract; and

(d) a supporting report which includes:

   (i) a general description of the methods which the Contractor intends to adopt, and of the major stages, in the execution of the Works, and

   (ii) details showing the Contractor's reasonable estimate of the number of each class of Contractor's Personnel and of each type of Contractor's Equipment, required on the Site for each major stage.

Unless the Engineer, within 21 days after receiving a programme, gives notice to the Contractor stating the extent to which it does not comply with the Contract, the Contractor shall proceed in accordance with the programme, subject to his other obligations under the Contract. The Employer's Personnel shall be entitled to rely upon the programme when planning their activities.

The Contractor shall promptly give notice to the Engineer of specific probable future events or circumstances which may adversely affect the work, increase the Contract Price or delay the execution of the Works. The Engineer may require the Contractor to submit an estimate of the anticipated effect of the future event or circumstances, and/or a proposal under Sub-Clause 13.3 [*Variation Procedure*].

If, at any time, the Engineer gives notice to the Contractor that a programme fails (to the extent stated) to comply with the Contract or to be consistent with actual progress and the Contractor's stated intentions, the Contractor shall submit a revised programme to the Engineer in accordance with this Sub-Clause.

In the Yellow Book paragraphs (a) and (b) at Sub-Clause 8.3 have been changed as follows.

(a) the order in which the Contractor intends to carry out the Works, including the anticipated timing of each stage of design, Contractor's Documents, procurement, manufacture, inspection, delivery to Site, construction, erection, testing, commissioning and trial operation;

(b) the periods for reviews under Sub-Clause 5.2 [*Contractor's Documents*] and for any other submissions, approvals and consents specified in the Employer's Requirements.

Sub-Clause 8.3 requires the Contractor to submit a detailed programme to the Engineer within 28 days after receiving the notice of the Commencement Date. The Contractor will obviously have started to prepare his programme at Tender stage and continued to plan his work during any negotiations and when he has received the Letter of Acceptance or Contract Agreement. However, he cannot prepare his final programme until he learns the actual calendar dates for the construction period which is when he receives the notice of the Commencement Date. The detailed programme may also include reduced working during certain periods of the year.

This Sub-Clause gives detailed requirements for the information to be included in this programme and these requirements may be amplified or extended in the Particular Conditions or Specifications. When deciding on the form of the programme and the detail to be included, the Contractor should remember that the programme will be used to demonstrate whether any delay situation will cause a delay to completion. In general terms the programme must include:

- the order in which the Contractor intends to carry out the Works;
- the anticipated timing of each stage from design, through procurement, manufacture, construction and testing, including the stages of the work of nominated Subcontractors;
- a report with a general description and details of the methods the Contractor intends to adopt and estimates of the numbers of personnel and type of equipment that will be required on Site.

The information required is extensive and requires the Contractor to have planned the work in detail. If the Engineer has any further requirements for the layout of the information, or particular computer software which is to be used, then these requirements must be given in the Particular Conditions, Specification or Employer's Requirements in order that the Contractor can allow for the costs in his Tender.

The Yellow Book requirement for the inclusion of the timing and details for commissioning and trial operation need to be clarified in the Employer's Requirements and Contractor's Proposal. Commissioning is not a defined term so will presumably have its usual meaning of 'bringing into operation'. This is a task which will be related to the trial operation. There is a sequence of post-installation events including testing, training, submission of documents, commissioning and trial operation which should be included in the programme. These tasks will sometimes need to be included in the Particular Conditions for Red Book Contracts. The

Red Book allows for the provision of Plant as part of the Permanent Works and any item of machinery or other Plant will need to be commissioned after installation and tests. The trial operation would normally refer to the operation of the completed project and so is applicable when the complete Works have been designed by the Contractor. However, there are circumstances when trial operation may be appropriate for Plant which has been designed by the Contractor under a Red Book Contract. In a Red Book contract the requirements for commissioning and trial operation must be amplified in the Specification, read in conjunction with Sub-Clauses 4.21 [*Progress Reports*] and 9.1 [*Contractor's Obligations*] and the Particular Conditions may also include requirements from Yellow Book Clause 5 [*Design*].

The Engineer is not expected or required to approve, or even to consent to, the programme. The Engineer has 21 days within which he can state that the programme does not comply with the Contract. The Contractor is then required to work in accordance with the programme – subject to his other obligations under the Contract. An intention or requirement of the programme cannot change any obligation under the Contract.

It is significant that the information required is stated as 'the Contractor intends' and 'the anticipated timing'. If circumstances cause a change in the Contractor's intentions or anticipated timing then he is presumably allowed to change the programme, provided of course that the revised programme meets the Time for Completion.

The information which is required in the programme and supporting report is also listed in the requirements for the Contractor's monthly progress report under Sub-Clause 4.21. The programme and the various reports will need to be prepared using the same format or computer software.

If the actual progress falls behind the programme, is in any way different to the programme, or the programme fails to comply with the Contract, the Contractor may be required to take action, i.e. either

- to submit a revised programme under the first or last paragraph of Sub-Clause 8.3, or
- to submit a revised programme and supporting report under Sub-Clause 8.6 showing how he proposes to expedite progress.

This Sub-Clause also states that the Employer's Personnel are entitled to rely on the programme when planning their activities so any change must be made known immediately to enable the Engineer and his staff to adjust their own plans to suit the change. If the Contractor works in advance of his programme, in order to allow for any future delays, then the Engineer may object on the grounds that he is not ready to issue additional drawings or to provide the appropriate supervision. The use of an 'early start' and 'late start' type of programme can be useful, or work in advance of the programme should be agreed with the Engineer. Any such advance working might also be highlighted in the monthly progress report.

The Contractor is required to give notice to the Engineer of any events or circumstances that may adversely affect the work, increase the Contract Price or delay the execution of the Works. This requirement for a notice from the Contractor covers virtually anything that has an adverse effect on the activities of the Contractor and not just matters that affect the programme or for which the Contractor intends to submit a claim. It is in addition to the requirement for claims notices under Sub-Clause 20.1 although a delay or price situation will frequently result in notices under both clauses. The Sub-Clause 8.3 notice must be given 'promptly', which is much quicker than the 'not later than 28 days' requirement for the Sub-Clause 20.1 notice. However, this notice appears to serve the same purpose as the potential delay notices under other Clauses, such as the delayed drawing or instruction notice under Sub-Clause 1.9 (RB).

The Sub-Clause 8.3 notice is in effect an 'early warning notice' and gives the Engineer the opportunity to take action to overcome the problem before the Contractor incurs delay or additional cost. There is no requirement for the Contractor to meet with the Engineer to discuss the problems and possible solutions, but the Sub-Clause does enable the Engineer to require the Contractor to submit estimates and proposals. For good management the Engineer would normally meet with the Contractor to discuss the potential problem and the best way to overcome the problem.

8.4   Extension of Time for Completion

The Contractor shall be entitled subject to Sub-Clause 20.1 [*Contractor's Claims*] to an extension of the Time for Completion if and to the extent that completion for the purposes of Sub-Clause 10.1 [*Taking Over of the Works and Sections*] is or will be delayed by any of the following causes:

(a)   a Variation (unless an adjustment to the Time for Completion has been agreed under Sub-Clause 13.3 [*Variation Procedure*]) or other substantial change in the quantity of an item of work included in the Contract;

(b)   a cause of delay giving an entitlement to extension of time under a Sub-Clause of these Conditions;

(c)   exceptionally adverse climatic conditions;

(d)   Unforeseeable shortages in the availability of personnel or Goods caused by epidemic or governmental actions; or

(e)   any delay, impediment or prevention caused by or attributable to the Employer, the Employer's Personnel, or the Employer's other contractors on the Site.

If the Contractor considers himself to be entitled to an extension of the Time for Completion, the Contractor shall give notice to the Engineer in accordance with Sub-Clause 20.1 [*Contractor's Claims*]. When determining each extension of time under Sub-Clause 20.1, the Engineer shall review previous determinations and may increase, but shall not decrease, the total extension of time.

In the Yellow Book the reference to a 'change in the quantity' in paragraph (a) is not relevant and has been omitted. Sub-Clause 8.4 lists the situations which may entitle the Contractor to an extension of the Time for Completion. It is not sufficient for the event to cause delay or disruption to the Contractor's work; the Contractor must demonstrate that it will actually delay completion under Sub-Clause 10.1. The Contractor must comply with the notice and other requirements of Sub-Clause 20.1, which means that the Engineer will then follow the procedures of Sub-Clause 3.5 in order to determine any extension of time.

Sub-Clause 3.5 does not give the Engineer a time period for making this determination although it must not be 'unreasonably withheld or delayed' under Sub-Clause 1.3. Any determination of an extension of time should be made quickly in order that the Contractor can revise his programme to suit any revision to the Date for Completion or can accelerate to meet the previous Date for Completion. If the determination is delayed then the Contractor might have a claim for the Costs of an acceleration which is not then necessary or the additional Costs or delay caused by the late determination.

Sub-Clause 8.4 only entitles the Contractor to an extension of time, which brings relief from delay damages under Sub-Clause 8.7, but not to additional payment. Where there is an overlap with another Sub-Clause the Contractor will generally submit his claim under the Sub-Clause which also allows for additional payment, in addition to the relevant paragraph of this Sub-Clause.

The matters listed are as follows.

(a)   *Variations.* Clause 13 gives the Engineer the power to issue instructions to vary the Works and the Engineer may ask for a proposal from the Contractor before issuing the instruction. If the Engineer has not asked for such a proposal then the Contractor must give notices promptly under Sub-Clause 8.3 and within 28 days under Sub-Clause 20.1 if he considers that the Variation may delay completion. The Contractor may also claim an extension of time if there is a substantial change in the quantity of an item of work, which would presumably occur as a consequence of the measurement procedure under Clause 12.

(b) *Other Sub-Clauses.* The other Sub-Clauses which entitle the Contractor to an extension of time are discussed under the relevant Sub-Clause:

1.9   Delayed Drawings or Instructions
2.1   Right of Access to the Site
4.7   Setting Out
4.12   Unforeseeable Physical Conditions
4.24   Fossils
7.4   Testing
10.3   Interference with Tests on Completion
13.7   Adjustments for Changes in Legislation
16.1   Contractor's Entitlement to Suspend Work
17.4   Consequences of Employer's Risks
19.4   Consequences of Force Majeure.

(c) *Climatic conditions.* To justify an extension of time the Contractor must demonstrate that the climatic conditions were exceptionally adverse and actually delayed completion. It will be necessary to submit records for the normal weather over a period of, say, five years. The Employer may already have such records and made them available at Tender stage under Sub-Clause 4.10 or the Contractor should have obtained all available information under Sub-Clause 4.10(b). In order to record the actual conditions, it will be necessary for the Contractor to have the necessary equipment in place from the start of the project, such that rainfall or other conditions are recorded automatically when they occur, even though such conditions may occur outside normal working hours. Claims for climatic conditions will only result in additional time, but not money, and they are specifically excluded from the unforeseeable physical conditions situations under Sub-Clause 4.12.

(d) *Shortages of personnel or Goods.* The shortage must have been unforeseeable by an experienced Contractor, as defined at Sub-Clause 1.1.6.8. and caused by epidemic or governmental action. Governmental action is not restricted to the government of the Country of the project.

(e) *Employer causes.* If the Employer causes a delay then the Contractor, as the other Party to the Contract, should be entitled to compensation. Part (e) gives an overall right to an extension of time but many of the events which are covered will also be covered under Employer's Risks as Sub-Clauses 17.3 and 17.4. The reference to the Employer's other Contractors on the Site must be read in conjunction with Sub-Clause 4.6, which refers to the reimbursement of cost, but not delays.

By comparison with the extension of time situations at Clause 44 of the previous FIDIC Contract (the Conditions of Contract for Works of Civil Engineering Construction, fourth edition, 1987), the wording of paragraph (c) remains unchanged, paragraphs (a) and (b) have been developed and clarified, paragraph (d) is new, paragraph (e) has been developed and the reference to the Employer's other contractors has been added. The previous paragraph (e) which referred to 'other special circumstances' has been omitted. This paragraph was always unpopular with Employers as being too general and imprecise. It remains to be seen whether Contractors will be now barred from extensions of time to which they might have been entitled under the previous Conditions. The provision at Sub-Clause 20.1 for claims 'under any Clause of these Conditions or otherwise in connection with the Contract', together with the development of paragraphs (a) to (e) and the new provision at Sub-Clause 8.5, should be sufficiently general to cover any situation for which a Contractor should reasonably be entitled to an extension.

8.5   Delays Caused by Authorities
If the following conditions apply, namely:

(a)   the Contractor has diligently followed the procedures laid down by the relevant legally constituted public authorities in the Country;
(b)   these authorities delay or disrupt the Contractor's work; and
(c)   the delay or disruption was Unforeseeable;

then this delay or disruption will be considered as a cause of delay under subparagraph (b) of Sub-Clause 8.4 [*Extension of Time for Completion*].

This Sub-Clause gives an additional entitlement to the grounds for an extension of time under Sub-Clause 8.4(b). The Sub-Clause does not require the Engineer to follow the procedures of Sub-Clause 3.5 in order to determine the extension but this will be required under the provisions of Sub-Clause 20.1.

The precise meaning of 'legally constituted public authorities in the Country' under the governing law is a potential source of dispute. The trend to privatise public bodies may reduce the scope of this Sub-Clause.

8.6   Rate of Progress
If, at any time:

(a)   actual progress is too slow to complete within the Time for Completion; and/or

(b) progress has fallen (or will fall) behind the current programme under Sub-Clause 8.3 [*Programme*];

other than as a result of a cause listed in Sub-Clause 8.4 [*Extension of Time for Completion*], then the Engineer may instruct the Contractor to submit, under Sub-Clause 8.3 [*Programme*], a revised programme and supporting report describing the revised methods which the Contractor proposes to adopt in order to expedite progress and complete within the Time for Completion.

Unless the Engineer notifies otherwise, the Contractor shall adopt these revised methods, which may require increases in the working hours and/or in the numbers of Contractor's Personnel and/or Goods, at the risk and cost of the Contractor. If these revised methods cause the Employer to incur additional costs, the Contractor shall subject to Sub-Clause 2.5 [*Employer's Claims*] pay these costs to the Employer, in addition to delay damages (if any) under Sub-Clause 8.7 below.

Sub-Clause 8.6 entitles the Engineer to instruct the Contractor to submit proposals to revise his programme and to accelerate the work in order to achieve completion by the due date. If the acceleration measures cause the Employer to incur additional Costs then the Employer may submit a claim under Sub-Clause 2.5 and the Engineer will make a determination under the procedures of Sub-Clause 3.5.

Sub-Clause 8.6 states that the provision only applies when the reason for the delay is not covered by Sub-Clause 8.4. Whether or not the delay was caused by a Sub-Clause 8.4 event depends on an Engineer's determination under Sub-Clause 3.5, or a subsequent decision by the Dispute Adjudication Board (DAB). If the Contractor decides to refer the matter to the DAB under Sub-Clause 20.4 then he should first give notices under Clause 20.1 and any other relevant clauses to claim reimbursement of his acceleration Costs together with any Employer's Costs and delay damages.

If the Contractor incurs acceleration Costs under this Sub-Clause and the DAB later decides that the Contractor is entitled to an extension of time then there will be a potential claim situation.

8.7 Delay Damages

If the Contractor fails to comply with Sub-Clause 8.2 [*Time for Completion*], the Contractor shall subject to Sub-Clause 2.5 [*Employer's Claims*] pay delay damages to the Employer for this default. These delay damages shall be the sum stated in the Appendix to Tender, which shall be paid for every day which shall elapse between the relevant Time for Completion and the date stated in the Taking-Over Certificate.

However, the total amount due under this Sub-Clause shall not exceed the maximum amount of delay damages (if any) stated in the Appendix to Tender.

These delay damages shall be the only damages due from the Contractor for such default, other than in the event of termination under Sub-Clause 15.2 [*Termination by Employer*] prior to completion of the Works. These damages shall not relieve the Contractor from his obligation to complete the Works, or from any other duties, obligations or responsibilities which he may have under the Contract.

The Appendix to Tender must state the daily sum and the maximum total amount of the damages due from the Contractor to the Employer if the Works are not completed by the due date. These figures are required to be given as percentages of the final Contract Price. That is the final sum, as Sub-Clause 14.1, after taking into account all adjustments for remeasurement, Variations and otherwise under the Contract. Hence the sum for delay damages cannot be determined finally until after agreement of the Final Statement.

By the normal definition of the word 'damages', the figures for delay damages should be a reasonable estimate of the actual losses which will be incurred by the Employer. If the governing law entitles the Employer to deduct 'penalties' then the Sub-Clause and the Appendix to Tender should be amended by the Particular Conditions.

The FIDIC Guidance for the Preparation of Particular Conditions includes an example Sub-Clause if the Employer decides to include an incentive for early completion. The principle of a bonus for early completion will appeal to many tenderers and act as an incentive to acceleration or to maintaining progress when the work proceeds ahead of the programme. However, it would only be applicable when the Employer is in a position to occupy and use the Works as soon as they are complete. This principle is recognised in the provision for accelerated completion in the value engineering provision at Sub-Clause 13.2. The example Sub-Clause refers to the occupation and use of Sections of the Works, additional information being provided in the Specification and bonus dates for Sections not being adjusted by the award of extensions of time. This Sub-Clause would need careful study and revision to suit the Employer's intentions.

8.8 Suspension of Work

The Engineer may at any time instruct the Contractor to suspend progress of part or all of the Works. During such suspension, the Contractor shall protect, store and secure such part or the Works against any deterioration, loss or damage.

The Engineer may also notify the cause for the suspension. If and to the extent that the cause is notified and is the responsibility of the Contractor, the following Sub-Clauses 8.9, 8.10 and 8.11 shall not apply.

Sub-Clause 8.8 entitles the Engineer to instruct the Contractor to suspend progress of part or all of the Works. Surprisingly, the Engineer is not obliged to give the reason for the suspension but 'may' notify the cause. Clearly the reasonable Engineer should tell the Contractor the reason and likely extent of the suspension in order that the Contractor can decide how to meet his obligation to 'protect, store and secure' that part of the Works.

8.9   Consequences of Suspension
If the Contractor suffers delay and/or incurs Cost from complying with the Engineer's instructions under Sub-Clause 8.8 [*Suspension of Work*] and/or from resuming the work, the Contractor shall give notice to the Engineer and shall be entitled subject to Sub-Clause 20.1 [*Contractor's Claims*] to:

(a) an extension of time for any such delay, if completion is or will be delayed, under Sub-Clause 8.4 [*Extension of Time for Completion*]; and

(b) payment of any such Cost, which shall be included in the Contract Price.

After receiving this notice, the Engineer shall proceed in accordance with Sub-Clause 3.5 [*Determinations*] to agree or determine these matters.

The Contractor shall not be entitled to an extension of time for, or to payment of the Cost incurred in, making good the consequences of the Contractor's faulty design, workmanship or materials, or of the Contractor's failure to protect, store or secure in accordance with Sub-Clause 8.8 [*Suspension of Work*].

The Contractor must give the usual notices under Clause 20.1 in order to claim any Costs and extension of time. This Sub-Clause also covers the Costs of resuming work, such as any remobilisation Costs.

8.10   Payment for Plant and Materials in Event of Suspension
The Contractor shall be entitled to payment of the value (as at the date of suspension) of Plant and/or Materials which have not been delivered to Site, if:

(a) the work on Plant or delivery of Plant and/or Materials has been suspended for more than 28 days; and

(b) the Contractor has marked the Plant and/or Materials as the Employer's property in accordance with the Engineer's instructions.

Any request for payment for Plant and/or Materials which have not been delivered to Site would presumably require notice from the Contractor and confirmation from the Engineer, either as an item in the monthly Statement under Sub-Clause 14.3 or as a claim under Sub-Clause 20.1.

8.11 Prolonged Suspension

If the suspension under Sub-Clause 8.8 [*Suspension of Work*] has continued for more than 84 days, the Contractor may request the Engineer's permission to proceed. If the Engineer does not give permission within 28 days after being requested to do so, the Contractor may, by giving notice to the Engineer, treat the suspension as an omission under Clause 13 [*Variations and Adjustments*] of the affected part of the Works. If the suspension affects the whole of the Works, the Contractor may give notice of termination under Sub-Clause 16.2 [*Termination by Contractor*].

If the Engineer waits for the full 28 days before replying to the request, then the suspension will have lasted 106 days, by which time the Contractor may have incurred substantial costs and disruption to planning his allocation of recourses to different projects. This would presumably be the time to cancel the suspended work.

If the suspension is not lifted and the Contractor chooses to treat suspension of part of the Works as an omission under Sub-Clause 13.1(d) then the omitted work will either be valued by agreement, or under Sub-Clause 12.4. Following omission under Sub-Clause 13.1(d) the omitted work cannot be carried out by others. If the whole of the Works was suspended and the Contractor decides to give notice of termination under Sub-Clause 16.2(f) then the payment will be made under the provisions of Sub-Clause 19.6, as for Force Majeure termination, plus loss of profit and other losses or damage under Sub-Clause 16.4(c). Clearly this would be expensive for the Employer, so sustained suspension should be avoided and should not be used for ulterior motives or as a weapon against the Contractor.

8.12 Resumption of Work

After the permission or instruction to proceed is given, the Contractor and the Engineer shall jointly examine the Works and the Plant and Materials affected by the suspension. The Contractor shall make good any deterioration or defect in or loss of the Works or Plant or Materials, which has occurred during the suspension.

If the Contractor and Engineer fail to agree on the results of their joint inspection then the Engineer would presumably issue instructions and the Contractor would have the option of giving notice under Sub-Clause 20.1 and any other relevant clause. The same procedure would be followed if there is a dispute about who pays the Costs of making good. The Contract insurances would have remained in place during the suspension and the insurer would have been notified of the suspension in accordance with Sub-Clause 18.1.

Chapter 18

Clause 9: Tests on Completion

Tests on Completion are the tests that are carried out after the Works have been completed and before the Engineer will issue the Taking-Over Certificate. The responsibilities and procedures for the 'Tests on Completion' are given at Clause 9, which also requires compliance with the testing procedures at Sub-Clause 7.4 and the submission of Contractor's Documents as Sub-Clause 4.1(d). The technical details of the required tests will be given in the Specification.

Under a Red Book Contract the Materials and other aspects of the Works are normally tested during construction and further tests before the issue of the Taking-Over Certificate should only be specified if testing at an earlier stage was not possible. If the Contract includes items of Plant, or other work which is designed by the Contractor to a performance specification, then the Yellow Book procedures will be appropriate.

The Yellow Book includes additional requirements for commissioning and trial operation. The tests before taking-over are inevitably more extensive, and the criteria for acceptance are more complex, under a Yellow Book Contract.

Definitions at Clause 1.1 relevant to this Clause include:

1.1.2.6	Employer's Personnel
1.1.3.4	Tests on Completion
1.1.3.5	Taking-Over Certificate
1.1.3.6	Tests after Completion
1.1.3.7	Defects Notification Period
1.1.5.5	Plant
1.1.5.6	Section
1.1.5.8	Works.

9.1 Contractor's Obligations

The Contractor shall carry out the Tests on Completion in accordance with this Clause and Sub-Clause 7.4 [*Testing*], after providing the documents in accordance with sub-paragraph (d) of Sub-Clause 4.1 [*Contractor's General Obligations*].

The Contractor shall give to the Engineer not less than 21 days' notice of the date after which the Contractor will be ready to carry out each of the Tests on Completion. Unless otherwise agreed, Tests on Completion shall be carried out within 14 days after this date, on such day or days as the Engineer shall instruct.

In considering the results of the Tests on Completion, the Engineer shall make allowances for the effect of any use of the Works by the Employer on the performance or other characteristics of the Works. As soon as the Works, or a Section, have passed any Tests on Completion, the Contractor shall submit a certified report of the results of these Tests to the Engineer.

In the Yellow Book the reference to Sub-Clause 4.1 is changed to refer to Sub-Clause 5.6 [*As-Built Documents*] and Sub-Clause 5.7 [*Operation and Maintenance Manuals*]. The Yellow Book includes additional paragraphs.

Unless otherwise stated in the Particular Conditions, the Tests on Completion shall be carried out in the following sequence:

(a) pre-commissioning tests, which shall include the appropriate inspections and ('dry' or 'cold') functional tests to demonstrate that each item of Plant can safely undertake the next stage, (b);

(b) commissioning tests, which shall include the specified operational tests to demonstrate that the Works or Section can be operated safely and as specified, under all available operating conditions; and

(c) trial operation, which shall demonstrate that the Works or Section perform reliably and in accordance with the Contract.

During trial operation, when the Works are operating under stable conditions, the Contractor shall give notice to the Engineer that the Works are ready for any other Tests on Completion, including performance tests to demonstrate whether the Works conform with criteria specified in the Employer's Requirements and with the Schedule of Guarantees.

Trial operation shall not constitute a taking-over under Clause 10 [*Employer's Taking Over*]. Unless otherwise stated in the Particular Conditions, any product produced by the Works during trial operation shall be the property of the Employer.

In considering the results of the Tests on Completion, the Engineer shall make allowances for the effect of any use of the Works by the Employer on the performance or other characteristics of the Works. As soon as the Works, or a Section, have passed each of the Tests on Completion described in sub-paragraph (a), (b) or (c), the Contractor shall submit a certified report of the results of these Tests to the Engineer.

Sub-Clause 8.2 requires that the Works have passed any Tests on Completion before issue of the Taking-Over Certificate under Clause 10. It is not stated whether the Tests on Completion can be carried out immediately the particular item is complete, or whether all Tests on Completion must be carried out immediately prior to the issue of the Taking-Over Certificate. In practice this will depend on the circumstances and any requirements should be detailed in the Specification.

Sub-Clause 9.1 states that the Tests on Completion cannot be carried out until the Contractor has provided the Engineer with the documents listed at Sub-Clause 4.1(d). This refers to the as-built drawings and the operation and maintenance manuals for any part of the Permanent Works which had been designed by the Contractor. The items required to be tested after they are complete will often be items of Plant which have been designed by the Contractor to meet a performance specification.

The Contract requires the documents to have been submitted to the Engineer, but does not require them to have been approved by the Engineer. However, Sub-Clause 4.1(d) requires these documents to be 'in accordance with the Specification and in sufficient detail for the Employer to operate, maintain, dismantle, reassemble, adjust and repair this part of the Works'. Hence the Employer will expect the Engineer to confirm that the submitted documents are acceptable.

The Contractor must give 21 days' notice of the date when he will be ready to carry out the Tests on Completion, which gives time for the Engineer to arrange for any specialist engineers to attend and for the Employer to make any necessary arrangements, particularly in parts of the Works which may already have been taken over by the Employer. The Employer may require that his staff who will maintain the Works should observe the tests. The tests must be carried out within 14 days after this date, on a date instructed by the Engineer.

The additional requirements in the Yellow Book are essential when the Works include Plant, as distinct from Materials. Where appropriate they should also be included in the Particular Conditions for a Red Book Contract. Further details of the tests and the criteria for acceptance must be given in the Employer's Requirements or Specification.

These tests are a sequence of pre-commissioning tests, commissioning tests and trial operation, together with performance tests which will be carried out during the trial operation. The performance tests will demonstrate 'whether the Works conform with criteria specified in the Employer's Requirements and with the Schedule of Guarantees'. However, tests at this stage are only interim tests, to check that the Works are ready for the Employer to take over and occupy the project in accordance with Clause 10. Compliance with the Employer's Requirements and the Schedule of Guarantees will also be checked during the Tests after Completion, as Clause 12, and at the End of the Defects

Notification Period, before the issue of the Performance Certificate, as Sub-Clause 11.9.

9.2 Delayed Tests

If the Tests on Completion are being unduly delayed by the Employer, Sub-Clause 7.4 [*Testing*] (fifth paragraph) and/or Sub-Clause 10.3 [*Interference with Tests on Completion*] shall be applicable.

If the Tests on Completion are being unduly delayed by the Contractor, the Engineer may by notice require the Contractor to carry out the Tests within 21 days after receiving the notice. The Contractor shall carry out the Tests on such day or days within that period as the Contractor may fix and of which he shall give notice to the Engineer.

If the Contractor fails to carry out the Tests on Completion within the period of 21 days, the Employer's Personnel may proceed with the Tests at the risk and cost of the Contractor. The Tests on Completion shall then be deemed to have been carried out in the presence of the Contractor and the results of the Tests shall be accepted as accurate.

If the Tests on Completion are delayed then the provisions of Sub-Clause 9.2 will apply. If the tests are delayed by the Employer then the Contractor can give notice to the Engineer under Sub-Clause 7.4 and follow the Sub-Clause 20.1 procedure to claim for an extension of time and additional payment. If the delay lasts for more than 14 days then, under Sub-Clause 10.3, the Employer is deemed to have taken over the Works or Section on the date when the Tests on Completion would otherwise have been completed. The tests must then be carried out as soon as practicable before the expiry date of the Defects Notification Period. The procedures for the Engineer to issue a Taking-Over Certificate and for any claims are given at Sub-Clause 10.3.

If the tests are delayed by the Contractor then the Engineer may give notice for the Contractor to carry out the tests within 21 days, or the Employer's Personnel may proceed with the tests, at the Contractor's risk and Cost.

9.3 Retesting

If the Works, or a Section, fail to pass the Tests on Completion, Sub-Clause 7.5 [*Rejection*] shall apply, and the Engineer or the Contractor may require the failed Tests, and Tests on Completion on any related work, to be repeated under the same terms and conditions.

Sub-Clause 9.3 requires that Sub-Clause 7.5 shall apply to 'the Works, or a Section', which has failed to pass the Tests on Completion. Sub-Clause 7.5

provides that the Engineer may reject the 'Plant, Materials or workmanship' and the Contractor must promptly make good the defect. The Engineer can require a repeat test.

9.4   Failure to Pass Tests on Completion

If the Works, or a Section, fail to pass the Tests on Completion repeated under Sub-Clause 9.3 [*Retesting*], the Engineer shall be entitled to:

(a)   order further repetition of Tests on Completion under Sub-Clause 9.3;

(b)   if the failure deprives the Employer of substantially the whole benefit of the Works or Section, reject the Works or Section (as the case may be), in which event the Employer shall have the same remedies as are provided in subparagraph (c) of Sub-Clause 11.4 [*Failure to Remedy Defects*]; or

(c)   issue a Taking-Over Certificate, if the Employer so requests.

In the event of subparagraph (c), the Contractor shall proceed in accordance with all other obligations under the Contract, and the Contract Price shall be reduced by such amount as shall be appropriate to cover the reduced value to the Employer as a result of this failure. Unless the relevant reduction for this failure is stated (or its method of calculation is defined) in the Contract, the Employer may require the reduction to be (i) agreed by both Parties (in full satisfaction of this failure only) and paid before this Taking-Over Certificate is issued, or (ii) determined and paid under Sub-Clause 2.5 [*Employer's Claims*] and Sub-Clause 3.5 [*Determinations*].

Sub-Clause 9.4 refers to failure by 'the Works, or a Section'. If a particular part of the Works, or a single item of Plant fails a test then the whole of the Works or Section has failed. If the Engineer then decides to order a repetition of the tests, as option (a), then his decision is a technical matter and may, or may not, resolve the problem. If the item being tested again fails the test, despite the making good as Sub-Clause 7.5, then the Engineer will consider other technical alternatives before going to options (b) or (c).

Sub-Clause 7.6 enables the Engineer to instruct the Contractor to remove and replace Plant or Materials or remove and re-execute other work. If the Contractor fails to carry out this instruction then the Employer is entitled to arrange for other persons to carry out the work and claim the Costs under Sub-Clause 2.5.

Option (b) refers to the procedure at sub-paragraph (c) of Sub-Clause 11.4. The Employer can terminate the Contract, in whole or in part, and recover all his Costs as defined at sub-paragraph (c). It is difficult to envisage circumstances where this could be appropriate under a Red

Book Contract and before invoking this procedure the Engineer should also consider alternative actions available under Sub-Clause 11.4.

Any acceptance of work that has failed a test must be agreed by the Employer and Contractor and must be confirmed as a Variation, signed by both Parties, stating the terms and conditions under which the work has been accepted.

Chapter 19

Clause 10: Employer's Taking Over

This Clause gives the procedures to be followed for the Works to be taken over by the Employer. The procedure can apply to the Works as a whole, or to any Section of the Works which has been defined in the Appendix to Tender.

Clause 10 in the Yellow Book is the same as in the Red Book. However, the detailed requirements for the work which must be completed before the Works can be taken over as listed at Sub-Clause 8.2, include the Tests on Completion, as Clause 9. The test requirements in the Yellow Book are more extensive, including commissioning and trial operation. It is also necessary to check that the Contractor's design complies with the Employer's Requirements.

Definitions at Sub-Clause 1.1 relevant to this Clause include:

1.1.3.4	Tests on Completion
1.1.3.5	Taking-Over Certificate
1.1.4.12	Statement
1.1.5.6	Section
1.1.5.8	Works
1.1.6.1	Contractor's Documents.

10.1 Taking-Over of the Works and Sections

Except as stated in Sub-Clause 9.4 [*Failure to Pass Tests on Completion*], the Works shall be taken over by the Employer when (i) the Works have been completed in accordance with the Contract, including the matters described in Sub-Clause 8.2 [*Time for Completion*] and except as allowed in subparagraph (a) below, and (ii) a Taking-Over Certificate for the Works has been issued, or is deemed to have been issued in accordance with this Sub-Clause.

The Contractor may apply by notice to the Engineer for a Taking-Over Certificate not earlier than 14 days before the Works will, in the Contractor's opinion, be complete and ready for taking over. If the Works are divided into Sections, the Contractor may similarly apply for a Taking-Over Certificate for each Section.

The Engineer shall, within 28 days after receiving the Contractor's application:

(a) issue the Taking-Over Certificate to the Contractor, stating the date on which the Works or Section were completed in accordance with the Contract, except for any minor outstanding work and defects which will not substantially affect the use of the Works or Section for their intended purpose (either until or whilst this work is completed and these defects are remedied); or

(b) reject the application, giving reasons and specifying the work required to be done by the Contractor to enable the Taking-Over Certificate to be issued. The Contractor shall then complete this work before issuing a further notice under this Sub-Clause.

If the Engineer fails either to issue the Taking-Over Certificate or to reject the Contractor's application within the period of 28 days, and if the Works or Section (as the case may be) are substantially in accordance with the Contract, the Taking-Over Certificate shall be deemed to have been issued on the last day of that period.

Sub-Clause 10.1 requires that the Works will be taken over when completed in accordance with the Contract. This requirement specifically includes the matters described at Sub-Clause 8.2, which are:

- passing the Tests on Completion, as Clause 9, and
- completing all the work as required by the Contract.

However, Sub-Clause 10.1(a) states that it is not necessary to complete 'any minor outstanding work and defects which will not substantially affect the use of the Works or Section for their intended purpose (either until or whilst this work is completed and these defects are remedied)'. This specific exclusion is a considerable improvement on the wording of previous Conditions, which referred to the Works being 'substantially completed'. It is now clear that some outstanding work or defects will not delay the issue of the Taking-Over Certificate, provided that they do not substantially affect the use of the Works for their intended purpose. The question of whether a particular item will 'substantially affect' such use will be a matter for the Engineer to exercise his judgement, but the emphasis on the use of the Works should help towards a clearer definition of when the Works are ready to be taken over by the Employer.

The minor outstanding work must be completed during the Defects Notification Period as instructed by the Engineer under Sub-Clause 11.1(a).

The procedure for the Employer to take over the Works is given at Sub-Clause 10.1 as follows.

(a) When the Contractor decides that the Works are within 14 days of being ready to be taken over, he issues a notice to apply to the Engineer for a Taking-Over Certificate.

(b) Within 28 days of receiving the Contractor's application, the Engineer must either:

    (i) issue the Taking-Over Certificate stating the date when the Works were completed in accordance with the Contract; or

    (ii) reject the application.

If the Engineer rejects the application he must give his reasons and specify the work that must be done by the Contractor to enable the Taking-Over Certificate to be issued. The Contractor must then complete this work and issue another notice.

If the Engineer fails either to issue the Taking-Over Certificate or to reject the application within the 28 day period then the Contract states that the Taking-Over Certificate shall be deemed to have been issued on the last day of the 28 day period, provided that the Works are substantially completed in accordance with the Contract.

The procedure to establish whether or not the Works are substantially completed in accordance with the Contract, in the absence of a statement by the Engineer, is not clear and could cause problems. Presumably the Contractor would first refer the matter direct to the Employer and then, if necessary, to the DAB or the Arbitrator.

The issue of the Taking-Over Certificate for the Works is the start of the 84 day period for the Contractor to issue his Statement at completion, which includes an estimate of any further claims, in accordance with Sub-Clause 14.10.

10.2 Taking-Over of Parts of the Works

The Engineer may, at the sole discretion of the Employer, issue a Taking-Over Certificate for any part of the Permanent Works.

The Employer shall not use any part of the Works (other than as a temporary measure which is either specified in the Contract or agreed by both Parties) unless and until the Engineer has issued a Taking-Over Certificate for this part. However, if the Employer does use any part of the Works before the Taking-Over Certificate is issued:

(a) the part which is used shall be deemed to have been taken over as from the date on which it is used;

(b) the Contractor shall cease to be liable for the care of such part as from this date; when responsibility shall pass to the Employer; and

(c) if requested by the Contractor, the Engineer shall issue a Taking-Over Certificate for this part.

After the Engineer has issued a Taking-Over Certificate for a part of the Works, the Contractor shall be given the earliest opportunity to take such steps as may be necessary to carry out any outstanding Tests on Completion. The Contractor shall carry out these Tests on Completion as soon as practicable before the expiry date of the relevant Defects Notification Period.

If the Contractor incurs Cost as a result of the Employer taking over and/or using a part of the Works, other than such use as is specified in the Contract or agreed by the Contractor, the Contractor shall (i) give notice to the Engineer and (ii) be entitled subject to Sub-Clause 20.1 [*Contractor's Claims*] to payment of any such Cost plus reasonable profit, which shall be included in the Contract Price. After receiving this notice, the Engineer shall proceed in accordance with Sub-Clause 3.5 [*Determinations*] to agree or determine this Cost and profit.

If a Taking-Over Certificate has been issued for a part of the Works (other than a Section), the delay damages thereafter for completion of the remainder of the Works shall be reduced. Similarly, the delay damages for the remainder of the Section (if any) in which this part is included shall also be reduced. For any period of delay after the date stated in this Taking-Over Certificate, the proportional reduction in these delay damages shall be calculated as the proportion which the value of the part so certified bears to the value of the Works or Section (as the case may be) as a whole. The Engineer shall proceed in accordance with Sub-Clause 3.5 [*Determinations*] to agree or determine these proportions. The provisions of this paragraph shall only apply to the daily rate of delay damages under Sub-Clause 8.7 [*Delay Damages*], and shall not affect the maximum amount of these damages.

The provisions of Sub-Clause 10.1 and 10.3 refer to the whole of the Works, or Sections of the Works which are designated in the Appendix to Tender. Sub-Clause 10.2 relates to parts of the Works that have not been designated as Sections.

Only the Employer has the right to decide that a certain part of the Works will be taken over before the remainder of the Works. This discretion may be exercised when the Employer wishes to use a part of the Works before the whole of the Works is complete. The Employer can require the Engineer to issue a Taking-Over Certificate and the Employer would then be responsible for the care of that part.

If the Employer's use of part of the Works is a temporary measure, which is specified in the Contract or agreed by both Parties, then a Taking-Over Certificate is not required. If the Employer uses a part of the Works without a Taking-Over Certificate then Sub-Clause 10.2 requires that:

(a) the part which is used shall be deemed to have been taken over as from the date on which it is used;

(b) the Contractor shall cease to be liable for the care of such part as from this date, when responsibility shall pass to the Employer; and

(c) if requested by the Contractor, the Engineer shall issue a Taking-Over Certificate for this part.

The taking over of a part of the Works was not envisaged in the Contract and is likely to cause problems for any Tests on Completion. Any such tests must be carried out as soon as practicable, but may have to be co-ordinated with tests in other parts of the Works.

Sub-Clause 10.2 provides that if the Contractor incurs Cost as a result of the Employer using and/or taking over a part of the Works then the Contractor will give notice and proceed as Sub-Clauses 20.1 and 3.5. The Contractor could then be entitled to his Cost plus reasonable profit.

This Sub-Clause does not refer to any entitlement for an extension of time but, if completion of another part of the Works has been delayed by this situation, the Contractor will presumably claim under a different clause, possibly Sub-Clause 8.4(e) as a delay attributable to the Employer.

The Sub-Clause also provides that the daily rate for any delay damages will be reduced in proportion to the value of any part of the Works for which a Taking-Over Certificate has been issued. The figure will be determined by the Engineer under Sub-Clause 3.5.

10.3 Interference with Tests on Completion

If the Contractor is prevented, for more than 14 days, from carrying out the Tests on Completion by a cause for which the Employer is responsible, the Employer shall be deemed to have taken over the Works or Section (as the case may be) on the date when the Tests on Completion would otherwise have been completed.

The Engineer shall then issue a Taking-Over Certificate accordingly, and the Contractor shall carry out the Tests on Completion as soon as practicable, before the expiry date of the Defects Notification Period. The Engineer shall require the Tests on Completion to be carried out by giving 14 days' notice and in accordance with the relevant provisions of the Contract.

If the Contractor suffers delay and/or incurs Cost as a result of this delay in carrying out the Tests on Completion, the Contractor shall give notice to the Engineer and shall be entitled subject to Sub-Clause 20.1 [*Contractor's Claims*] to:

(a) an extension of time for any such delay, if completion is or will be delayed, under Sub-Clause 8.4 [*Extension of Time for Completion*]; and

(b) payment of any such Cost plus reasonable profit, which shall be included in the Contract Price.

After receiving this notice, the Engineer shall proceed in accordance with Sub-Clause 3.5 [*Determinations*] to agree or determine these matters.

Sub-Clause 10.3 states that the Works shall be deemed to have been taken over by the Employer if the Contractor is prevented, for more than 14 days, from carrying out the Tests on Completion by a cause for which the Employer is responsible. The Engineer is required to issue a Taking-Over Certificate for the date on which the tests would have been completed if they had not been delayed by this cause.

If the Contractor suffers delay and/or incurs Costs as a result of this delay to the Tests on Completion he can give notice under Sub-Clause 10.3 and follow the procedures of Sub-Clauses 20.1 and 3.5.

The delay to the tests may be due to more than one cause, or the critical cause may be disputed. The Contractor's claim would include a statement that a certain cause was critical and establish the responsibility for the critical cause.

When the cause which prevented the Tests on Completion from being carried out has been removed, the Engineer can require them to be carried out by giving 14 days' notice. The Contractor is then obliged to carry out the tests as soon as practicable and before the expiry date of the Defects Notification Period. In the unlikely event that this cause continues to the end of the Defects Notification Period then the Engineer will need to consider what action to take, by agreement with the Employer and Contractor. The situation would be outside the provisions of the Contract and therefore outside the authority of the Engineer.

10.4 Surfaces Requiring Reinstatement
Except as otherwise stated in a Taking-Over Certificate, a certificate for a Section or part of the Works shall not be deemed to certify completion of any ground or other surfaces requiring reinstatement.

Sub-Clause 10.4 covers the situation when the ground or other surface needs to be reinstated after the Works are complete. Final reinstatement may not be physically possible until after the Contractor has completed the Works, or even until the end of the Defects Notification Period. This Sub-Clause states that a Taking-Over Certificate shall not be deemed to cover such reinstatement unless it is stated in the Certificate. The completion of reinstatement would become 'minor outstanding work' to be carried out during the Defects Notification Period, or as an unfulfilled obligation under Sub-Clause 11.10.

Chapter 20

Clause 11: Defects Liability

Clause 11 deals with the procedures during the Defects Notification Period, immediately after the Works have been taken over by the Employer. During this period the Contractor is responsible for correcting any defects. If, for any reason, the Employer does not fully occupy and use the project immediately after taking it over then the Employer will lose the benefits of the full Defects Notification Period.

The duration of the Defects Notification Period is stated in the Appendix to Tender. Most of the items in the Appendix to Tender have been left blank in the FIDIC form, for details to be inserted by the Employer before calling Tenders, but the figure of 365 days has been printed for the Defects Notification Period. This period may need to be changed by the Employer in the Tender documents. Whilst a period of one year will generally be suitable for civil engineering projects, a longer period may be required for electrical, mechanical or building services work. For example, performance tests on air conditioning plant must be carried out during hot weather, may be specified as Tests after Completion and are often followed by balancing and adjustment of the plant. For the Defects Notification Period to include a full hot-weather season after the completion of the balancing will require a two-year or 730-day period.

The procedures under Clause 11 generally require notifications and actions by the Employer, whereas similar actions before Completion would have been undertaken by the Engineer. This is a logical change because the Employer has occupied the Works, will be aware of any defects or other problems and the Contractor will need to liaise with the Employer in order to carry out repairs. The Employer will need to make the appropriate arrangements to identify any defects and must designate a representative to liaise with the Contractor. In practice, as the Engineer is now defined as Employer's Personnel, it may be convenient for these tasks to be carried out by the Engineer.

During this period the Engineer has certain powers and responsibilities, as stated in the Sub-Clauses, but no longer has the power to issue instructions for Variations. Under Sub-Clause 13.1 Variations can only be issued *prior* to the issue of the Taking-Over Certificate.

If any claims or disputes arise during the Disputes Notification Period the provisions of Clause 20 will still apply. The Dispute Adjudication Board is still operative during this period. Under the Yellow Book any failure to meet the performance specifications during the Defects Notification Period would be a defect.

Definitions at Clause 1.1 relevant to this Clause include:

1.1.3.6 Tests after Completion
1.1.3.7 Defects Notification Period
1.1.3.8 Performance Certificate
1.1.5.5 Plant.

11.1 Completion of Outstanding Work and Remedying Defects

In order that the Works and Contractor's Documents, and each Section, shall be in the condition required by the Contract (fair wear and tear excepted) by the expiry date of the relevant Defects Notification Period or as soon as practicable thereafter, the Contractor shall:

(a) complete any work which is outstanding on the date stated in a Taking-Over Certificate, within such reasonable time as is instructed by the Engineer; and

(b) execute all work required to remedy defects or damage, as may be notified by (or on behalf) of the Employer on or before the expiry date of the Defects Notification Period for the Works or Section (as the case may be).

If a defect appears or damage occurs, the Contractor shall be notified accordingly, by (or on behalf of) the Employer.

Sub-Clause 11.1 gives the overall requirement and procedures for the Defects Notification Period. During the Defects Notification Period, the Works have been occupied and are being used by the Employer. At the end of the period, the Works must be in the condition required by the Contract, with the exception of 'fair wear and tear'. Routine maintenance and problems caused by the Employer's use of the Works are the responsibility of the Employer. This means that:

- any work which was outstanding at the date of the Taking-Over Certificate will have been completed, and
- any defects or damage which have been notified to the Contractor by the Employer will have been repaired.

Any defect will be notified to the Contractor by (or on behalf of) the Employer. Any such notification should be copied to the Engineer, in order that he can take any necessary action under other Sub-Clauses.

In earlier Conditions of Contracts this period was known as the 'Maintenance Period' or the 'Defects Liability Period'. The change to the name 'Defects Notification Period' emphasises that the Contractor's liability is to repair any defects that have been notified during the period.

11.2   Cost of Remedying Defects

All work referred to in sub-paragraph (b) of Sub-Clause 11.1 [*Completion of Outstanding Work and Remedying Defects*] shall be executed at the risk and cost of the Contractor, if and to the extent that the work is attributable to:

(a)   any design for which the Contractor is responsible;
(b)   Plant, Materials or workmanship not being in accordance with the Contract; or
(c)   failure by the Contractor to comply with any other obligation.

If and to the extent that such work is attributable to any other cause, the Contractor shall be notified promptly by (or on behalf of) the Employer, and Sub-Clause 13.3 [*Variation Procedure*] shall apply.

In the Yellow Book the list of items of work for which the Contractor is liable for the cost of remedying defects is extended to include the additional responsibilities for the design and performance of the Works. The Red Book paragraphs (a) to (c) are replaced by the following.

(a)   the design of the Works, other than a part of the design for which the Employer is responsible (if any);
(b)   Plant, Materials or workmanship not being in accordance with the Contract;
(c)   improper operation or maintenance which was attributable to matters for which the Contractor is responsible (under Sub-Clauses 5.5 to 5.7 or otherwise); or
(d)   failure by the Contractor to comply with any other obligation.

Sub-Clause 11.2 explains the procedure by which the liability for the Cost of the repair is established. The defect or damage has been notified by the Employer under Sub-Clause 11.1(b). If the Employer decides that the work is not the Contractor's liability then the Contractor must be notified promptly and the Cost to be paid to the Contractor is decided by the Engineer as a Variation, using the procedures at Sub-Clause 13.3.

The Defects Notification Period does not give the Employer the right to use the Contractor to carry out routine maintenance and repairs to damage caused by the Employer's Personnel. Paragraphs (a) to (c) in the Red Book and (a) to (d) in the Yellow Book list the types of defects that must be repaired at the Contractor's Cost. Any other work must be paid for by the Employer. Whilst category (c) may seem to cover a wide range of problems, it is still necessary for the Employer to state and prove with which obligation the Contractor has failed to comply.

11.3   Extension of Defects Notification Period

The Employer shall be entitled subject to Sub-Clause 2.5 [*Employer's Claims*] to an extension of the Defects Notification Period for the Works or a Section if and to the extent that the Works, Section or a major item of Plant (as the case may be, and after taking over) cannot be used for the purposes for which they are intended by reason of a defect or damage. However, a Defects Notification Period shall not be extended by more than two years.

If delivery and/or erection of Plant and/or Materials was suspended under Sub-Clause 8.8 [*Suspension of Work*] or Sub-Clause 16.1 [*Contractor's Entitlement to Suspend Work*], the Contractor's obligations under this Clause shall not apply to any defects or damage occurring more than two years after the Defects Notification Period for the Plant and/or Materials would otherwise have expired.

The duration of the Defects Notification Period is stated in the Appendix to Tender but may be extended under Sub-Clause 11.3. If the Employer considers that he is entitled to an extension of this period, then either the Employer or the Engineer must give notice to the Contractor. The notice must be given, under Sub-Clause 2.5, as soon as practicable after the Employer became aware of the circumstances and before the expiry of the period. The Engineer will then make a determination under Sub-Clause 3.5.

To establish an entitlement to an extension, the Employer must prove that the whole or a Section of the Works or a major item of Plant could not be used for the purpose for which it was intended due to a defect or damage. The Defects Notification Period for the whole, or the Section of the Works or the major item of Plant could then be extended for an appropriate period, which must not exceed two years.

If the delivery and/or erection of Plant and/or Materials was suspended under Sub-Clause 8.8 or Sub-Clause 16.1 then the calendar dates of the Defects Notification Period will be delayed. However, under Sub-Clause 11.3, the Contractor's obligation to repair defects or damage shall not apply to any defect or damage that occurs more than two years after the Defects Notification Period for that Plant and/or Materials would have expired. This limitation presumably takes precedence over the other requirements in this Clause and refers specifically to problems with Plant and/or Materials.

11.4   Failure to Remedy Defects

If the Contractor fails to remedy any defect or damage within a reasonable time, a date may be fixed by (or on behalf of) the Employer, on or by which the defect or damage is to be remedied. The Contractor shall be given reasonable notice of this date.

If the Contractor fails to remedy the defect or damage by this notified date and this remedial work was to be executed at the cost of the Contractor under Sub-Clause 11.2 [*Cost of Remedying Defects*], the Employer may (at his option):

(a)   carry out the work himself or by others, in a reasonable manner and at the Contractor's cost, but the Contractor shall have no responsibility for this work; and the Contractor shall subject to Sub-Clause 2.5 [*Employer's Claims*] pay to the Employer the costs reasonably incurred by the Employer in remedying the defect or damage;

(b)   require the Engineer to agree or determine a reasonable reduction in the Contract Price in accordance with Sub-Clause 3.5 [*Determinations*]; or

(c)   if the defect or damage deprives the Employer of substantially the whole benefit of the Works or any major part of the Works, terminate the Contract as a whole, or in respect of such major part which cannot be put to the intended use. Without prejudice to any other rights, under the Contract or otherwise, the Employer shall then be entitled to recover all sums paid for the Works or for such part (as the case may be), plus financing costs and the cost of dismantling the same, clearing the Site and returning Plant and Materials to the Contractor.

Before taking any action the Employer's preference must be discussed with the Engineer and Contractor, in an attempt to reach agreement on the proposed action, and any appropriate notices given to the Contractor. The Employer may:

- make other arrangements to carry out the work and claim the Cost against the Contractor, under Sub-Clause 2.5, or
- accept the work including the defect and reduce the Contract price, under the procedures of Sub-Clause 3.5 (this is a practical procedure and can be used when the remedial work would cause substantial inconvenience or damage and the Employer would prefer to accept the out of specification work), or

- terminate the Contract as a whole or in respect of the relevant part of the Works. This would obviously be a very serious action and would result in the Employer claiming substantial sums of money from the Contractor. The termination procedures at Clause 15 would apply, with the additional requirements of Sub-Clause 11.4(c).

As with the similar provision at Sub-Clause 9.4, it is difficult to envisage circumstances where the provisions at subparagraph (c) would be appropriate under a Red Book Contract.

11.5   Removal of Defective Work

If the defect or damage cannot be remedied expeditiously on the Site and the Employer gives consent, the Contractor may remove from the Site for the purposes of repair such items of Plant as are defective or damaged.

This consent may require the Contractor to increase the amount of the Performance Security by the full replacement cost of these items, or to provide other appropriate security.

The Employer must give his consent before any item of Plant is removed from the Site for repair. Before giving consent the Employer will want to know how long the repair will take and what action is proposed to enable the Works to be used during its absence. The situation envisaged at Sub-Clause 11.5 could result in an extension to the Defects Notification Period under Sub-Clause 11.3.

11.6   Further Tests

If the work of remedying of any defect or damage may affect the performance of the Works, the Engineer may require the repetition of any of the tests described in the Contract. The requirement shall be made by notice within 28 days after the defect or damage is remedied.

These tests shall be carried out in accordance with the terms applicable to the previous tests, except that they shall be carried out at the risk and cost of the Party liable, under Sub-Clause 11.2 [*Cost of Remedying Defects*], for the cost of the remedial work.

It is logical that if work that has previously been subject to tests has been repaired because of a defect then the original tests should be repeated. However, the details of the tests may need to be modified to suit the different circumstances now that the Works have been occupied by the Employer. Any modification would need to be agreed by the Parties. This provision is particularly important in a Yellow Book Contract.

11.7 (RB)   Right of Access

Until the Performance Certificate has been issued, the Contractor shall have such right of access to the Works as is reasonably required in order to comply with this Clause, except as may be inconsistent with the Employer's reasonable security restrictions.

In the Yellow Book Sub-Clause 11.7 is replaced by:

11.7 (YB)   Right of Access

Until the Performance Certificate has been issued, the Contractor shall have the right of access to all parts of the Works and to records of the operation and performance of the Works, except as may be inconsistent with the Employer's reasonable security restrictions.

Obviously the Contractor needs access to the Site in order to carry out his obligations. Times and arrangements must be agreed, to suit both the Employer and the Contractor. The Contractor may also need office and storage facilities on Site in order to meet his obligations during the Defects Notification Period. The details must be agreed between the Contractor and the Engineer. The removal of these facilities and any reinstatement would be covered by Sub-Clauses 10.4 and 11.11 concerning surfaces requiring reinstatement and clearance of the Site.

In the Yellow Book the Contractor is entitled to additional access to the Works during the Defects Notification period. This enables the Contractor to observe and check the operation of the Works and the performance records that are being kept by the Employer. The Contractor's design responsibilities are based on the requirement that the performance shall comply with the Employer's Requirements. If the Works fail to meet these requirements then there would be a defect requiring correction. It is therefore important that the Contractor has the opportunity to check that the Works are being operated and maintained in accordance with his design. Any problems or failures in operation or maintenance should be reported by the Contractor in order to avoid allegations of design failure or failure to pass the Tests after Completion.

11.8   Contractor to Search

The Contractor shall, if required by the Engineer, search for the cause of any defect, under the direction of the Engineer. Unless the defect is to be remedied at the cost of the Contractor under Sub-Clause 11.2 [*Cost of Remedying Defects*], the Cost of the search plus reasonable profit shall be agreed or determined by the Engineer in accordance with Sub-Clause 3.5 [*Determinations*] and shall be included in the Contract Price.

After the Employer has notified the Contractor of the defect, a technical assessment of the problem will be made by the Engineer. Sub-Clause 11.8 enables the Engineer to give instructions to the Contractor to investigate the problem. This Sub-Clause entitles the Contractor to additional payment, but does not refer to giving notice under Sub-Clause 20.1. However, any such payment could be disputed and so the procedures of Sub-Clause 20.1 should be followed.

11.9   Performance Certificate

Performance of the Contractor's obligations shall not be considered to have been completed until the Engineer has issued the Performance Certificate to the Contractor, stating the date on which the Contractor completed his obligations under the Contract.

The Engineer shall issue the Performance Certificate within 28 days after the latest of the expiry dates of the Defects Notification Periods, or as soon thereafter as the Contractor has supplied all the Contractor's Documents and completed and tested all the Works, including remedying any defects. A copy of the Performance Certificate shall be issued to the Employer.

Only the Performance Certificate shall be deemed to constitute acceptance of the Works.

The Performance Certificate is issued when the Engineer is satisfied that the Contractor has fulfilled his obligations during the Defects Notification Period. The delay of 28 days from the end of the Defects Notification Period allows time for a joint inspection of the Works and for the Contractor to complete any outstanding work.

The final sentence of Sub-Clause 11.9 confirms the Contract requirements, such as Sub-Clause 3.2(a), which stipulate that any failure to notice and report, at the time, any item of work that does not comply with the Specifications does not mean that the work has been accepted.

The receipt of the Performance Certificate starts the 56 day period for the Contractor to submit a draft final account which includes all outstanding claims.

11.10   Unfulfilled Obligations

After the Performance Certificate has been issued, each Party shall remain liable for the fulfilment of any obligation which remains unperformed at that time. For the purposes of determining the nature and extent of unperformed obligations, the Contract shall be deemed to remain in force.

Sub-Clause 11.9 required that the Performance Certificate states the date on which the Contractor completed his obligations under the Contract.

This is clearly inconsistent with the reference at Sub-Clause 11.10 to 'Unfulfilled Obligations'. However, there are some obligations which cannot be carried out until after the issue of the Performance Certificate, such as:

- clearance of the Site under Sub-Clause 11.11 and reinstatement under Sub-Clause 10.4;
- the application for Final Payment Certificate under Sub-Clause 14.11;
- investigation and correction of any latent defects which are not noticed until after the issue of the Performance Certificate, but for which the Contractor may have a liability under the applicable law.

11.11   Clearance of Site

Upon receiving the Performance Certificate, the Contractor shall remove any remaining Contractor's Equipment, surplus material, wreckage, rubbish and Temporary Works from the Site.

If all these items have not been removed within 28 days after the Employer receives a copy of the Performance Certificate, the Employer may sell or otherwise dispose of any remaining items. The Employer shall be entitled to be paid the costs incurred in connection with, or attributable to, such sale or disposal and restoring the Site.

Any balance of the moneys from the sale shall be paid to the Contractor. If these moneys are less than the Employer's costs, the Contractor shall pay the outstanding balance to the Employer.

The time periods for actions under Sub-Clause 11.11 start from the receipt of the Performance Certificate by the Contractor and Employer. The dates of receipt must be recorded by the Engineer. The requirements for the Contractor's final Site clearance may also be the subject of regulations under the governing law.

Chapter 21

Clause 12 (RB): Measurement and Evaluation

Clause 12 in the Red Book is written for a remeasurement contract in which the Accepted Contract Amount is based on estimated quantities but the Contractor is obliged to carry out all the work which is required by the Specification and Drawings and is paid for the actual quantities of work which he has executed. The Clause covers the procedures for the measurement and evaluation of the Works that have been executed, or have been omitted by a Variation.

The Red Book is clear that the quantities in the Bill of Quantities are only estimates. Hence any changes due to remeasurement are not Variations, but are part of the original obligations of both Parties. If the Employer, for his own internal accounting purposes, requires the additional Cost due to changes in quantities to be confirmed by a Variation order then this is just an administrative procedure and does not indicate that the change is a Variation.

If the Contract is based on a lump sum, or is on a cost-plus or other basis, then Clause 12 must be omitted from the General Conditions and alternative arrangements included in the Particular Conditions. Sub-Clause 14.1 of the FIDIC Guidance for the Preparation of Particular Conditions includes recommendations for Contracts on a cost-plus or lump sum basis. If a Red Book Contract includes some lump sum items then these must be paid from a Schedule of Payments as Sub-Clause 14.4.

Definitions at Sub-Clause 1.1 relevant to this Clause include:

1.1.1.7 (RB)	Schedules
1.1.1.10 (RB)	Bill of Quantities
1.1.4.2	Contract Price
1.1.5.2	Goods
1.1.5.3	Materials
1.1.5.4	Permanent Works
1.1.5.8	Works
1.1.6.9	Variation.

12.1 (RB)   Works to be Measured

The Works shall be measured, and valued for payment, in accordance with this Clause.

Whenever the Engineer requires any part of the Works to be measured, reasonable notice shall be given to the Contractor's Representative, who shall:

(a)   promptly either attend or send another qualified representative to assist the Engineer in making the measurement; and

(b)   supply any particulars requested by the Engineer.

If the Contractor fails to attend or send a representative, the measurement made by (or on behalf of) the Engineer shall be accepted as accurate.

Except as otherwise stated in the Contract, wherever any Permanent Works are to be measured from records, these shall be prepared by the Engineer. The Contractor shall, as and when requested, attend to examine and agree the records with the Engineer, and shall sign the same when agreed. If the Contractor does not attend, the records shall be accepted as accurate.

If the Contractor examines and disagrees the records, and/or does not sign them as agreed, then the Contractor shall give notice to the Engineer of the respects in which the records are asserted to be inaccurate. After receiving this notice, the Engineer shall review the records and either confirm or vary them. If the Contractor does not so give notice to the Engineer within 14 days after being requested to examine the records, they shall be accepted as accurate.

The procedures for measurement of the Works are given at Sub-Clause 12.1 as follows.

- The Engineer decides that he requires a part of the Works to be measured and notifies the Contractor.
- The Contractor attends and assists the Engineer in making the measurement.
- Alternatively, the Contractor fails to attend and the Engineer's measurements are accepted as accurate.

If a part of the Works is to be measured from records of its construction then the details should be specified in the Tender documents. A similar procedure applies in that the Engineer prepares the records and the Contractor examines and agrees or disagrees with the records.

If the Engineer requires the Contractor to carry out the work for either measurement or the preparation of records then this should be stated in the Specification. In practice the Contractor often does play a greater part in this work than is required by the Contract. The Contractor is more likely to have the staff and equipment available and some Contractors prefer to make the measurements themselves, rather than assist the Engineer. The Engineer will then check and confirm the Contractor's measurement.

The Contract does not stipulate any fixed periods or timing for the measurement and this is a matter for the Engineer. The timing of measurement notifications will depend on the progress of the Works and the completion of convenient parts or items in the Bill of Quantities, although any work which is to be buried or covered up must be measured before it is buried or covered. The Contractor will have notified the Engineer under Sub-Clause 7.3 before the Work is buried or covered up.

The measurement must be completed in time for the Contractor to prepare and submit his Statement at Completion, as Sub-Clause 14.10, but does not have to be related to interim payments. The provision for interim payments, at Sub-Clause 14.3, is based on 'the estimated value of the Works executed' and not on a final valuation. The estimated value may be based on an interim or approximate measurement and will be adjusted when the final measurement figures have been agreed.

12.2 (RB) Method of Measurement

Except as otherwise stated in the Contract and notwithstanding local practice:

(a) measurement shall be made of the net actual quantity of each item of the Permanent Works; and

(b) the method of measurement shall be in accordance with the Bill of Quantities or other applicable Schedules.

The procedure for the actual measurement of the different work items can be standardised for different projects and for consistency within a project by the use of a published standard method of measurement. The FIDIC Conditions of Contract do not require the use of a standard method of measurement but Sub-Clause 12.2 states that the method of measurement will be in accordance with the Bill of Quantities 'or other applicable Schedules'. If a standard method of measurement, such as the Civil Engineering Standard Method of Measurement published by The Institution of Civil Engineers, is to be used then this requirement should be stated in the Particular Conditions.

Alternatively, the Bill of Quantities should include a detailed explanation of the method of measurement which will be used. For example, the phrase 'net actual quantity' needs to be explained. It will not mean the actual quantity which has been executed by the Contractor. Particularly for work below ground level, the Contractor may have provided additional concrete, or carried out additional excavation, to suit his method of working. Net actual quantity would then mean the minimum quantities that would be required in order to provide the Permanent Works.

12.3 (RB)   Evaluation

Except as otherwise stated in the Contract, the Engineer shall proceed in accordance with Sub-Clause 3.5 [*Determinations*] to agree or determine the Contract Price by evaluating each item of work, applying the measurement agreed or determined in accordance with the above Sub-Clauses 12.1 and 12.2 and the appropriate rate or price for the item.

For each item of work, the appropriate rate or price for the item shall be the rate or price specified for such item in the Contractor, if there is no such item, specified for similar work. However, a new rate or price shall be appropriate for an item of work if:

(a)   (i)   the measured quantity of the item is changed by more than 10% from the quantity of this item in the Bill of Quantities or other Schedule,

   (ii)   this change in quantity multiplied by such specified rate for this item exceeds 0.01% of the Accepted Contract Amount,

   (iii)   this change in quantity directly changes the Cost per unit quantity of this item by more than 1%, and

   (iv)   this item is not specified in the Contract as a 'fixed rate item'; or

(b)   (i)   the work is instructed under Clause 13 [*Variations and Adjustments*],

   (ii)   no rate or price is specified in the Contract for this item, and (iii) no specified rate or price is appropriate because the item of work is not of similar character, or is not executed under similar conditions, as any item in the Contract.

Each new rate or price shall be derived from any relevant rates or prices in the Contract, with reasonable adjustments to take account of the matters described in sub-paragraph (a) and/or (b), as applicable. If no rates or prices are relevant for the derivation of a new rate or price, it shall be derived from the reasonable Cost of executing the work, together with reasonable profit, taking account of any other relevant matters.

Until such time as an appropriate rate or price is agreed or determined, the Engineer shall determine a provisional rate or price for the purposes of interim Payment Certificates.

Sub-Clause 12.3 requires the Engineer to agree or determine the Contract Price by applying the measurement and the appropriate rate or price for each item. The appropriate rate or price is stated to be the Contract rate or price for the item, or for similar work, unless:

- the measured quantity has changed by more than the amounts stated at Sub-Clause 12.3(a) and the item is not specified as a 'fixed rate item', or
- the work is a Variation under Clause 13 and there is no appropriate rate or price in the Contract.

The percentage figures given at sub-paragraphs (a) (i) and (ii) are probably too low and will result in a requirement to discuss an excessive number of new rates, which may be virtually unchanged from the original rates. The MDB Edition, which is discussed later in this book, has used 25% and 0.25%. Item (a) (iii) refers to changes of Cost, which is defined as expenditure reasonably incurred by the Contractor for the particular item. Only the Contractor knows this figure and he will probably be unwilling, or even unable, to provide an accurate figure.

Any evaluation or new rate or price will be determined by the Engineer in accordance with the procedures in Sub-Clause 3.5. That is, the Engineer will consult with both Parties and try to reach agreement. Failing agreement the Engineer will make a fair determination. Either Party has the right to invoke the Clause 20 dispute procedures if it is not satisfied with the Engineer's determination.

12.4 (RB)   Omissions

Whenever the omission of any work forms part (or all) of a Variation, the value of which has not been agreed, if:

(a)   the Contractor will incur (or has incurred) cost which, if the work had not been omitted, would have been deemed to be covered by a sum forming part of the Accepted Contract Amount;

(b)   the omission of the work will result (or has resulted) in this sum not forming part of the Contract Price; and

(c)   this cost is not deemed to be included in the evaluation of any substituted work;

then the Contractor shall give notice to the Engineer accordingly, with supporting particulars. Upon receiving this notice, the Engineer shall proceed in accordance with Sub-Clause 3.5 [*Determinations*] to agree or determine this cost, which shall be included in the Contract Price.

When any work is omitted it is likely that the Contractor will already have incurred some expenditure in the preparation, provision of Goods and ordering Materials, if not in the actual execution of work on the Site. This Sub-Clause requires the Engineer to make a fair assessment of any such Cost.

Chapter 22

Clause 12 (YB): Tests after Completion

The procedure for payment by measurement of work executed is not appropriate for a Contract with design by the Contractor and so Red Book Clause 12 [*Measurement and Evaluation*] is omitted from the Yellow Book. The Yellow Book Clause 12 [*Tests After Completion*] refers to additional tests which are to be carried out after the Works have been occupied by the Employer, following the issue of the Taking-Over Certificate. The procedures described in this Clause do not just relate to individual items of Plant but to tests of the Works as a whole, or to a Section which the Contract requires to be taken over as a separate entity. The basic requirement in the Yellow Book is that the completed project must meet the Employer's Requirements so the tests must be carried out when the project is being used by the Employer in order to confirm that performance requirements are being met. The procedures for these tests differ from the Tests on Completion because the Site is now occupied and controlled by the Employer and not by the Contractor.

Definitions at Sub-Clause 1.1 relevant to this Clause include:

1.1.1.5 (YB)	Employer's Requirements
1.1.1.7 (YB)	Contractor's Proposal
1.1.3.6	Tests after Completion
1.1.3.7	Defects Notification Period
1.1.4.3	Cost
1.1.4.11	Retention Money
1.1.5.5	Plant
1.1.5.6	Section
1.1.5.8	Works.

12.1 (YB)   Procedure for Tests after Completion

If Tests after Completion are specified in the Contract, this Clause shall apply. Unless otherwise stated in the Particular Conditions, the Employer shall:

(a)   provide all electricity, equipment, fuel, instruments, labour, materials, and suitably qualified and experienced staff, as are necessary to carry out the Tests after Completion efficiently; and

(b)   carry out the Tests after Completion in accordance with the manuals supplied by the Contractor under Sub-Clause 5.7 [*Operation and Maintenance Manuals*] and such guidance as the Contractor may be required to give during the course of these Tests; and in the presence of such Contractor's Personnel as either Party may reasonably request.

The Tests after Completion shall be carried out as soon as is reasonably practicable after the Works or Section have been taken over by the Employer. The Employer shall give to the Contractor 21 days' notice of the date after which the Tests after Completion will be carried out. Unless otherwise agreed, these Tests shall be carried out within 14 days after this date, on the day or days determined by the Employer.

If the Contractor does not attend at the time and place agreed, the Employer may proceed with the Tests after Completion, which shall be deemed to have been made in the Contractor's presence, and the Contractor shall accept the readings as accurate.

The results of the Tests after Completion shall be compiled and evaluated by both Parties. Appropriate account shall be taken of the effect of the Employer's prior use of the Works.

By definition, the Tests after Completion are carried out after the project has been handed over and occupied by the Employer. Hence the Employer is required to provide all the Materials, services and staff required to carry out the tests. The tests are to be carried out in accordance with the operation and maintenance manuals which have been provided by the Contractor under Sub-Clause 5.7. However, the requirements for the tests should have been given in the Employer's Requirements, with more details in the Contractor's Proposal.

This Sub-Clause includes the procedures for the Employer to inform the Contractor when he is ready to carry out the tests and for the results to be evaluated by both Parties. It is important that these tests are carried out as soon as possible after handover. The tests may reveal problems that require further action and it is essential that all problems are resolved before the end of the Defects Notification Period.

12.2 (YB)   Delayed Tests

If the Contractor incurs Cost as a result of any unreasonable delay by the Employer to the Tests after Completion, the Contractor shall (i) give notice to the Engineer and (ii) be entitled subject to Sub-Clause 20.1

[*Contractor's Claims*] to payment of any such Cost plus reasonable profit, which shall be included in the Contract Price.

After receiving this notice, the Engineer shall proceed in accordance with Sub-Clause 3.5 [*Determinations*] to agree or determine this Cost and profit.

If, for reasons not attributable to the Contractor, a Test after Completion on the Works or any Section cannot be completed during the Defects Notification Period (or any other period agreed upon by both Parties), then the Works or Section shall be deemed to have passed this Test after Completion.

This Sub-Clause follows the usual claims procedures if the Contractor has incurred Cost due to the Employer having delayed these tests.

Sub-Clause 14.9 requires that the Tests after Completion must have been completed before the first half of the Retention Money is certified by the Engineer for payment to the Contractor. Hence, if the tests are delayed by the Employer then the Contractor's claim will include the Cost of the delay in the payment of the Retention Money.

12.3 (YB) Retesting

If the Works, or a Section, fail to pass the Tests after Completion:

(a) sub-paragraph (b) of Sub-Clause 11.1 [*Completion of Outstanding Work and Remedying Defects*] shall apply; and

(b) either Party may then require the failed Tests, and the Tests after Completion on any related work, to be repeated under the same terms and conditions.

If and to the extent that this failure and retesting are attributable to any of the matters listed in sub-paragraphs (a) to (d) of Sub-Clause 11.2 [*Cost of Remedying Defects*] and cause the Employer to incur additional costs, the Contractor shall subject to Sub-Clause 2.5 [*Employer's Claims*] pay these costs to the Employer.

This Sub-Clause confirms that the Contractor must execute any work that is necessary to correct the problem which caused the Works or Section to fail the test. Either Party may require that the failed tests are repeated.

If the failure is attributable to the Contractor then the Employer can claim any additional Costs that have been incurred. In order to prove that the failure was due to some cause attributable to the Contractor, it is necessary to establish exactly why the tests failed and which Party is liable for the failure. This may be easily established or may need investigation. The Contract does not give procedures for establishing the cause and liability for the failure but the Sub-Clause includes a reference to Sub-Clause 11.1 [*Completion of Outstanding Work and Remedying Defects*].

It is therefore logical to assume that the procedures at Sub-Clause 11.8 [*Contractor to Search*] should also apply. This requires the Contractor to search for the cause of a defect, under the direction of the Engineer, and to be paid for the Cost of the search unless the defect is to be remedied at the cost of the Contractor.

12.4 (YB)   Failure to Pass Tests after Completion

If the following conditions apply, namely:

(a) the Works, or a Section, fail to pass any or all of the Tests after Completion;

(b) the relevant sum payable as non-performance damages for this failure is stated (or its method of calculation is defined) in the Contract; and

(c) the Contractor pays this relevant sum to the Employer during the Defects Notification Period;

then the Works or Section shall be deemed to have passed these Tests after Completion.

If the Works, or a Section, fail to pass a Test after Completion and the Contractor proposes to make adjustments or modifications to the Works or such Section, the Contractor may be instructed by (or on behalf of) the Employer that right of access to the Works or Section cannot be given until a time that is convenient to the Employer. The Contractor shall then remain liable to carry out the adjustments or modifications and to satisfy this Test, within a reasonable period of receiving notice by (or on behalf of) the Employer of the time that is convenient to the Employer. However, if the Contractor does not receive this notice during the relevant Defects Notification Period, the Contractor shall be relieved of this obligation and the Works or Section (as the case may be) shall be deemed to have passed this Test after Completion.

If the Contractor incurs additional Cost as a result of any unreasonable delay by the Employer in permitting access to the Works or Plant by the Contractor, either to investigate the causes of a failure to pass a Test after Completion or to carry out any adjustments or modifications, the Contractor shall (i) give notice to the Engineer and (ii) be entitled subject to Sub-Clause 20.1 [*Contractor's Claims*] to payment of any such Cost plus reasonable profit, which shall be included in the Contract Price.

After receiving this notice, the Engineer shall proceed in accordance with Sub-Clause 3.5 [*Determinations*] to agree or determine this Cost and profit.

Sub-clause 12.4 includes a reference to non-performance damages for failure to pass any of the Tests after Completion. The sum payable, or its method of calculation, must be stated in the Contract, but unfortunately there is no provision for this in the Appendix to Tender. This provision must also be considered with the provisions at Sub-Clause 11.4 for the situation if the Contractor fails to remedy any defects. Failure to pass a test could be considered to be a defect and be subject to further discussion on this basis.

The wording of this Sub-Clause is clear that it is the Works or Section, as a whole, which passes or fails the Tests after Completion. If any one test fails then the whole of the Works or Section has failed.

Chapter 23

Clause 13: Variations and Adjustments

Clause 13 covers the procedures for work being added, omitted, or changed from the original contract work, together with other matters which may increase or decrease the Contract Price. Under the Yellow Book the scope of the changes that may be instructed by the Engineer is restricted, which reflects the Contractor's responsibility for the design and the performance of the Works at completion. Under Sub-Clause 13.3 the Contractor must acknowledge receipt of any Engineer's instruction for a Variation.

In any construction project there will be a need to change the initial requirements as the construction proceeds on the Site. This may be a matter of the Employer changing his mind about some requirement, or the Engineer may need to issue further information which involves changes to the initial requirements, or it may be necessary to correct a mistake in the information issued to the Contractor. An instruction can be given to change an item of the Works which has been completed and the Cost of making the change will be included in the valuation of the Variation. However, instructions for changes cannot be given after the issue of the Taking-Over Certificate for the Works.

The FIDIC Conditions allow the Engineer, but not the Employer, to issue an instruction to change the Works. The Contractor is not permitted to change the Permanent Works unless the Engineer has instructed or approved the Variation. If the Employer wants to make any changes he must request that the Engineer issues an instruction. If the Employer gives an instruction direct to the Contractor then the Contractor must obtain the Engineer's confirmation and instruction before he executes the change. Strict adherence to these requirements is essential for the Engineer to maintain technical and financial control over the project.

Sub-Clause 3.3 gives the Engineer the power to issue instructions which may, or may not, constitute a Variation under Clause 13. If the Contractor considers that an instruction constitutes a Variation then he should confirm the instruction as a Variation, by acknowledging receipt and stating that it is as required by Sub-Clause 13.3. If the Engineer disagrees then the Contractor must still comply with the instruction but can follow the appropriate claim procedures under Sub-Clause 20.1.

Definitions at Sub-Clause 1.1 relevant to Clause 13 include:

1.1.1.5 (YB)	Employer's Requirements
1.1.1.7 (RB)	Schedules
1.1.1.10 (RB)	Bill of Quantities and Daywork Schedule
1.1.1.10 (YB)	Schedule of Guarantees and Schedule of Payments
1.1.3.1	Base Date
1.1.3.5	Taking-Over Certificate
1.1.4.2	Contract Price
1.1.4.3	Cost
1.1.4.10	Provisional Sum
1.1.5.2	Goods
1.1.5.4	Permanent Works
1.1.5.8	Works
1.1.6.2	Country
1.1.6.9	Variation.

13.1 (RB)   Right to Vary

Variations may be initiated by the Engineer at any time prior to issuing the Taking-Over Certificate for the Works, either by an instruction or by a request for the Contractor to submit a proposal.

The Contractor shall execute and be bound by each Variation, unless the Contractor promptly gives notice to the Engineer stating (with supporting particulars) that the Contractor cannot readily obtain the Goods required for the Variation. Upon receiving this notice, the Engineer shall cancel, confirm or vary the instruction.

Each Variation may include:

(a) changes to the quantities of any item of work included in the Contract (however, such changes do not necessarily constitute a Variation);

(b) changes to the quality and other characteristics of any item of work;

(c) changes to the levels, positions and/or dimensions of any part of the Works;

(d) omission of any work unless it is to be carried out by others;

(e) any additional work, Plant, Materials or services necessary for the Permanent Works, including any associated Tests on Completion, boreholes and other testing and exploratory work; or

(f) changes to the sequence or timing of the execution of the Works.

The Contractor shall not make any alteration and/or modification of the Permanent Works, unless and until the Engineer instructs or approves a Variation.

13.1 (YB)   Right to Vary

Variations may be initiated by the Engineer at any time prior to issuing the Taking-Over Certificate for the Works, either by an instruction or by a request for the Contractor to submit a proposal. A Variation shall not comprise the omission of any work which is to be carried out by others.

The Contractor shall execute and be bound by each Variation, unless the Contractor promptly gives notice to the Engineer stating (with supporting particulars) that (i) the Contractor cannot readily obtain the Goods required for the Variation, (ii) it will reduce the safety or suitability of the Works, or (iii) it will have an adverse impact on the achievement of the Schedule of Guarantees. Upon receiving this notice, the Engineer shall cancel, confirm or vary the instruction.

Under the Red Book, the Engineer can issue instructions to change a wide range of matters concerning the Works, as listed at Sub-Clause 13.1(a) to (f). However, these are all matters that concern the Permanent Works, which have been defined in the Contract, and do not result in a change to the scope or size of the Works. The Engineer cannot issue instructions under this Clause for additional work unless it is 'necessary for the Permanent Works', as Sub-Clause 13.1(e). If the Employer wants the Contractor to carry out work which changes the scope of the Works then he must negotiate a change to the Contract.

The Contractor can object that he cannot readily obtain the Goods, that is Equipment, Plant, Materials or Temporary Works, and the Engineer can either cancel, confirm or vary the instruction. However, the Contractor cannot object to the instruction because of difficulties in obtaining management staff or labour.

A significant change to previous FIDIC Conditions of Contracts is that the Engineer can initiate the Variation either by issuing an instruction or 'by a request for the Contractor to submit a proposal'. A request for a proposal is not just a matter of submitting a price for a proposed Variation. The Engineer may ask for a detailed technical proposal, together with details of the impact on the programme and on other aspects of the Works.

Where, under a Red Book Contract, the Contractor is responsible for a significant part of the design, consideration should be given to restricting the Engineer's power to vary that part of the Works, as stipulated in the Yellow Book.

The Yellow Book definition of a Variation covers an instruction to change either the Employer's Requirements or the Works, which has been confirmed by the Engineer to be a Variation. That is, the instruction has time or payment implications which will be valued by the Engineer as Sub-Clause 13.3. As with the Red Book, the Variation can be initiated by the Engineer either as an instruction or a request for a proposal and must not be to omit work which is to be carried out by others.

Because the Contractor under the Yellow Book has additional responsibilities, there are additional reasons by which the Contractor can object to the Variation.

Point (i) refers to difficulties in obtaining the necessary Goods, which is the same as the Red Book.

Point (ii) refers to a reduction in the safety of the Works, which clearly refers to the Contractor's responsibilities as the designer of the Works. The reference to suitability is not so clear but presumably refers to the designer's responsibility to meet the performance specification.

Point (iii) refers to the Schedule of Guarantees, which must be provided by the Contractor under the Yellow Book.

The Engineer can then either cancel, confirm or vary the instruction. If the Engineer confirms an instruction following objections by the Contractor then the Employer is taking responsibility for the potential problems which have been notified by the Contractor. If the Variation has design or safety implications then it could also bring additional responsibilities to both the Employer and the Engineer under the applicable law.

13.2 (RB) Value Engineering

The Contractor may, at any time, submit to the Engineer a written proposal which (in the Contractor's opinion) will, if adopted, (i) accelerate completion, (ii) reduce the cost to the Employer of executing, maintaining or operating the Works, (iii) improve the efficiency or value to the Employer of the completed Works, or (iv) otherwise be of benefit to the Employer.

The proposal shall be prepared at the cost of the Contractor and shall include the items listed in Sub-Clause 13.3 [*Variation Procedure*].

If a proposal, which is approved by the Engineer, includes a change in the design of part of the Permanent Works, then unless otherwise agreed by both Parties:

(a) the Contractor shall design this part;

(b) subparagraphs (a) to (d) of Sub-Clause 4.1 [*Contractor's General Obligations*] shall apply; and

(c) if this change results in a reduction in the contract value of this part, the Engineer shall proceed in accordance with Sub-Clause 3.5 [*Determinations*] to agree or determine a fee, which shall be included in the Contract Price. This fee shall be half (50%) of the difference between the following amounts:

(i) such reduction in contract value, resulting from the change, excluding adjustments under Sub-Clause 13.7 [*Adjustments for Changes in Legislation*] and Sub-Clause 13.8 [*Adjustments for Changes in Cost*], and

223

(ii) the reduction (if any) in the value to the Employer of the varied works, taking account of any reductions in quality, anticipated life or operational efficiencies.

However, if amount (i) is less than amount (ii), there shall not be a fee.

13.2 (YB)   Value Engineering

The Contractor may, at any time, submit to the Engineer a written proposal which (in the Contractor's opinion) will, if adopted, (i) accelerate completion, (ii) reduce the cost to the Employer of executing, maintaining or operating the Works, (iii) improve the efficiency or value to the Employer of the completed Works, or (iv) otherwise be of benefit to the Employer.

The proposal shall be prepared at the cost of the Contractor and shall include the items listed in Sub-Clause 13.3 [*Variation Procedure*].

The provision for value engineering is another significant addition to previous FIDIC Contracts. This provision enables the Employer to benefit from the Contractor's experience and proposals. However, the procedures that have been introduced may not encourage Contractors to put forward proposals.

If the Contractor wishes to submit a proposal that will benefit the Employer in any of the ways listed in the first paragraph of Sub-Clause 13.2 then he must prepare, at his own Cost, a proposal which includes the information which is required for a Variation proposal under Sub-Clause 13.3.

Under the Red Book, the third paragraph of Sub-Clause 13.2 draws a distinction between proposals that include a change in the design of part of the Permanent Works and those that do not include a design change. If the proposal includes a design change then, unless the Parties agree otherwise, the Contractor shall design the changed part of the Works and receive a fee, provided that the reduction in Contract value is greater than any reduction in the value of the Works to the Employer. The fee is calculated by the Engineer, following the Sub-Clause 3.5 procedure. If the proposal does not include a design change then the Contractor will have to rely on any benefit from savings in his own Costs.

The preparation of a value engineering proposal could involve the Contractor in substantial costs which may, or may not, be recovered. Any proposal should be discussed and agreed in principle before the Contractor incurs costs that may not be recoverable.

Under the Yellow Book, any value engineering proposal becomes a Variation and is valued as such by the Engineer.

13.3   Variation Procedure

If the Engineer requests a proposal, prior to instructing a Variation, the Contractor shall respond in writing as soon as practicable, either by giving reasons why he cannot comply (if this is the case) or by submitting:

(a)   a description of the proposed work to be performed and a programme for its execution;

(b)   the Contractor's proposal for any necessary modifications to the programme according to Sub-Clause 8.3 [*Programme*] and to the Time for Completion; and

(c)   the Contractor's proposal for evaluation of the Variation.

The Engineer shall, as soon as practicable after receiving such proposal (under Sub-Clause 13.2 [*Value Engineering*] or otherwise), respond with approval, disapproval or comments. The Contractor shall not delay any work whilst awaiting a response.

Each instruction to execute a Variation, with any requirements for the recording of Costs, shall be issued by the Engineer to the Contractor, who shall acknowledge receipt.

Each Variation shall be evaluated in accordance with Clause 12 [*Measurement and Evaluation*], unless the Engineer instructs or approves otherwise in accordance with this Clause.

The Yellow Book includes provision for a design proposal under sub-paragraph (a). The different payment terminology at sub-paragraph (c) is also shown by the replacement of the final paragraph of Sub-Clause 13.3 by the following.

Upon instructing or approving a Variation, the Engineer shall proceed in accordance with Sub-Clause 3.5 [*Determinations*] to agree or determine adjustments to the Contract Price and the Schedule of Payments. These adjustments shall include reasonable profit, and shall take account of the Contractor's submissions under Sub-Clause 13.2 [*Value Engineering*] if applicable.

When the Engineer is considering whether to issue instructions for a Variation he has the option of first asking the Contractor for a proposal. The Contractor can either give the reasons why he cannot comply or provide 'a description of the proposed work to be performed', modifications to the programme and date for Completion and his proposal for the evaluation of the Variation. There is no time limit on the provision of this proposal, only that it must be submitted 'as soon as practicable'.

The purpose of this Sub-Clause is apparently to reduce potential disputes by encouraging agreement of the consequences of Variations before the instruction is issued. If the Contractor considers that to prepare a proposal is likely to be time consuming or the time and cost implications are uncertain then he may either find a reason not to submit a proposal, or give high estimates for the programme modification and evaluation. The proposal could then be subject to discussion before the Engineer decides to issue the Variation.

The Sub-Clause 13.3 proposal is not a firm offer to carry out the Variation for a fixed price and time extension. Payment will be made by measurement in accordance with Clause 12, unless the Engineer decides otherwise. The Engineer can ask for records of Costs. Any extension of time would be determined under the procedures at Sub-Clause 8.4.

Sub-Clause 13.3, unlike Sub-Clause 13.2, does not state that the proposal shall be made at the Contractor's Cost, so Costs could presumably be claimed, or would be covered in the valuation of the Variation.

If a Variation affects the work which is currently being executed by the Contractor then the Engineer would need to issue the instructions immediately, without waiting for a proposal. The Contractor must not delay any work during this process, which could result in a need for the Variation to include the removal of completed work. The Cost of any disruption caused by the Variation must also be considered, possibly requiring a separate claim under Sub-Clause 20.1.

Under the Red Book, Variations are to be valued in accordance with Clause 12. Omissions will be valued in accordance with Sub-Clause 12.4.

Under the Yellow Book, the Engineer will value Variations as a determination under Sub-Clause 3.5.

The procedure for the valuation of omissions, which is given at Sub-Clause 12.4 of the Red Book, has been omitted from the Yellow Book. However, the requirement for fairness, at Sub-Clause 3.5, should result in a similar procedure.

13.4 Payment in Applicable Currencies

If the Contract provides for payment of the Contract Price in more than one currency, then whenever an adjustment is agreed, approved or determined as stated above, the amount payable in each of the applicable currencies shall be specified. For this purpose, reference shall be made to the actual or expected currency proportions of the Cost of the varied work, and to the proportions of various currencies specified for payment of the Contract Price.

This Sub-Clause requires the currency provisions in the Contract to be carried through into the evaluation of a Variation. It does not address the problem of changes in exchange rates between the Base Date and the Variation date, but it would presumably give the opportunity for the Contractor to raise any problems for discussion.

13.5 Provisional Sums

Each Provisional Sum shall only be used, in whole or in part, in accordance with the Engineer's instructions, and the Contract Price shall be adjusted accordingly. The total sum paid to the Contractor shall include only such amounts, for the work, supplies or services to which the Provisional Sum relates, as the Engineer shall have instructed. For each Provisional Sum, the Engineer may instruct:

(a) work to be executed (including Plant, Materials or services to be supplied) by the Contractor and valued under Sub-Clause 13.3 [*Variation Procedure*]; and/or

(b) Plant, Materials or services to be purchased by the Contractor, from a nominated Subcontractor (as defined in Clause 5 [*Nominated Subcontractors*]) or otherwise; and for which there shall be included in the Contract Price:

   (i) the actual amounts paid (or due to be paid) by the Contractor, and

   (ii) a sum for overhead charges and profit, calculated as a percentage of these actual amounts by applying the relevant percentage rate (if any) stated in the appropriate Schedule. If there is no such rate, the percentage rate stated in the Appendix to Tender shall be applied.

The Contractor shall, when required by the Engineer, produce quotations, invoices, vouchers and accounts or receipts in substantiation.

In the Yellow Book the reference to a Nominated Subcontractor at sub-paragraph (b) has been omitted.

A Provisional Sum is defined as a sum of money, which is included in the Contract Price, but has been allocated for a particular part of the Works, or the supply of Plant, Materials or services, as specified in the Contract. The money can only be used when instructed by the Engineer. The instruction may take the form of a Variation for additional work, which is then valued in accordance with Sub-Clause 13.3. Alternatively it may be an instruction for the purchase of Plant, Materials or services. This would be valued as the actual amount paid, based on invoices, plus a percentage for overheads and profit. The percentage must be stated in the Appendix to Tender. Under the Red Book, the Engineer has the option of stating the source to be used, which becomes a nominated Subcontractor; however, under the Yellow Book, this would not be appropriate. The Provisional Sum can only be used for the specified purpose. Any money surplus to these requirements cannot be used for other work and will result in a reduction in the Contract Price. If a sum of money which is included as a Provisional Sum is actually intended to be a contingency sum then this must be clearly defined in the Particular Conditions.

13.6 Daywork

For work of a minor or incidental nature, the Engineer may instruct that a Variation shall be executed on a daywork basis. The work shall then be valued in accordance with the Daywork Schedule included in the Contract, and the following procedure shall apply. If a Daywork Schedule is not included in the Contract, this Sub-Clause shall not apply.

Before ordering Goods for the work, the Contractor shall submit quotations to the Engineer. When applying for payment, the Contractor shall submit invoices, vouchers and accounts or receipts for any Goods.

Except for any items for which the Daywork Schedule specifies that payment is not due, the Contractor shall deliver each day to the Engineer accurate statements in duplicate which shall include the following details of the resources used in executing the previous day's work:

(a)   the names, occupations and time of Contractor's Personnel;
(b)   the identification, type and time of Contractor's Equipment and Temporary Works; and
(c)   the quantities and types of Plant and Materials used.

One copy of each statement will, if correct, or when agreed, be signed by the Engineer and returned to the Contractor. The Contractor shall then submit priced statements of these resources to the Engineer, prior to their inclusion in the next Statement under Sub-Clause 14.3 [*Application for Interim Payment Certificates*].

In the Yellow Book, 'daywork schedule' is not a defined term. However, if the Contract is to include provision for payment on a daywork basis it is still necessary to include a daywork schedule in the Contract.

Payment on a daywork basis means that the Contractor submits daily records of the resources used in the execution of the previous day's work, including the information which is listed at Sub-Clause 13.6, and is paid at the rates stated in the Daywork Schedule. If there is no Daywork Schedule in the Contract, then payment cannot be made on a daywork basis.

It is therefore important that a Daywork Schedule is included in the Tender documents, completed by the Contractor and included with the Letter of Tender and Letter of Acceptance so as to form part of the Contract. For a Daywork Schedule to be agreed later would require the Employer's agreement, as an addition to the Contract.

Sub-Clause 13.6 restricts the use of Daywork to work 'of a minor or incidental nature'. Minor or incidental work generally creates more disruption than is normal for the total Cost of the work, so daywork rates are usually high. If the Engineer wants to negotiate a rate on a cost-plus basis he will expect the rates to show a reduction on the daywork rates.

13.7 Adjustments for Changes in Legislation

The Contract Price shall be adjusted to take account of any increase or decrease in Cost resulting from a change in the Laws of the Country (including the introduction of new Laws and the repeal or modification of existing Laws) or in the judicial or official governmental interpretation of such Laws, made after the Base Date, which affect the Contractor in the performance of obligations under the Contract.

If the Contractor suffers (or will suffer) delay and/or incurs (or will incur) additional Cost as a result of these changes in the Laws or in such inter-pretations, made after the Base Date, the Contractor shall give notice to the Engineer and shall be entitled subject to Sub-Clause 20.1 [*Contractor's Claims*] to:

(a) an extension of time for any such delay, if completion is or will be delayed, under Sub-Clause 8.4 [*Extension of Time for Completion*]; and

(b) payment of any such Cost, which shall be included in the Contract Price.

After receiving this notice, the Engineer shall proceed in accordance with Sub-Clause 3.5 [*Determinations*] to agree or determine these matters.

Sub-Clause 13.7 refers to increases or decreases in Cost due to changes in legislation. The Sub-Clause only refers to changes in the Laws of the Country. If the governing law is different to the Laws of the Country, or the Contractor is carrying out work in a different country, as discussed in the commentary on Sub-Clause 1.4, then the provisions of this Sub-Clause would not apply. If the Contractor suffers delay or additional Cost then he submits a claim under the procedures of Sub-Clause 20.1. Similarly, if there is a possible decrease in Cost then the Employer would have to submit a claim under Sub-Clause 2.5.

Changes in legislation will normally mean the introduction of new laws or regulations. The possibility of a change in the interpretation of the law introduces a more difficult subject with subjective opinions. Also, it is not unknown for a country's legal system to change, for new countries to be created or for country borders to move and for a site to effectively move into a different country. Any additional Costs would be claimed under

Sub-Clause 20.1 and the legal basis of the claim discussed in relation to the particular circumstances.

Changes in legislation may affect several items of work in different ways and it is important to ensure that the additional payment does not duplicate other payments.

13.8   Adjustments for Changes in Cost

In this Sub-Clause, 'table of adjustment data' means the completed table of adjustment data included in the Appendix to Tender. If there is no such table of adjustment data, this Sub-Clause shall not apply.

If this Sub-Clause applies, the amounts payable to the Contractor shall be adjusted for rises or falls in the cost of labour, Goods and other inputs to the Works, by the addition or deduction of the amounts determined by the formulae prescribed in this Sub-Clause. To the extent that full compensation for any rise or fall in Costs is not covered by the provisions of this or other Clauses, the Accepted Contract Amount shall be deemed to have included amounts to cover the contingency of other rises and falls in costs.

The adjustment to be applied to the amount otherwise payable to the Contractor, as valued in accordance with the appropriate Schedule and certified in Payment Certificates, shall be determined from formulae for each of the currencies in which the Contract Price is payable. No adjustment is to be applied to work valued on the basis of Cost or current prices. The formulae shall be of the following general type:

$$Pn = a + b \frac{Ln}{Lo} + c \frac{En}{Eo} + d \frac{Mn}{Mo} + \cdots$$

where:

'Pn' is the adjustment multiplier to be applied to the estimated contract value in the relevant currency of the work carried out in period 'n', this period being a month unless otherwise stated in the Appendix to Tender;

'a' is a fixed coefficient, stated in the relevant table of adjustment data, representing the non-adjustable portion in contractual payments; 'b', 'c', 'd', ... are coefficients representing the estimated proportion of each cost element related to the execution of the Works, as stated in the relevant table of adjustment data; such tabulated cost elements may be indicative of resources such as labour, equipment and materials;

'Ln', 'En', 'Mn', ... are the current cost indices or reference prices for period 'n', expressed in the relevant currency of payment, each of which is applicable to the relevant tabulated cost element on the date 49 days prior to the last day of the period (to which the

230

particular Payment Certificate relates); and 'Lo', 'Eo', 'Mo', . . . are the base cost indices or reference prices, expressed in the relevant currency of payment, each of which is applicable to the relevant tabulated cost element on the Base Date.

The cost indices or reference prices stated in the table of adjustment data shall be used. If their source is in doubt, it shall be determined by the Engineer. For this purpose, reference shall be made to the values of the indices at stated dates (quoted in the fourth and fifth columns respectively of the table) for the purposes of clarification of the source; although these dates (and thus these values) may not correspond to the base cost indices.

In cases where the 'currency of index' (stated in the table) is not the relevant currency of payment, each index shall be converted into the relevant currency of payment at the selling rate, established by the central bank of the Country, of this relevant currency on the above date for which the index is required to be applicable.

Until such time as each current cost index is available, the Engineer shall determine a provisional index for the issue of Interim Payment Certificates. When a current cost index is available, the adjustment shall be recalculated accordingly.

If the Contractor fails to complete the Works within the Time for Completion, adjustment of prices thereafter shall be made using either (i) each index or price applicable on the date 49 days prior to the expiry of the Time for Completion of the Works, or (ii) the current index or price: whichever is more favourable to the Employer.

The weightings (coefficients) for each of the factors of cost stated in the table(s) of adjustment data shall only be adjusted if they have been rendered unreasonable, unbalanced or inapplicable, as a result of Variations.

If the Employer wishes to include provision to reimburse the Contractor for changes in the Cost of labour, equipment, Materials, or other items then the table in the Appendix to Tender must be completed in accordance with the provisions of Sub-Clause 13.8. This is a new provision for FIDIC and will need to be assessed following experience of the use of the formula.

To decide on the various coefficients to be included in the adjustment formula, together with the other information which is required, will not be a simple matter and will depend on the information which is available for the Country, as well as on the details of the project. Similarly, the administration and evaluation of Cost adjustments will be time consuming for both the Contractor and the Engineer and could lead to disputes as to the correct evaluation.

Employers who currently use different procedures for evaluation of inflation costs may prefer to continue to use their own procedures and make the appropriate provisions in the Particular Conditions.

International circumstances may result in a significant increase in the price of a single material, which is not reflected in the general price increases. This situation is not covered in the FIDIC Contracts, but may be covered in an 'unforeseen or exceptional circumstances' provision in the governing law, or by a government regulation.

Chapter 24

Clause 14: Contract Price and Payment

In the Red Book the Contract Price is defined at Sub-Clause 1.1.4.2 as 'the price defined in Sub-Clause 14.1', which includes any adjustments which are provided for in the Contract. The Contract Price must be distinguished from the Accepted Contract Amount, which is defined at Sub-Clause 1.1.4.1 as 'the amount accepted in the Letter of Acceptance'. The Accepted Contract Amount is fixed, but the Contract Price can change and will probably increase, due to the measurement of actual quantities, Variations and other adjustments. The Contract Agreement states that the Employer will pay the Contractor 'the Contract Price at the times and in the manner prescribed by the Contract'.

In the Yellow Book, the references to remeasurement are omitted and replaced by references to the Accepted Contract Amount as a lump sum. Payments are made in accordance with a Schedule and are subject to adjustment in accordance with the Contract. Where the Red or Yellow Books include provision for some payments to be made as instalments of a lump sum then the provisions of Sub-Clause 14.4 will apply.

Clause 14 also includes, at the second paragraph of Sub-Clause 14.4, a requirement for the Contractor to provide a quarterly estimate of payments.

The FIDIC Guidance for the Preparation of Particular Conditions includes the statement:

> When writing the Particular Conditions, consideration should be given to the amount and timing of payment(s) to the Contractor. A positive cash flow is clearly of benefit to the Contractor, and tenderers will take account of the interim payment procedures when preparing their tenders.

This statement is extremely important. The structure of the FIDIC payment and bonding procedures is such that the Contractor is unlikely to achieve a positive cash flow throughout the project, but the Employer's interests are covered by the bonds and the work which has been completed by the time he makes an interim payment. Hence all tenderers will study the provisions for payment, including the advance payment, and may include an allowance for the Contractor having to pay interest on any negative cash flow. It is therefore important that consideration is given to the cash flow situation in both the preparation of the Particular Conditions and the administration of the Contract. The time periods for the measurement of work on Site, the submission of the Contractor's statement, issue of the Engineer's certificate and the payment to the Contractor are such that the work on Site will normally be several months further advanced by the time the Employer actually makes the payment. This fact should be taken into account when preparing the Contract documents, considering the percentage and limit of retention as Sub-Clause 14.3(c) and calculating an interim payment.

Definitions at Sub-Clause 1.1 relevant to this Clause include:

1.1.1.3	Letter of Acceptance
1.1.1.4	Letter of Tender
1.1.1.6 (YB)	Schedules
1.1.1.7 (RB)	Schedules
1.1.1.8	Tender
1.1.1.10 (RB)	Bill of Quantities and Daywork Schedule
1.1.1.10 (YB)	Schedule of Guarantees and Schedule of Payments
1.1.3.2	Commencement Date
1.1.4.1	Accepted Contract Amount
1.1.4.2	Contract Price
1.1.4.3	Cost
1.1.4.4	Final Payment Certificate
1.1.4.5	Final Statement
1.1.4.6	Foreign Currency
1.1.4.7	Interim Payment Certificate
1.1.4.8	Local Currency
1.1.4.9	Payment Certificate
1.1.4.10	Provisional Sum
1.1.4.11	Retention Money
1.1.4.12	Statement
1.1.6.2	Country
1.1.6.6	Performance Security.

14.1 (RB)   The Contract Price
Unless otherwise stated in the Particular Conditions:

(a)   the Contract Price shall be agreed or determined under Sub-Clause 12.3 [*Evaluation*] and be subject to adjustments in accordance with the Contract;

(b)   the Contractor shall pay all taxes, duties and fees required to be paid by him under the Contract, and the Contract Price shall not be adjusted for any of these costs except as stated in Sub-Clause 13.7 [*Adjustments for Changes in Legislation*];

(c) any quantities which may be set out in the Bill of Quantities or other Schedule are estimated quantities and are not to be taken as the actual and correct quantities:

(i)   of the Works which the Contractor is required to execute, or

(ii) for the purposes of Clause 12 [*Measurement and Evaluation*]; and

(d) the Contractor shall submit to the Engineer, within 28 days after the Commencement Date, a proposed breakdown of each lump sum price in the Schedules. The Engineer may take account of the breakdown when preparing Payment Certificates, but shall not be bound by it.

In the Yellow Book, Sub-Clause 14.1 is replaced by the following.

14.1 (YB)   The Contract Price
Unless otherwise stated in the Particular Conditions:

(a) the Contract Price shall be the lump sum Accepted Contract Amount and be subject to adjustments in accordance with the Contract;

(b) the Contractor shall pay all taxes, duties and fees required to be paid by him under the Contract, and the Contract Price shall not be adjusted for any of these costs, except as stated in Sub-Clause 13.7 [*Adjustments for Changes in Legislation*];

(c) any quantities which may be set out in a Schedule are estimated quantities and are not to be taken as the actual and correct quantities of the Works which the Contractor is required to execute; and

(d) any quantities or price data which may be set out in a Schedule shall be used for the purposes stated in the Schedule and may be inapplicable for other purposes.

However, if any part of the Works is to be paid according to quantity supplied or work done, the provisions for measurement and evaluation shall be as stated in the Particular Conditions. The Contract Price shall be determined accordingly, subject to adjustments in accordance with the Contract.

Sub-Clause 14.1 gives the following four general requirements, which relate to other Sub-Clauses.

● The Contract Price, which is stated in the Contract Agreement to be the amount which the Employer will pay to the Contractor, is agreed or determined by the Engineer. The Engineer will determine the Contract Price in accordance with Sub-Clause 12.3, as the sum of the valuations of each item of work, including any Variations, together with other adjustments.

Under a Red Book Contract, if payment is to be made on a lump sum basis then the Guidance for the Preparation of Particular Conditions gives an alternative wording:

> (a) the Contract Price shall be the lump sum Accepted Contract Amount and be subject to adjustments in accordance with the Contract.

For a lump sum contract it is essential that full details of the Employer's requirements are given in the Tender documents to enable the Contractor to submit a realistic Tender. Any uncertainties in the Tender documents, or additional information issued by the Engineer, are likely to result in claims.

The Guidance suggests that Clause 12 and the last sentence of Sub-Clause 13.3 should be deleted for a lump sum Contract. Variations should be valued by the Engineer using the procedures of Sub-Clause 3.5. The Sub-Clause 13.3 procedure for the Contractor to submit a proposal before a Variation is issued would seem to be essential if disputes are to be avoided. Sub-Clause 14.1(b), (c) and (d) may also need to be revised for a lump sum Contract.

These proposed changes have already been incorporated into the Yellow Book.

- Sub-Clause 1.13(b) requires the Contractor to pay all taxes, duties and fees. The Employer only reimburses any of these which are the result of changes in legislation as Sub-Clause 13.7. If the Employer intends to reimburse any other charges they must be defined in the Particular Conditions. The Guidance for the Preparation of Particular Conditions includes suggested Sub-Clauses if Sub-Clause 14.1(b) is not to apply. These Sub-Clauses, in the Particular Conditions, would have priority over the relevant part of Sub-Clause 1.13(b).
- Sub-Clause 14.1(c) must be revised if the quantities in the Bill of Quantities or other Schedules are to be taken as the actual and correct quantities.
- Sub-Clause 14.1(d) (RB) imposes another requirement on the Contractor. Within 28 days from the Commencement Date the Contractor must provide a proposed breakdown of every lump sum price in the Schedules. These breakdowns are only proposals, for the information of the Engineer, but should be consistent with other financial submissions. The Engineer is not bound to follow the Contractor's breakdown but should be prepared to discuss any queries or changes to the breakdown. Sub-Clause 14.1(d) (YB) requires that the Schedules will include the purposes for which the quantities or price data should be used.

The final paragraph of Sub-Clause 14.1 (YB) requires the Particular Conditions to include the provisions if any measurement is required. The Guidance for the Preparation of Particular Conditions includes a suggested Sub-Clause, which states that if the value is not agreed then the Engineer will make a determination under Sub-Clause 3.5. This is consistent with the procedure for the valuation of Variations, as Sub-Clause 13.3 (YB). The suggested Sub-Clause then repeats Sub-Clauses 12.1 and 12.2(a) from the Red Book. Sub-Clause 12.2(b) is not repeated, presumably because the Yellow Book does not normally include a Bill of Quantities. However, if a Yellow Book Contract includes for the measurement of work which may be controversial then some method of measurement should be included.

14.2 Advance Payment

The Employer shall make an advance payment, as an interest-free loan for mobilisation, when the Contractor submits a guarantee in accordance with this Sub-Clause. The total advance payment, the number and timing of instalments (if more than one), and the applicable currencies and proportions, shall be as stated in the Appendix to Tender.

Unless and until the Employer receives this guarantee, or if the total advance payment is not stated in the Appendix to Tender, this Sub-Clause shall not apply.

The Engineer shall issue an Interim Payment Certificate for the first instalment after receiving a Statement (under Sub-Clause 14.3 [*Application for Interim Payment Certificates*]) and after the Employer receives (i) the Performance Security in accordance with Sub-Clause 4.2 [*Performance Security*], and (ii) a guarantee in amounts and currencies equal to the advance payment. This guarantee shall be issued by an entity and from within a country (or other jurisdiction) approved by the Employer, and shall be in the form annexed to the Particular Conditions or in another form approved by the Employer.

The Contractor shall ensure that the guarantee is valid and enforceable until the advance payment has been repaid, but its amount may be progressively reduced by the amount repaid by the Contractor as indicated in the Payment Certificates. If the terms of the guarantee specify its expiry date, and the advance payment has not been repaid by the date 28 days prior to the expiry date, the Contractor shall extend the validity of the guarantee until the advance payment has been repaid.

The advance payment shall be repaid through percentage deductions in Payment Certificates. Unless other percentages are stated in the Appendix to Tender:

(a) deductions shall commence in the Payment Certificate in which the total of all certified interim payments (excluding the advance payment and deductions and repayments of retention) exceeds ten per cent (10%) of the Accepted Contract Amount less Provisional Sums; and

(b) deductions shall be made at the amortisation rate of one quarter (25%) of the amount of each Payment Certificate (excluding the advance payment and deductions and repayments of retention) in the currencies and proportions of the advance payment, until such time as the advance payment has been repaid.

If the advance payment has not been repaid prior to the issue of the Taking-Over Certificate for the Works or prior to termination under Clause 15 [*Termination by Employer*], Clause 16 [*Suspension and Termination by Contractor*] or Clause 19 [*Force Majeure*] (as the case may be), the whole of the balance then outstanding shall immediately become due and payable by the Contractor to the Employer.

If the Employer intends to make an advance payment then the relevant information must be provided in the Appendix to Tender. The figure for the advance payment is given as a percentage of the Accepted Contract Amount and the currency in which it is to be paid must be stated. If the advance payment is to be paid in instalments then the number and timing of instalments must be stated.

In accordance with Sub-Clause 14.7(a), the first instalment of the advance payment must be paid by the later of:

- 42 days from issuing the Letter of Acceptance, or
- 21 days from receiving the Performance Security under Sub-Clause 4.2 and the Advance Payment Guarantee and other documents under Sub-Clause 14.2.

The Contractor should ensure that the Performance Security and Advance Payment Guarantee are submitted to the Employer within 21 days from the Letter of Acceptance. The forms which are acceptable to the Employer should have been annexed to the Particular Conditions, preferably as the FIDIC Annex C or D and E.

The procedure for payment, given at Sub-Clause 14.2, is as follows.

- The Contractor submits a Statement for the first instalment under Sub-Clause 14.3. This Statement should be submitted immediately after the Letter of Acceptance, so that the various time periods can be concurrent, rather than consecutive.
- The Engineer must issue an Interim Payment Certificate immediately after receiving the Statement. The Engineer does not have the usual 28 day period, as Sub-Clause 14.6, to issue his Certificate because this would prevent the Employer from making payment by the due date. If the Engineer fails to issue the Certificate then the

provisions of Sub-Clause 16.1, for the Contractor first to give notice to suspend or reduce the rate of work and eventually Sub-Clause 16.2(b), for the Contractor to terminate the Contract, would apply.

- The Employer must have received the Performance Security and Advance Payment Guarantee. If these documents have not been received then the Engineer can delay issuing the Interim Payment Certificate. Some Employers may also require that the insurance documents have also been received.
- The Employer pays within 21 days from receiving the Performance Security and Advance Payment Guarantee, or within 42 days from issuing the Letter of Acceptance if this is later. This 42 day period coincides with the 42 day period for the Commencement Date, although the advance payment period starts from the Employer issuing the Letter of Acceptance and the Commencement Date period from its receipt by the Contractor. If the Employer fails to pay within these periods then the provisions of Sub-Clauses 16.1, for the Contractor to give notice to suspend or reduce the rate of work, and Sub-Clause 16.2(c), for the Contractor to terminate the Contract, will apply. The Contractor will also be entitled to finance charges as Sub-Clause 14.8.

The advance payment is stated at the first sentence of Sub-Clause 14.2 to be an 'interest-free loan for mobilisation', so any delay in payment could result in the Contractor claiming that his mobilisation will be delayed. Similarly, if payment is made but mobilisation is slow then the Employer could ask whether the payment has been used for its proper purpose.

The payment procedures are appropriate for the first instalment, which must be paid as soon as possible after the Letter of Acceptance. If the Particular Conditions state that the advance payment will be made in several instalments then the procedures for the further instalments must also be stated. For the payment to be an advance for mobilisation then the total advance payment must be paid quickly and be related to the timing of the Contractor's mobilisation costs. If the timing of instalments is intended to relate to further mobilisation costs which will arise during the project then the timing of the date for payment must relate to these costs. Sub-Clause 14.3(d) allows for advance payments to be included in the Contractor's statements for Interim Payment Certificates. However, this would not comply with the requirements for an advance payment due to the lengthy time period between the Contractor's statement and the receipt of payment.

Sub-Clause 14.2 requires that repayment of the advance payment will commence when the certified interim payments exceed 10% of the Accepted Contract Amount and will be calculated as 25% of the amount of each Payment Certificate. The Guidance for the Preparation of Particular Conditions states that these figures were calculated on the assumption that the total advance payment is less than 22% of the Accepted Contract Amount. If the total advance payment is more than 22% of the Accepted Contract Amount, which seems unlikely, then the repayments should be increased. If it is substantially less than 22% the repayments could be reduced. Any outstanding balance must be repaid immediately on the issue of the Taking-Over Certificate for the Works or prior to termination under Clauses 15, 16 or 19.

14.3   Application for Interim Payment Certificates

The Contractor shall submit a Statement in six copies to the Engineer after the end of each month, in a form approved by the Engineer, showing in detail the amounts to which the Contractor considers himself to be entitled, together with supporting documents which shall include the report on the progress during this month in accordance with Sub-Clause 4.21 [*Progress Reports*].

The Statement shall include the following items, as applicable, which shall be expressed in the various currencies in which the Contract Price is payable, in the sequence listed:

(a)   the estimated contract value of the Works executed and the Con-tractor's Documents produced up to the end of the month (including Variations but excluding items described in sub-paragraphs (b) to (g) below);

(b)   any amounts to be added and deducted for changes in legislation and changes in cost, in accordance with Sub-Clause 13.7 [*Adjust-ments for Changes in Legislation*] and Sub-Clause 13.8 [*Adjustments for Changes in Cost*];

(c)   any amount to be deducted for retention, calculated by applying the percentage of retention stated in the Appendix to Tender to the total of the above amounts, until the amount so retained by the Employer reaches the limit of Retention Money (if any) stated in the Appendix to Tender;

(d)   any amounts to be added and deducted for the advance payment and repayments in accordance with Sub-Clause 14.2 [*Advance Payment*];

(e)   any amounts to be added and deducted for Plant and Materials in accordance with Sub-Clause 14.5 [*Plant and Materials intended for the Works*];

(f)   any other additions or deductions which may have become due under the Contract or otherwise, including those under Clause 20 [*Claims, Disputes and Arbitration*]; and

(g) the deduction of amounts certified in all previous Payment Certificates.

Under the Yellow Book interim payments are made as required by the Schedules, which may not be monthly. Hence, Sub-Clause 14.3 allows for the periods for payment to be stated in the Contract.

The procedure for the Contractor to receive payments from the Employer starts with the Contractor's application for payment. The Contractor submits a Statement to the Engineer each month giving the amounts that he is claiming, together with supporting documents. The Statement is submitted 'after the end of each month' and the sooner the Contractor collects the necessary information and submits the Statement, the sooner he will be paid. The Statement must be 'in a form approved by the Engineer' and include the items listed as (a) to (g), in the order in which they are listed. Agreement on the form and layout of the Statement is important and if the Engineer has any particular requirements they should be stated in the Particular Conditions.

Item (a) refers to 'the estimated contract value of the Works executed'. This will include any Works which have been measured in accordance with Clause 12, together with an estimate of the value of work which has not yet been measured by the Engineer.

Item (f) refers to amounts due as claims under Clause 20. This will include the claims and interim claims described at Sub-Clause 20.1. The reference to Clause 20 emphasises the importance of claims being submitted under Clause 20 in addition to the notices under other clauses, such as Sub-Clause 1.9.

Item (g) refers to the deduction of amounts previously certified, but does not require a Statement of any amounts which have been certified by the Engineer but were not paid by the Employer. The Contractor should normally confirm the Certificates that have been paid and the due dates for unpaid Certificates. The Contractor is entitled to finance charges for delayed payments 'without formal notice or certification', as Sub-Clause 14.8, but it would obviously be prudent to include a calculation of any finance charges under item (f).

When submitting the first Statement the Contractor should demonstrate that he has received, or state when he expects to receive, the Employer's approval to the Performance Security. Under Sub-Clause 14.6 the Engineer will not certify any payment until the Performance Security has been approved by the Employer. Under Sub-Clause 1.3, the approval must not be 'unreasonably withheld or delayed'. If the Contract includes provision for an advance payment then the Performance Security will already have been approved before payment of the advance payment. The timing of the first monthly Statement for work executed will depend on the progress of the Works being such that the net amount due to be paid exceeds the minimum amount of Interim Payment Certificates stated in the Appendix to Tender.

The Contractor's Statement should be sent by a method that requires a receipt. Sub-Clause 14.7 requires the Employer to make payment of the sum which is certified by the Engineer within 56 days from the date the Engineer receives the Contractor's Statement.

The supporting documents with the Contractor's Statement must be complete, as required by Sub-Clause 14.3, and must include the Contractor's monthly progress report under Sub-Clause 4.21.

14.4   Schedule of Payments

If the Contract includes a schedule of payments specifying the instalments in which the Contract Price will be paid, then unless otherwise stated in this schedule:

(a)   the instalments quoted in this schedule of payments shall be the estimated contract values for the purposes of sub-paragraph (a) of Sub-Clause 14.3 [*Application for Interim Payment Certificates*];

(b)   Sub-Clause 14.5 [*Plant and Materials intended for the Works*] shall not apply; and

(c)   if these instalments are not defined by reference to the actual progress achieved in executing the Works, and if actual progress is found to be less than that on which this schedule of payments was based, then the Engineer may proceed in accordance with Sub-Clause 3.5 [*Determinations*] to agree or determine revised instalments, which shall take account of the extent to which progress is less than that on which the instalments were previously based.

If the Contract does not include a schedule of payments, the Contractor shall submit non-binding estimates of the payments which he expects to become due during each quarterly period. The first estimate shall be submitted within 42 days after the Commencement Date. Revised estimates shall be submitted at quarterly intervals, until the Taking-Over Certificate has been issued for the Works.

If the Contract Price is to be paid in instalments then the Contract must include a Schedule of Payments, giving the timing and details of the instalments, subject to the provisions of Sub-Clause 14.4. The schedule must be clear and unambiguous and relate to the Contractor's programme and the actual progress which has been recorded on the Site. Subparagraph (c) allows the Engineer to reduce the payment if actual progress is less than had been assumed. Logically the Engineer should also increase the payment if actual progress is greater than had been assumed.

The Schedule of Payments is particularly important for a Yellow Book Contract. Whereas the Red Book includes provision, at Clause 12, for the Works to be measured and valued for payment, the Yellow Book relies only on the Schedule of Payments in order to calculate the estimated contract value for interim payments as Sub-Clause 14.3(a).

If the Contract does not include a Schedule of Payments then the Contractor must submit estimates of the amount he expects will become due during each quarterly period. The first estimate must be submitted within 42 days after the Commencement Date, that is, during the first half of that quarter. Further estimates are required 'at quarterly intervals', but the next estimate is not necessarily required exactly three months after the first estimate. The dates for submission should be agreed between the Contractor and the Engineer. This requirement replaces the provision for a cash flow estimate in earlier FIDIC Conditions of Contracts. If the Employer requires the estimate to include particular details, then the requirements must be stated in the Particular Conditions. The estimates should also relate to the Contractor's programme.

14.5 Plant and Materials intended for the Works

If this Sub-Clause applies, Interim Payment Certificates shall include, under subparagraph (e) of Sub-Clause 14.3, (i) an amount for Plant and Materials which have been sent to the Site for incorporation in the Permanent Works, and (ii) a reduction when the contract value of such Plant and Materials is included as part of the Permanent Works under subparagraph (a) of Sub-Clause 14.3 [*Application for Interim Payment Certificates*].

If the lists referred to in subparagraphs (b)(i) or (c)(i) below are not included in the Appendix to Tender, this Sub-Clause shall not apply.

The Engineer shall determine and certify each addition if the following conditions are satisfied:

(a) the Contractor has:
  (i) kept satisfactory records (including the orders, receipts, Costs and use of Plant and Materials) which are available for inspection, and
  (ii) submitted a statement of the Cost of acquiring and delivering the Plant and Materials to the Site, supported by satisfactory evidence;
  and either:
(b) the relevant Plant and Materials:
  (i) are those listed in the Appendix to Tender for payment when shipped,
  (ii) have been shipped to the Country, en route to the Site, in accordance with the Contract; and
  (iii) are described in a clean shipped bill of lading or other evidence of shipment, which has been submitted to the Engineer together

with evidence of payment of freight and insurance, any other documents reasonably required, and a bank guarantee in a form and issued by an entity approved by the Employer in amounts and currencies equal to the amount due under this Sub-Clause: this guarantee may be in a similar form to the form referred to in Sub-Clause 14.2 [*Advance Payment*] and shall be valid until the Plant and Materials are properly stored on Site and protected against loss, damage or deterioration; or

(c) the relevant Plant and Materials:
  (i) are those listed in the Appendix to Tender for payment when delivered to the Site, and
  (ii) have been delivered to and are properly stored on the Site, are protected against loss, damage or deterioration, and appear to be in accordance with the Contract.

The additional amount to be certified shall be the equivalent of eighty percent of the Engineer's determination of the cost of the Plant and Materials (including delivery to Site), taking account of the documents mentioned in this Sub-Clause and of the contract value of the Plant and Materials.

The currencies for this additional amount shall be the same as those in which payment will become due when the contract value is included under sub-paragraph (a) of Sub-Clause 14.3 [*Application for Interim Payment Certificates*]. At that time, the Payment Certificate shall include the applicable reduction which shall be equivalent to, and in the same currencies and proportions as, this additional amount for the relevant Plant and Materials.

It is normal practice for the Employer to make interim payments for Plant and Materials that have been allocated to the Works but which are not yet incorporated into the Works. The Appendix to Tender has provision for the Employer to list the Plant and Materials for which payment will be made, either when they have been shipped to the Country, or when they have been delivered to the Site.

If payment is to be made for Plant and Materials that have been shipped to the Country then the Contractor must provide a bank guarantee for the amount due. The guarantee must be similar to the Advance Payment Guarantee and approved by the Engineer. The amounts to be paid and the necessary supporting documents are described at Sub-Clause 14.5.

14.6 Issue of Interim Payment Certificates

No amount will be certified or paid until the Employer has received and approved the Performance Security. Thereafter, the Engineer shall, within 28 days after receiving a Statement and supporting documents, issue to the Employer an Interim Payment Certificate which shall state the amount which the Engineer fairly determines to be due, with supporting particulars.

However, prior to issuing the Taking-Over Certificate for the Works, the Engineer shall not be bound to issue an Interim Payment Certificate in an amount which would (after retention and other deductions) be less than the minimum amount of Interim Payment Certificates (if any) stated in the Appendix to Tender. In this event, the Engineer shall give notice to the Contractor accordingly.

An Interim Payment Certificate shall not be withheld for any other reason, although:

(a)   if any thing supplied or work done by the Contractor is not in accordance with the Contract, the cost of rectification or replacement may be withheld until rectification or replacement has been completed; and/or

(b)   if the Contractor was or is failing to perform any work or obligation in accordance with the Contract, and had been so notified by the Engineer, the value of this work or obligation may be withheld until the work or obligation has been performed.

The Engineer may in any Payment Certificate make any correction or modification that should properly be made to any previous Payment Certificate. A Payment Certificate shall not be deemed to indicate the Engineer's acceptance, approval, consent or satisfaction.

The Engineer must decide the amount which is due to be paid to the Contractor and issue a certificate, including supporting particulars, within 28 days after receiving the Contractor's Statement. The calculation of the sum due must be made strictly in accordance with the provisions of the Contract, including the provisions at Sub-Clause 14.6(a) and (b). Under Sub-Clause 14.6 the Engineer 'fairly determines' the amount. If the Contractor is not satisfied with the figure he can give notice under Sub-Clause 20.1.

If the Engineer fails to issue the Interim Payment Certificate the Contractor may give 21 days' notice and then suspend or reduce the rate of work, under Sub-Clause 16.1. If the Engineer has still failed to issue the Interim Payment Certificate after 56 days from receipt of the Contractor's Statement and supporting documents then the Contractor may terminate the Contract under Sub-Clause 16.2(b). These provisions emphasise the importance of regular interim payments to enable the Contractor to carry out his obligations. If the problem is caused by the Engineer, rather than the Employer, then the Employer could offer to make an interim payment, of an agreed amount, while the problem is rectified.

14.7   Payment
The Employer shall pay to the Contractor:

(a) the first instalment of the advance payment within 42 days after issuing the Letter of Acceptance or within 21 days after receiving the documents in accordance with Sub-Clause 4.2 [*Performance Security*] and Sub-Clause 14.2 [*Advance Payment*], whichever is later;

(b) the amount certified in each Interim Payment Certificate within 56 days after the Engineer receives the Statement and supporting documents; and

(c) the amount certified in the Final Payment Certificate within 56 days after the Employer receives this Payment Certificate.

Payment of the amount due in each currency shall be made into the bank account, nominated by the Contractor, in the payment country (for this currency) specified in the Contract.

Interim payments must be made within 56 days after the Engineer receives the Contractor's Statement and supporting documents. For the Final Payment the 56 day period for payment starts when the Employer receives the Payment Certificate. The Employer has the benefit of the cash flow estimates provided under Sub-Clause 14.4, together with advice from the Engineer, so it should be possible for these periods to be reduced in the Particular Conditions. Anything which can be done to improve the Contractor's cash flow should result in lower tenders and savings in the overall project cost.

The Employer's obligation is to pay the sum which is certified by the Engineer, without any deductions. If the Employer is entitled to any deduction or payment from the Contractor then the amount will have been claimed under Sub-Clause 2.5, subject to the exceptions listed. The total of any deductions will then be listed in the Engineer's Certificate and should have been included in the Contractor's Statement under Sub-Clause 14.3(f). If the Employer has a query concerning the Engineer's Interim Payment Certificate then the payment must still be made and any correction included in the next month's certificate.

If the Employer fails to comply with these requirements then the Contractor may give 21 days' notice and then suspend or reduce the rate of work under Sub-Clause 16.1. The Contractor may terminate the Contract if payment is not received within 42 days of the due date under Sub-Clause 16.2(c).

14.8   Delayed Payment
If the Contractor does not receive payment in accordance with Sub-Clause 14.7 [*Payment*], the Contractor shall be entitled to receive

financing charges compounded monthly on the amount unpaid during the period of delay. This period shall be deemed to commence on the date for payment specified in Sub-Clause 14.7 [*Payment*], irrespective (in the case of its sub-paragraph (b)) of the date on which any Interim Payment Certificate is issued.

Unless otherwise stated in the Particular Conditions, these financing charges shall be calculated at the annual rate of three percentage points above the discount rate of the central bank in the country of the currency of payment, and shall be paid in such currency.

The Contractor shall be entitled to this payment without formal notice or certification, and without prejudice to any other right or remedy.

Sub-Clause 14.8 gives the procedures for calculating the financing charges which are due to the Contractor if a payment is not made by the due date.

The financing charges will be included in the Contractor's Statements and the Payment Certificates under Sub-Clause 14.3(f) and so are carried forward if the next Certificate is not paid. Financing charges are damages – the reimbursement of money which has been deemed to be spent as a consequence of a breach of Contract – but should still be checked against the provisions of the applicable law.

14.9 (RB)   Payment of Retention Money

When the Taking-Over Certificate has been issued for the Works, the first half of the Retention Money shall be certified by the Engineer for payment to the Contractor. If a Taking-Over Certificate is issued for a Section or part of the Works, a proportion of the Retention Money shall be certified and paid. This proportion shall be two-fifths (40%) of the proportion calculated by dividing the estimated contract value of the Section or part, by the estimated final Contract Price.

Promptly after the latest of the expiry dates of the Defects Notification Periods, the outstanding balance of the Retention Money shall be certified by the Engineer for payment to the Contractor. If a Taking-Over Certificate was issued for a Section, a proportion of the second half of the Retention Money shall be certified and paid promptly after the expiry date of the Defects Notification Period for the Section. This proportion shall be two-fifths (40%) of the proportion calculated by dividing the estimated contract value of the Section by the estimated final Contract Price.

However, if any work remains to be executed under Clause 11 [*Defects Liability*], the Engineer shall be entitled to withhold certification of the estimated cost of this work until it has been executed.

When calculating these proportions, no account shall be taken of any adjustments under Sub-Clause 13.7 [*Adjustments for Changes in Legislation*] and Sub-Clause 13.8 [*Adjustments for Changes in Cost*].

In the Yellow Book Sub-Clause 14.9 is replaced by the following.

14.9 (YB)   Payment of Retention Money

When the Taking-Over Certificate has been issued for the Works, and the Works have passed all specified tests (including the Tests after Completion, if any), the first half of the Retention Money shall be certified by the Engineer for payment to the Contractor. If a Taking-Over Certificate is issued for a Section, the relevant percentage of the first half of the Retention Money shall be certified and paid when the Section passes all tests.

Promptly after the latest of the expiry dates of the Defects Notification Periods, the outstanding balance of the Retention Money shall be certified by the Engineer for payment to the Contractor. If a Taking-Over Certificate was issued for a Section, the relevant percentage of the second half of the Retention Money shall be certified and paid promptly after the expiry date of the Defects Notification Period for the Section.

However, if any work remains to be executed under Clause 11 [*Defects Liability*] or Clause 12 [*Tests after Completion*], the Engineer shall be entitled to withhold certification of the estimated cost of this work until it has been executed.

The relevant percentage for each Section shall be the percentage value of the Section as stated in the Appendix to Tender. If the percentage value of a Section is not stated in the Appendix to Tender, no percentage of either half of the Retention Money shall be released under this Sub-Clause in respect of such Section.

Sub-Clause 14.9 (RB) gives the procedures for the Employer to pay Retention Money, which has been deducted from Interim Payment Certificates as Sub-Clause 14.3(c). The first half of the Retention Money is to be certified by the Engineer when the Taking-Over Certificate has been issued for the Works. For a Section or part of the Works, 40% of the proportion by value will be certified. No time periods are stated for the certification and payment and Sub-Clause 14.3(c) concerning the deduction of retention does not refer to the payment of retention. The Contractor should ensure that the retention is included in a Statement as soon as possible, not waiting for the Statement at Completion as Sub-Clause 14.10. It should then be possible for the Certificate and payment to be issued well within the periods of 28 and 56 days from the Statement.

The outstanding balance of the Retention Money is to be certified 'promptly' after the latest of the expiry dates of the Defects Notification Period, subject to a possible deduction for the estimated cost of any defects work under Clause 11 which has not been completed. The use of the word 'promptly' could cause problems but it surely implies a matter of a few days, rather than weeks. Again, it would be prudent for the Contractor to issue a request for payment, asking that the certificate will be issued and payment made well within the 28 and 56 day periods.

The FIDIC Guidance for the Preparation of Particular Conditions includes an example Sub-Clause for use if the Employer is prepared to agree to early release of all or part of the Retention Money against a bank guarantee. When the Retention Money reaches 60% of the limit in the Appendix to Tender the Employer makes a payment of 50% of the limit, against the bank guarantee. The 50% of the limit which is due when the Taking-Over Certificate is issued is paid at that time and the Guarantee continues in force until any defects have been corrected, as specified for the Performance Certificate.

When considering whether to accept a bank guarantee, or to reduce or even omit the requirement for Retention Money, the Employer should consider the cash flow benefits to the Contractor and the positive value of work on Site that has been executed but not yet paid for.

In the Yellow Book, the payment of the first half of the Retention Money is not due until the Works have passed the Tests after Completion. The timing of the Tests after Completion depends on the Employer being ready for the tests, which may not be until after the Employer has completed preparations and the Works have been occupied. The Contractor's cash flow will clearly suffer from any delay and the inclusion of a Retention Money Guarantee, as the example form at Annex F, must be recommended. This early release of Retention Money requires an additional Sub-Clause, as discussed for Sub-Clause 14.9 (RB).

Arrangements for the calculation of Retention Money in relation to a Section of the Works is different in the Yellow Book from the Red Book, due to the different method of valuing parts of the Works.

14.10   Statement at Completion

Within 84 days after receiving the Taking-Over Certificate for the Works, the Contractor shall submit to the Engineer six copies of a Statement at completion with supporting documents, in accordance with Sub-Clause 14.3 [*Application for Interim Payment Certificates*], showing:

(a) the value of all work done in accordance with the Contract up to the date stated in the Taking-Over Certificate for the Works;

(b) any further sums which the Contractor considers to be due; and

(c) an estimate of any other amounts which the Contractor considers will become due to him under the Contract. Estimated amounts shall be shown separately in this Statement at completion.

The Engineer shall then certify in accordance with Sub-Clause 14.6 [*Issue of Interim Payment Certificates*].

The Statement at completion can only be issued following the issue of the Taking-Over Certificate for all of the Works. Before the issue of this certificate, the Contractor has been able to submit Statements for Interim Payment Certificates. It is in the Contractor's interest to prepare the Statement in advance for issue well within the 84 day period.

The Statement at completion must include amounts or estimates for every payment for which the Contractor considers the Employer has a liability, including all claims and potential claims, or the Employer may reject liability under Sub-Clause 14.14(b). However, if the Contractor has followed the notices and procedures under Sub-Clause 20.1 this further submission would be a reminder and record rather than a new submission.

14.11   Application for Final Payment Certificate

Within 56 days after receiving the Performance Certificate, the Contractor shall submit, to the Engineer, six copies of a draft final statement with supporting documents showing in detail in a form approved by the Engineer:

(a)   the value of all work done in accordance with the Contract; and
(b)   any further sums which the Contractor considers to be due to him under the Contract or otherwise.

If the Engineer disagrees with or cannot verify any part of the draft final statement, the Contractor shall submit such further information as the Engineer may reasonably require and shall make such changes in the draft as may be agreed between them. The Contractor shall then prepare and submit to the Engineer the final statement as agreed. This agreed statement is referred to in these Conditions as the 'Final Statement'.

However if, following discussions between the Engineer and the Contractor and any changes to the draft final statement which are agreed, it becomes evident that a dispute exists, the Engineer shall deliver to the Employer (with a copy to the Contractor) an Interim Payment Certificate for the agreed parts of the draft final statement. Thereafter, if the dispute is finally resolved under Sub-Clause 20.4 [*Obtaining Dispute Adjudication Board's Decision*] or Sub-Clause 20.5 [*Amicable Settlement*], the Contractor shall then prepare and submit to the Employer (with a copy to the Engineer) a Final Statement.

Sub-Clauses 14.10 and 14.11 give the procedures for the Contractor to submit Statements and the Engineer to certify interim payments, following the issue of the Taking-Over Certificate and the Performance

Certificate. The Employer must make the interim payments within 56 days from the Contractor's Statement in accordance with Sub-Clause 14.7(b).

The Final Statement, following the Performance Certificate, is first submitted as a draft, which is discussed between the Contractor and the Engineer. If the draft statement is agreed then the Contractor submits a Final Statement. However, if there are matters which cannot be agreed they are considered under the Clause 20 disputes procedures. Any sums which have been agreed must be paid on an Interim Payment Certificate and the draft Final Statement remains open until the disputes are eventually resolved. By the time the agreed matters have been finalised it may be too late for the Employer to pay within 56 days from when the Engineer received the draft Final Statement. The Sub-Clause does not require the Contractor to submit a further interim Statement before the Engineer prepares this Interim Payment Certificate so the Contractor could be entitled to financing charges under Sub-Clause 14.8.

If the dispute is resolved by the DAB or by amicable settlement, then the Contractor must prepare a Final Statement to start the payment sequence. However, if the dispute is resolved by arbitration then any payment must be made on the Arbitration Tribunal's Award and additional Contract documentation is not necessary.

14.12   Discharge

When submitting the Final Statement, the Contractor shall submit a written discharge which confirms that the total of the Final Statement represents full and final settlement of all moneys due to the Contractor under or in connection with the Contract. This discharge may state that it becomes effective when the Contractor has received the Performance Security and the outstanding balance of this total, in which event the discharge shall be effective on such date.

Sub-Clause 14.12 requires the Contractor to include with the Final Statement confirmation that it covers all moneys due to him under or in connection with the Contract. The Final Statement must cover any claims that have been, or should have been, submitted. However, Sub-Clause 11.10 refers to the continuing liability for any obligations which have not been fulfilled at the issue of the Performance Certificate. Sub-Clause 14.14 also refers to the Employer's continuing liability under certain Clauses.

If parts of the draft Final Statement are eventually settled in arbitration then the Contractor does not seem to have to submit a Final Statement and hence would not submit a discharge. The submissions to the arbitration tribunal would normally cover any amounts which the Contractor considers to be due.

14.13   Issue of Final Payment Certificate

Within 28 days after receiving the Final Statement and written discharge in accordance with Sub-Clause 14.11 [*Application for Final Payment Certificate*] and Sub-Clause 14.12 [*Discharge*], the Engineer shall issue, to the Employer, the Final Payment Certificate which shall state:

(a)   the amount which is finally due; and
(b)   after giving credit to the Employer for all amounts previously paid by the Employer and for all sums to which the Employer is entitled, the balance (if any) due from the Employer to the Contractor or from the Contractor to the Employer, as the case may be.

If the Contractor has not applied for a Final Payment Certificate in accordance with Sub-Clause 14.11 [*Application for Final Payment Certificate*] and Sub-Clause 14.12 [*Discharge*], the Engineer shall request the Contractor to do so. If the Contractor fails to submit an application within a period of 28 days, the Engineer shall issue the Final Payment Certificate for such amount as he fairly determines to be due.

When the Final Statement has eventually been agreed between the Contractor and the Engineer, it is submitted to the Engineer together with the Sub-Clause 14.12 discharge.

Sub-Clause 14.13 gives the procedures for the Engineer to issue the Final Payment Certificate. If the Contractor does not make the proper application for the Final Payment Certificate then the Engineer issues a Certificate for the amount he 'fairly determines to be due'. Under this procedure the Contractor has not submitted a written discharge and the Engineer should demonstrate that all claims which have been received have been considered and dealt with in accordance with the Contract.

The Employer must pay the amount in the Final Payment Certificate within 56 days from receipt, in accordance with Sub-Clause 14.7(c).

14.14   Cessation of Employer's Liability

The Employer shall not be liable to the Contractor for any matter or thing under or in connection with the Contract or execution of the Works, except to the extent that the Contractor shall have included an amount expressly for it:

(a)   in the Final Statement and; also

(b)   (except for matters or things arising after the issue of the Taking-Over Certificate for the Works) in the Statement at completion described in Sub-Clause 14.10 [*Statement at Completion*].

However, this Sub-Clause shall not limit the Employer's liability under his indemnification obligations, or the Employer's liability in any case of fraud, deliberate default or reckless misconduct by the Employer.

Sub-Clause 14.14 refers to the Employer's liability 'for any matter or thing under or in connection with the Contract or execution of the Works'. If the Contractor is not satisfied with any valuation, the response to any claim, or anything else whatsoever related to the Contract, then he must ensure that the matter is mentioned in the Final Statement, together with an amount of money in compensation. The Employer can disclaim liability for any matter that is not mentioned and valued in the Final Statement.

The nearest equivalent Clause for cessation of the Contractor's liability is Sub-Clause 11.9 for the issue of the Performance Certificate. However, after the Performance Certificate has been issued, both Parties still remain liable for unfulfilled obligations, as Sub-Clause 11.10. For the Employer, Sub-Clause 11.10 appears to be superseded and the general liability presumably ceases with the Final Statement, except for the exceptions noted in Sub-Clause 14.14. Sub-Clause 14.14 must be considered in conjunction with any provisions in the governing law.

14.15   Currencies of Payment

The Contract Price shall be paid in the currency or currencies named in the Appendix to Tender. Unless otherwise stated in the Particular Conditions, if more than one currency is so named, payments shall be made as follows:

(a)   if the Accepted Contract Amount was expressed in Local Currency only:
  (i)   the proportions or amounts of the Local and Foreign Currencies, and the fixed rates of exchange to be used for calculating the payments, shall be as stated in the Appendix to Tender, except as otherwise agreed by both Parties;
  (ii) payments and deductions under Sub-Clause 13.5 [*Provisional Sums*] and Sub-Clause 13.7 [*Adjustments for Changes in Legislation*] shall be made in the applicable currencies and proportions; and
  (iii) other payments and deductions under sub-paragraphs (a) to (d) of Sub-Clause 14.3 [*Application for Interim Payment Certificates*] shall be made in the currencies and proportions specified in sub-paragraph (a)(i) above;

(b) payment of the damages specified in the Appendix to Tender shall be made in the currencies and proportions specified in the Appendix to Tender;

(c) other payments to the Employer by the Contractor shall be made in the currency in which the sum was expended by the Employer, or in such currency as may be agreed by both Parties;

(d) if any amount payable by the Contractor to the Employer in a particular currency exceeds the sum payable by the Employer to the Contractor in that currency, the Employer may recover the balance of this amount from the sums otherwise payable to the Contractor in other currencies; and

(e) if no rates of exchange are stated in the Appendix to Tender, they shall be those prevailing on the Base Date and determined by the central bank of the Country.

Sub-Clause 14.15 must be read together with the Appendix to Tender and the FIDIC form for the Letter of Tender, which are printed at the end of the Conditions of Contract and are reproduced in Appendix A4 of this book. These documents allow for different provisions for the currency of payment and the documents must be clear as to the precise provisions that will apply.

The FIDIC form for the Letter of Tender includes provision for the Contractor to insert the currency or currencies in which the Contract Price will be paid. This conforms to the first option in the Appendix to Tender. Alternatively, the Employer can stipulate the currency of payment in the Appendix to Tender, or the percentages of the Contract Price which will be paid in different currencies, together with the rates of exchange.

If only one currency is named in the Letter of Tender or the Appendix to Tender then all payments will be made in that currency. However, if the Letter of Acceptance gives the Accepted Contract Amount in the Local Currency, but the Letter of Tender or the Appendix to Tender allow for different currencies then the provisions of Sub-Clause 14.15(a) will apply. Sub-Clauses 14.15(b) to (e) will apply whenever the Letter of Tender or Appendix to Tender allow for more than one currency.

The Letter of Acceptance is generally written following some negotiations and any queries or problems concerning currencies for payment should be clarified and agreed at that stage.

If the parts of the Contract Price which are to be paid in different currencies are to be based on the Cost of different items, such as items of Plant, Materials or labour, then suitable provision, in sufficient detail to avoid misunderstanding, must be made in the Particular Conditions.

The provisions for the currencies of payment do not include any provision for changes in the rates of exchange. If rates of exchange are to be adjusted to allow for currency fluctuations then suitable provision must be included in the Particular Conditions.

The FIDIC Guidance for the Preparation of Particular Conditions includes an example Sub-Clause for a single-currency Contract, with all payments in Local Currency. The Local Currency is assumed to be fully convertible, with the Employer being liable for any additional Costs if the situation should change.

Chapter 25

Clause 15: Termination by Employer

Clause 15 describes the circumstances in which the Employer is entitled to terminate the Contract, the procedures that must be followed and the financial arrangements that will apply.

Termination is an extremely serious step, which inevitably causes hardship to both Parties and should not be invoked without considerable discussion and attempts to overcome any problems and rectify the situation. If the Contractor objects to the termination and a DAB or Arbitrator later decides that the Employer was not entitled to terminate then the financial consequences to the Employer would be substantial.

If the Employer does decide to terminate the Contract it is essential that he follows the correct procedures. The governing law may also have requirements in addition to, or which supersede, the Contract procedures.

Definitions at Sub-Clause 1.1 relevant to this Clause include:

1.1.2.9   DAB
1.1.6.4   Force Majeure
1.1.6.5   Laws
1.1.6.6   Performance Security.

15.1   Notice to Correct
If the Contractor fails to carry out any obligation under the Contract, the Engineer may by notice require the Contractor to make good the failure and to remedy it within a specified reasonable time.

When the Engineer writes a letter to the Contractor requiring him to make good a failure to carry out some obligation, it may refer to a relatively minor matter or it may be an obligation which is crucial to the success of the project. However, it could be the first step towards termination of the Contract.

A 'Notice to Correct' under Sub-Clause 15.1 is the starting point of one of the routes towards termination of the Contract by the Employer. To avoid possible disputes as to whether the termination procedure was followed correctly, any Notice to Correct should refer specifically to Sub-Clause 15.1. The issue of such a notice may be a sensible additional step in some of the alternative routes to termination, in order to empha- sise the seriousness of the situation as perceived by the Engineer and to give the Contractor a final warning as to the consequences of failure to comply with the particular obligation.

15.2   Termination by Employer
The Employer shall be entitled to terminate the Contract if the Contractor:

(a) fails to comply with Sub-Clause 4.2 [*Performance Security*] or with a notice under Sub-Clause 15.1 [*Notice to Correct*];

(b) abandons the Works or otherwise plainly demonstrates the intention not to continue performance of his obligations under the Contract;

(c) without reasonable excuse fails:
   (i)   to proceed with the Works in accordance with Clause 8 [*Commencement, Delays and Suspension*], or
   (ii) to comply with a notice issued under Sub-Clause 7.5 [*Rejection*] or Sub-Clause 7.6 [*Remedial Work*], within 28 days after receiving it;

(d) subcontracts the whole of the Works or assigns the Contract without the required agreement;

(e) becomes bankrupt or insolvent, goes into liquidation, has a receiving or administration order made against him, compounds with his creditors, or carries on business under a receiver, trustee or manager for the benefit of his creditors, or if any act is done or event occurs which (under applicable Laws) has a similar effect to any of these acts or events; or

(f) gives or offers to give (directly or indirectly) to any person any bribe, gift, gratuity, commission or other thing of value, as an inducement or reward:
   (i)   for doing or forbearing to do any action in relation to the Contract, or
   (ii) for showing or forbearing to show favour or disfavour to any person in relation to the Contract;

or if any of the Contractor's Personnel, agents or Subcontractors gives or offers to give (directly or indirectly) to any person any such inducement or reward as is described in this sub-paragraph (f). However, lawful inducements and rewards to Contractor's Personnel shall not entitle termination.

In any of these events or circumstances, the Employer may, upon giving 14 days' notice to the Contractor, terminate the Contract and expel the Contractor from the Site. However, in the case of sub-paragraph (e) or (f), the Employer may by notice terminate the Contract immediately.

The Employer's election to terminate the Contract shall not prejudice any other rights of the Employer, under the Contract or otherwise.

The Contractor shall then leave the Site and deliver any required Goods, all Contractor's Documents, and other design documents made by or for him, to the Engineer. However, the Contractor shall use his best efforts to comply immediately with any reasonable instructions included in the notice (i) for the assignment of any subcontract, and (ii) for the protection of life or property or for the safety of the Works.

After termination, the Employer may complete the Works and/or arrange for any other entities to do so. The Employer and these entities may then use any Goods, Contractor's Documents and other design documents made by or on behalf of the Contractor.

The Employer shall then give notice that the Contractor's Equipment and Temporary Works will be released to the Contractor at or near the Site. The Contractor shall promptly arrange their removal, at the risk and cost of the Contractor. However, if by this time the Contractor has failed to make a payment due to the Employer, these items may be sold by the Employer in order to recover this payment. Any balance of the proceeds shall then be paid to the Contractor.

The Employer is entitled to terminate the Contract either because of some default by the Contractor, as listed in this Sub-Clause, or for convenience, under Sub-Clause 15.5. Sub-Clause 19.6 also includes provision for termination, by either Party, if the execution of substantially all of the Works in progress is prevented by Force Majeure for a continuous period of 84 days. The provisions are very wide and include actions by a Subcontractor who may have acted without the knowledge or consent of the Contractor. In these circumstances a provision to require the Contractor to terminate the subcontract would seem to be more appropriate than termination of the Contract.

The circumstances described at subparagraphs (a) to (d) refer to failures to carry out his obligations in accordance with specific Clauses of the Contract. These could include failure to carry out some minor obligation which would seem to be an excessively harsh remedy for a minor default. Other Sub-Clauses, such as 11.4(c), for failure to remedy defects, also entitle the Employer to terminate all or part of the Contract and in these circumstances the Employer should also follow the Clause 15 procedures, together with any requirements of the particular Sub-Clause.

These procedures require the Employer, as distinct from the Engineer, to give 14 days' notice of the termination. This gives a final opportunity for the Contractor to comply with the relevant obligation or to discuss the matter with the Engineer or direct with the Employer.

Subparagraphs (e) and (f) refer to insolvency and bribery, which entitle the Employer to give notice terminating the Contract immediately. If the

Employer intends to terminate the Contract under any of these provisions he must be careful to ensure that there is legally acceptable proof of the circumstances. Whilst the insolvency or similar situation under subparagraph (e) should be capable of being proved, the bribery circumstances under subparagraph (f) could be very difficult to prove unless there has been a criminal prosecution. Even an admission of guilt may not be sufficient, if it is denied by the Contractor and not supported by independent evidence which would be acceptable in a Court of Law.

The termination notice is required to include any instructions concerning safety and the assignment of subcontracts and should also include any other instructions concerning the Contractor's departure from the Site and the valuation of the Works. Any of the termination provisions should be checked against the governing law before being invoked.

15.3   Valuation at Date of Termination

As soon as practicable after a notice of termination under Sub-Clause 15.2 [*Termination by Employer*] has taken effect, the Engineer shall proceed in accordance with Sub-Clause 3.5 [*Determinations*] to agree or determine the value of the Works, Goods and Contractor's Documents, and any other sums due to the Contractor for work executed in accordance with the Contract.

The Engineer will agree or determine the sums due to the Contractor 'as soon as practicable' after the notice of termination. Whilst the agreement of the value of some items may require lengthy negotiations, any measurement of work executed or agreement of Materials on Site must be carried out immediately, preferably during the period between the notice and the Contractor's departure from the Site.

15.4   Payment after Termination

After a notice of termination under Sub-Clause 15.2 [*Termination by Employer*] has taken effect, the Employer may:

(a)   proceed in accordance with Sub-Clause 2.5 [*Employer's Claims*];

(b)   withhold further payments to the Contractor until the costs of execution, completion and remedying of any defects, damages for delay in completion (if any), and all other costs incurred by the Employer, have been established; and/or

(c)   recover from the Contractor any losses and damages incurred by the Employer and any extra costs of completing the Works, after allowing for any sum due to the Contractor under Sub-Clause 15.3 [*Valuation at Date of Termination*]. After recovering any such losses, damages and extra costs, the Employer shall pay any balance to the Contractor.

Subparagraphs (a) to (c) refer to three procedures whereby the Employer may recover money from the Contractor. However, the word 'may' in the opening sentence of this Sub-Clause could lead to confusion. The choice of (a), (b) and/or (c) will depend on the circumstances and the Employer must follow the Contract procedures.

Subparagraphs (a) and (b) refer to procedures for the correction of problems caused by the Contractor whose Contract has been terminated. Subparagraph (a) requires that claims which would be covered by Sub-Clause 2.5 are to follow the procedure of Sub-Clause 2.5. Similarly claims under (b) arose from actions by this Contractor and should, as far as is practical, follow the same procedure.

The procedure for subparagraph (c) is more difficult. If the termination occurs early in the project, or there is a delay before a new Contractor can start on Site, the extra Costs incurred by the Employer could be substantial and may be disputed by the Contractor. Any such claim by the Employer would also seem to be covered by Sub-Clause 2.5. The Employer must ensure that all the necessary records are kept to substantiate any such claim.

Any dispute which arises under the termination procedure could be referred to the DAB. The final paragraph of Sub-Clause 20.2 (RB) states that the appointment of the full term DAB expires when it has given its decision on the last dispute which has been referred to it or when the discharge as Sub-Clause 14.12 has become effective. The Sub-Clause 14.12 discharge depends on the issue of the Contractor's Final Statement. It is possible that this will not be agreed until after the Works have been completed by the replacement Contractor and the Employer has established any extra Costs that he has incurred. Under Sub-Clause 20.2 (YB) for an ad hoc DAB the appointment of the DAB expires when it has given its decision on the dispute for which it was appointed.

15.5 Employer's Entitlement to Termination

The Employer shall be entitled to terminate the Contract, at any time for the Employer's convenience, by giving notice of such termination to the Contractor. The termination shall take effect 28 days after the later of the dates on which the Contractor receives this notice or the Employer returns the Performance Security. The Employer shall not terminate the Contract under this Sub-Clause in order to execute the Works himself or to arrange for the Works to be executed by another contractor.

After this termination, the Contractor shall proceed in accordance with Sub-Clause 16.3 [*Cessation of Work and Removal of Contractor's*

Equipment] and shall be paid in accordance with Sub-Clause 19.6 [*Optional Termination, Payment and Release*].

The Employer is entitled to terminate the Contract at any time for his own convenience, i.e. without needing to show any default by the Contractor or other justification. However, the consequences of such action may be against the interests of the Employer in that the Employer is not permitted to complete the Works. However, there can be circumstances when the Employer no longer requires the project and so termination is necessary.

For this termination for convenience, the financial Cost to the Employer follows the Force Majeure termination procedure at Sub-Clause 19.6, which is more beneficial to the Contractor than Sub-Clause 15.4. However, it does not include compensation for loss of profit, which seems unreasonable when the Employer has decided on termination for his own convenience and not due to any default by the Contractor.

Chapter 26

Clause 16: Suspension and Termination by Contractor

Payment by the Employer to the Contractor, in accordance with the provisions of the Contract, is an essential requirement of any construction contract. This obligation on the Employer is clearly stated in the FIDIC Contract Agreement and the procedures for payment are given at Clause 14. When a Contractor prepares his Tender he will base his calculations on the assumption that the money he pays out, for labour and Materials, will be reimbursed in accordance with the provisions of the Contract. If this does not happen then the Contractor may have no alternative but to stop work. Clause 16 enables the Contractor to reduce the rate of work, suspend all work or terminate the Contract if the Employer fails to comply with his obligations for payment or to provide the information concerning his financial arrangements as required by Sub-Clause 2.4.

Definitions at Sub-Clause 1.1 relevant to this Clause include:

1.1.4.9   Payment Certificate
1.1.5.1   Contractor's Equipment
1.1.6.4   Force Majeure
1.1.6.6   Performance Security.

16.1   Contractor's Entitlement to Suspend Work

If the Engineer fails to certify in accordance with Sub-Clause 14.6 [*Issue of Interim Payment Certificates*] or the Employer fails to comply with Sub-Clause 2.4 [*Employer's Financial Arrangements*] or Sub-Clause 14.7 [*Payment*], the Contractor may, after giving not less than 21 days' notice to the Employer, suspend work (or reduce the rate of work) unless and until the Contractor has received the Payment Certificate, reasonable evidence or payment, as the case may be and as described in the notice.

The Contractor's action shall not prejudice his entitlements to financing charges under Sub-Clause 14.8 [*Delayed Payment*] and to termination under Sub-Clause 16.2 [*Termination by Contractor*].

If the Contractor subsequently receives such Payment Certificate, evidence or payment (as described in the relevant Sub-Clause and in the above notice) before giving a notice of termination, the Contractor shall resume normal working as soon as is reasonably practicable.

If the Contractor suffers delay and/or incurs Cost as a result of suspending work (or reducing the rate of work) in accordance with this Sub-Clause, the Contractor shall give notice to the Engineer and shall be entitled subject to Sub-Clause 20.1 [*Contractor's Claims*] to:

(a) an extension of time for any such delay, if completion is or will be delayed, under Sub-Clause 8.4 [*Extension of Time for Completion*]; and

(b) payment of any such Cost plus reasonable profit, which shall be included in the Contract Price.

After receiving this notice, the Engineer shall proceed in accordance with Sub-Clause 3.5 [*Determinations*] to agree or determine these matters.

The Contractor is entitled to reduce the rate of work or suspend work if:

- the Employer fails to provide information concerning his financial arrangements as Sub-Clause 2.4, or
- the Engineer fails to issue an Interim Payment Certificate as Sub-Clause 14.6, or
- the Employer fails to pay the Contractor the sum due as Sub-Clause 14.7.

If the Contractor wishes to invoke the provisions of this Sub-Clause he must give at least 21 days' notice and describe the information, Certificate or payment which he has not received. If the information, Certificate or payment is not received during the notice period then the Contractor can reduce or suspend work, but must resume normal working 'as soon as is reasonably practicable' if the information, Certificate or payment is received before he gives a notice of termination under Sub-Clause 16.2.

When the Contractor takes action to reduce or suspend work he will inevitably incur additional Costs and delay, which may delay completion. The Contractor should then give notice under Sub-Clause 16.1 and follow the procedures of Sub-Clauses 8.4 and 20.1. The Engineer will endeavour to reach agreement or make a determination in accordance with Sub-Clause 3.5. The Contractor's Costs would include the Cost of resuming work and he is also entitled to profit on those Costs.

16.2 Termination by Contractor

The Contractor shall be entitled to terminate the Contract if:

(a) the Contractor does not receive the reasonable evidence within 42 days after giving notice under Sub-Clause 16.1 [*Contractor's Entitlement to Suspend Work*] in respect of a failure to comply with Sub-Clause 2.4 [*Employer's Financial Arrangements*];

(b) the Engineer fails, within 56 days after receiving a Statement and supporting documents, to issue the relevant Payment Certificate;

(c) the Contractor does not receive the amount due under an Interim Payment Certificate within 42 days after the expiry of the time stated in Sub-Clause 14.7 [*Payment*] within which payment is to be made (except for deductions in accordance with Sub-Clause 2.5 [*Employer's Claims*]);

(d) the Employer substantially fails to perform his obligations under the Contract;

(e) the Employer fails to comply with Sub-Clause 1.6 [*Contract Agreement*] or Sub-Clause 1.7 [*Assignment*];

(f) a prolonged suspension affects the whole of the Works as described in Sub-Clause 8.11 [*Prolonged Suspension*]; or

(g) the Employer becomes bankrupt or insolvent, goes into liquidation, has a receiving or administration order made against him, compounds with his creditors, or carries on business under a receiver, trustee or manager for the benefit of his creditors, or if any act is done or event occurs which (under applicable Laws) has a similar effect to any of these acts or events.

In any of these events or circumstances, the Contractor may, upon giving 14 days' notice to the Employer, terminate the Contract. However, in the case of subparagraph (f) or (g), the Contractor may by notice terminate the Contract immediately.

The Contractor's election to terminate the Contract shall not prejudice any other rights of the Contractor, under the Contract or otherwise.

Sub-Clause 16.2 lists the reasons that would entitle the Contractor to terminate the Contract, including failure to comply with the requirements of Sub-Clause 16.1. The Contractor must give 14 days' notice before he terminates the Contract except that he may terminate immediately in case of prolonged suspension as Sub-Clause 8.11 or the Employer becoming bankrupt or having any of the problems listed at paragraph (g) of this Sub-Clause. The Contractor may also terminate the Contract in the event of prolonged Force Majeure as Sub-Clause 19.6.

Before taking action the Contractor must ensure that he has legally acceptable proof that the Employer has failed to meet the relevant obligation. In the examples such as failure to make payment, this should be easy to establish. However, for a provision such as (d) 'the Employer substantially fails to perform his obligations under the Contract' it will be more difficult to establish proof that would satisfy the Dispute Adjudication Board or Arbitration Tribunal if the Employer should dispute the termination. Any significant failure on the part of the Employer would presumably have been the subject of correspondence and probably have already resulted in claims under other Clauses of the Contract.

16.3   Cessation of Work and Removal of Contractor's Equipment

After a notice of termination under Sub-Clause 15.5 [*Employer's Entitlement to Termination*], Sub-Clause 16.2 [*Termination by Contractor*] or Sub-Clause 19.6 [*Optional Termination, Payment and Release*] has taken effect, the Contractor shall promptly:

(a)   cease all further work, except for such work as may have been instructed by the Engineer for the protection of life or property or for the safety of the Works;

(b)   hand over Contractor's Documents, Plant, Materials and other work, for which the Contractor has received payment; and

(c)   remove all other Goods from the Site, except as necessary for safety, and leave the Site.

This Sub-Clause gives the requirements for the Contractor to leave the Site and applies to Sub-Clauses 15.5 and 19.6 as well as to Sub-Clause 16.2.

16.4   Payment on Termination

After a notice of termination under Sub-Clause 16.2 [*Termination by Contractor*] has taken effect, the Employer shall promptly:

(a)   return the Performance Security to the Contractor;

(b)   pay the Contractor in accordance with Sub-Clause 19.6 [*Optional Termination, Payment and Release*]; and

(c)   pay to the Contractor the amount of any loss of profit or other loss or damage sustained by the Contractor as a result of this termination.

Under Sub-Clause 16.2 the termination is caused by failure by the Employer, so the Contractor is entitled to receive back his Performance Security and receive loss of profit and other losses or damage in addition to payment as Sub-Clause 19.6.

Chapter 27

Clause 17: Risk and Responsibility

The FIDIC form for the Contract Agreement states clearly that the Contractor is responsible for the execution and completion of the Works and will remedy any defects in the Works. In return, the Employer will pay the Contract Price to the Contractor. Clause 17 refers to risks and responsibilities for which one Party indemnifies the other Party against losses and some additional risks for which the Employer accepts responsibility for the Cost of repairing any damage to the Works. These are not all-inclusive lists and must be considered in conjunction with the risks and responsibilities stated or implied in other clauses of the Contract.

Clause 17 also contains an important Sub-Clause which limits the liability of the Parties for consequential loss and also limits the total liability of the Contractor.

The legal meaning of the phrase 'indemnify and hold harmless' should be checked under the governing law.

Definitions at Sub-Clause 1.1 which are relevant to this Clause include:

1.1.2.6   Employer's Personnel
1.1.2.7   Contractor's Personnel
1.1.5.2   Goods
1.1.5.8   Works
1.1.6.1   Contractor's Documents
1.1.6.4   Force Majeure
1.1.6.8   Unforeseeable.

17.1   Indemnities
The Contractor shall indemnify and hold harmless the Employer, the Employer's Personnel, and their respective agents, against and from all claims, damages, losses and expenses (including legal fees and expenses) in respect of:

(a)   bodily injury, sickness, disease or death, of any person whatsoever arising out of or in the course of or by reason of the Contractor's design (if any), the execution and completion of the Works and the remedying of any defects, unless attributable to any negligence, wilful act or breach of the Contract by the Employer, the Employer's Personnel, or any of their respective agents; and

(b) damage to or loss of any property, real or personal (other than the Works), to the extent that such damage or loss:

(i)   arises out of or in the course of or by reason of the Contractor's design (if any), the execution and completion of the Works and the remedying of any defects, and

(ii) is attributable to any negligence, wilful act or breach of the Contract by the Contractor, the Contractor's Personnel, their respective agents, or anyone directly or indirectly employed by any of them.

The Employer shall indemnify and hold harmless the Contractor, the Contractor's Personnel, and their respective agents, against and from all claims, damages, losses and expenses (including legal fees and expenses) in respect of (1) bodily injury, sickness, disease or death, which is attributable to any negligence, wilful act or breach of the Contract by the Employer, the Employer's Personnel, or any of their respective agents, and (2) the matters for which liability may be excluded from insurance cover, as described in sub-paragraphs (d)(i), (ii) and (iii) of Sub-Clause 18.3 [*Insurance Against Injury to Persons and Damage to Property*].

Sub-Clause 17.1 includes separate indemnities from the Contractor and the Employer. The indemnities cover similar losses, which are different due to the different roles of the Parties. Both indemnities cover the other Party's personnel as well as that Party itself. This is a considerable extension of the normal contractual obligations to the other Party to the Contract. Employer's Personnel includes anyone who has been notified to the Contractor. It is important that any specialist advisers or other visitors to Site are notified to the Contractor so as to be covered by the indemnity. Contractor's Personnel includes employees of Subcontractors and 'any other personnel assisting the Contractor in the execution of the Works', but the names of the individuals do not have to be notified to the Engineer.

These indemnities must be considered in conjunction with the insurance provisions at Clause 18 and cover losses that may be excluded from the insurance cover. The indemnities must also be considered together with the indemnities at other Sub-Clauses, such as:

1.13 failure to give notices required by Law and comply with regulations;

4.2   claims under Performance Security;

4.14 interference with the convenience of the public;

4.16   claims from transport of Goods;

5.2   objection to nominated Subcontractor;

17.5   intellectual and industrial property rights.

17.2   Contractor's Care of the Works

The Contractor shall take full responsibility for the care of the Works and Goods from the Commencement Date until the Taking-Over Certificate is issued (or is deemed to be issued under Sub-Clause 10.1 [*Taking Over of the Works and Sections*]) for the Works, when responsibility for the care of the Works shall pass to the Employer. If a Taking-Over Certificate is issued (or is so deemed to be issued) for any Section or part of the Works, responsibility for the care of the Section or part shall then pass to the Employer.

After responsibility has accordingly passed to the Employer, the Contractor shall take responsibility for the care of any work which is outstanding on the date stated in a Taking-Over Certificate, until this outstanding work has been completed.

If any loss or damage happens to the Works, Goods or Contractor's Documents during the period when the Contractor is responsible for their care, from any cause not listed in Sub-Clause 17.3 [*Employer's Risks*], the Contractor shall rectify the loss or damage at the Contractor's risk and cost, so that the Works, Goods and Contractor's Documents conform with the Contract.

The Contractor shall be liable for any loss or damage caused by any actions performed by the Contractor after a Taking-Over Certificate has been issued. The Contractor shall also be liable for any loss or damage which occurs after a Taking-Over Certificate has been issued and which arose from a previous event for which the Contractor was liable.

The Contractor's responsibility is not limited by the extent of the insurance cover which is required by Clause 18.

17.3   Employer's Risks

The risks referred to in Sub-Clause 17.4 below are:

(a) war, hostilities (whether war be declared or not), invasion, act of foreign enemies;

(b) rebellion, terrorism, revolution, insurrection, military or usurped power, or civil war, within the Country;

(c) riot, commotion or disorder within the Country by persons other than the Contractor's Personnel and other employees of the Contractor and Subcontractors;

(d) munitions of war, explosive materials, ionising radiation or contamination by radio-activity, within the Country, except as may be attributable to the Contractor's use of such munitions, explosives, radiation or radio-activity;

(e) pressure waves caused by aircraft or other aerial devices travelling at sonic or supersonic speeds;

(f) use or occupation by the Employer of any part of the Permanent Works, except as may be specified in the Contract;

(g) design of any part of the Works by the Employer's Personnel or by others for whom the Employer is responsible; and

(h) any operation of the forces of nature which is Unforeseeable or against which an experienced contractor could not reasonably have been expected to have taken adequate preventative precautions.

In the Yellow Book the words 'if any' are added after 'responsible' in sub-paragraph (g). The list of Employer's risks includes the items listed at Sub-Clause 19.1 as constituting Force Majeure with the following changes and additions:

(a) no change;

(b) the Employer's risks are restricted to actions within the Country;

(c) the Employer's risks are restricted to actions within the Country and do not include strikes or lockouts;

(d) the Employer's risks are restricted to actions within the Country;

(e) the Employer's risks are not included under Force Majeure;

(f) the Employer's risks are not included under Force Majeure;

(g) the Employer's risks are not included under Force Majeure;

(h) covers similar situations to the Force Majeure natural catastrophes, but is both more general and more restrictive.

Items (f) and (g) are situations for which the Employer must take responsibility. For some other items a shared responsibility might be considered more appropriate. However, if the Employer is local and the Contractor is from overseas then it might be appropriate for the Employer to accept the risk. The provision of insurance must also be considered.

17.4 Consequences of Employer's Risks

If and to the extent that any of the risks listed in Sub-Clause 17.3 above results in loss or damage to the Works, Goods or Contractor's Documents, the Contractor shall promptly give notice to the Engineer and shall rectify this loss or damage to the extent required by the Engineer.

If the Contractor suffers delay and/or incurs Cost from rectifying this loss or damage, the Contractor shall give a further notice to the Engineer and shall be entitled subject to Sub-Clause 20.1 [*Contractor's Claims*] to:

(a) an extension of time for any such delay, if completion is or will be delayed, under Sub-Clause 8.4 [*Extension of Time for Completion*]; and

(b) payment of any such Cost, which shall be included in the Contract Price. In the case of sub-paragraphs (f) and (g) of Sub-Clause 17.3 [*Employer's Risks*], reasonable profit on the Cost shall also be included.

After receiving this further notice, the Engineer shall proceed in accordance with Sub-Clause 3.5 [*Determinations*] to agree or determine these matters.

Some of the items listed at Sub-Clause 17.3 are similar to events which are noted elsewhere in the Contract as giving justification for a claim by the Contractor. Any claims should always be considered together with the provisions for Force Majeure at Clause 19. The distinction is that the Employer's risk is only for rectifying the loss or damage which has occurred to the Works, Goods or Contractor's Documents. It does not cover other Costs that may have been incurred by the Contractor. When damage occurs the Contractor must give the usual notices to the Engineer but is only required to rectify the loss or damage to the extent which is required by the Engineer.

17.5   Intellectual and Industrial Property Rights

In this Sub-Clause, 'infringement' means an infringement (or alleged infringement) of any patent, registered design, copyright, trade mark, trade name, trade secret or other intellectual or industrial property right relating to the Works; and 'claim' means a claim (or proceedings pursuing a claim) alleging an infringement.

Whenever a Party does not give notice to the other Party of any claim within 28 days of receiving the claim, the first Party shall be deemed to have waived any right to indemnity under this Sub-Clause.

The Employer shall indemnify and hold the Contractor harmless against and from any claim alleging an infringement which is or was:

(a) an unavoidable result of the Contractor's compliance with the Contract; or

(b) a result of any Works being used by the Employer:

(i)   for a purpose other than that indicated by, or reasonably to be inferred from, the Contract, or

(ii) in conjunction with any thing not supplied by the Contractor, unless such use was disclosed to the Contractor prior to the Base Date or is stated in the Contract.

The Contractor shall indemnify and hold the Employer harmless against and from any other claim which arises out of or in relation to (i) the manufacture, use, sale or import of any Goods, or (ii) any design for which the Contractor is responsible.

If a Party is entitled to be indemnified under this Sub-Clause, the indemnifying Party may (at its cost) conduct negotiations for the settlement of the claim, and any litigation or arbitration which may arise from it. The other Party shall, at the request and cost of the indemnifying Party, assist in contesting the claim. This other Party (and its Personnel) shall not make any admission which might be prejudicial to the indemnifying Party, unless the indemnifying Party failed to take over the conduct of any negotiations, litigation or arbitration upon being requested to do so by such other Party.

In the Yellow Book the word 'Contract' in sub-paragraph (a) is replaced by 'Employer's Requirements' and the fourth paragraph is replaced by:

The Contractor shall indemnify and hold the Employer harmless against and from any other claim which arises out of or in relation to (i) the Contractor's design, manufacture, construction or execution of the Works, (ii) the use of Contractor's Equipment, or (iii) the proper use of the Works.

Sub-Clause 17.5 includes separate indemnities from the Employer and the Contractor. The indemnities cover claims which are made against the other Party by someone who alleges that their rights have been infringed. Unlike Sub-Clause 17.1, these indemnities do not include legal fees and expenses of the innocent Party. The details differ in that the roles of the Parties, and hence the details of possible claims, are different.

In order to exercise the right to this indemnity, notice must be given within 28 days of receiving the claim from the person who alleges infringement. Notice should be given at the earliest possible date and failure to give prompt notice of the claim might restrict the ability of the indemnifying Party to defend the claim.

17.6   Limitation of Liability

Neither Party shall be liable to the other Party for loss of use of any Works, loss of profit, loss of any contract or for any indirect or consequential loss or damage which may be suffered by the other Party in connection with the Contract, other than under Sub-Clause 16.4 [*Payment on Termination*] and Sub-Clause 17.1 [*Indemnities*].

The total liability of the Contractor to the Employer, under or in connection with the Contract other than under Sub-Clause 4.19 [*Electricity, Water and Gas*], Sub-Clause 4.20 [*Employer's Equipment and Free-Issue*

Material], Sub-Clause 17.1 [*Indemnities*] and Sub-Clause 17.5 [*Intellectual and Industrial Property Rights*], shall not exceed the sum stated in the Particular Conditions or (if a sum is not so stated) the Accepted Contract Amount.

This Sub-Clause shall not limit liability in any case of fraud, deliberate default or reckless misconduct by the defaulting Party.

Sub-Clause 17.6 removes any liability of either Party to the other for losses other than for direct Costs, except for indemnities under Sub-Clause 17.1 and the Contractor's losses as Sub-Clause 16.4(c) for losses on termination following default by the Employer.

The Contractor's total liability to the Employer is restricted to the Accepted Contract Amount or the sum stated in the Particular Conditions, except under the Sub-Clauses listed. There is no similar limitation on the Employer's liability.

Both Parties' liability for fraud and certain other causes remains in accordance with the applicable law and is not limited by this Sub-Clause. The meaning and enforcement of this Sub-Clause could be controversial and will depend on any relevant provisions in the applicable law.

Chapter 28

Clause 18: Insurance

Clause 18 covers the requirements for construction insurances for the Works and Contractor's Equipment, injury to persons, damage to property and for the Contractor's Personnel.

The arrangement of Sub-Clauses has changed completely from the previous FIDIC Contracts. Whilst the basic requirements are similar, many of the details have changed and policies which met the requirements of the previous Conditions will need to be checked and modified to meet the new requirements.

The FIDIC Contracts Guide acknowledges that all the insurance cover described in this Clause may not be available. The available cover will depend on the type of Works and the Country in which the cover is being sought. It is therefore essential that the Employer checks on the available cover when preparing the Particular Conditions. Specialist advice from an insurance expert will be necessary.

When all or part of the design is being carried out by the Contractor then Professional Indemnity Insurance to cover the design liability may also be required. This may cause a problem because of the fitness for purpose requirement at Sub-Clause 4.1 (RB) and Clause 5 (YB).

The Multilateral Development Banks Harmonised Edition (the MDB Edition) is reviewed in Part 4 of this book. In the Introduction to the MDB Edition, FIDIC suggest that the Employer should consider a dedicated single policy for the project which would cover all the insurance requirements. Details of the policy should be included in the invitation to tender.

Definitions at Sub-Clause 1.1 relevant to this Clause include:

1.1.1.2 Contract Agreement
1.1.1.3 Letter of Acceptance
1.1.1.8 Tender
1.1.2.6 Employer's Personnel
1.1.2.7 Contractor's Personnel
1.1.3.1 Base Date
1.1.3.5 Taking-Over Certificate

18.1   General Requirements for Insurances

In this Clause, 'insuring Party' means, for each type of insurance, the Party responsible for effecting and maintaining the insurance specified in the relevant Sub-Clause.

Wherever the Contractor is the insuring Party, each insurance shall be effected with insurers and in terms approved by the Employer. These terms shall be consistent with any terms agreed by both Parties before the date of the Letter of Acceptance. This agreement of terms shall take precedence over the provisions of this Clause.

Wherever the Employer is the insuring Party, each insurance shall be effected with insurers and in terms consistent with the details annexed to the Particular Conditions.

If a policy is required to indemnify joint insured, the cover shall apply separately to each insured as though a separate policy had been issued for each of the joint insured. If a policy indemnifies additional joint insured, namely in addition to the insured specified in this Clause, (i) the Contractor shall act under the policy on behalf of these additional joint insured except that the Employer shall act for Employer's Personnel, (ii) additional joint insured shall not be entitled to receive payments directly from the insurer or to have any other direct dealings with the insurer, and (iii) the insuring Party shall require all additional joint insured to comply with the conditions stipulated in the policy.

Each policy insuring against loss or damage shall provide for payments to be made in the currencies required to rectify the loss or damage. Payments received from insurers shall be used for the rectification of the loss or damage.

The relevant insuring Party shall, within the respective periods stated in the Appendix to Tender (calculated from the Commencement Date), submit to the other Party:

(a) evidence that the insurances described in this Clause have been effected; and

(b) copies of the policies for the insurances described in Sub-Clause 18.2 [*Insurance for Works and Contractor's Equipment*] and Sub-Clause 18.3 [*Insurance against Injury to Persons and Damage to Property*].

When each premium is paid, the insuring Party shall submit evidence of payment to the other Party. Whenever evidence or policies are submitted, the insuring Party shall also give notice to the Engineer.

Each Party shall comply with the conditions stipulated in each of the insurance policies. The insuring Party shall keep the insurers informed of any relevant changes to the execution of the Works and ensure that insurance is maintained in accordance with this Clause.

Neither Party shall make any material alteration to the terms of any insurance without the prior approval of the other Party. If an insurer makes (or attempts to make) any alteration, the Party first notified by the insurer shall promptly give notice to the other Party.

If the insuring Party fails to effect and keep in force any of the insurances it is required to effect and maintain under the Contract, or fails to provide satisfactory evidence and copies of policies in accordance with this Sub-Clause, the other Party may (at its option and without prejudice to any other right or remedy) effect insurance for the relevant coverage and pay the premiums due. The insuring Party shall pay the amount of these premiums to the other Party, and the Contract Price shall be adjusted accordingly.

Nothing in this Clause limits the obligations, liabilities or responsibilities of the Contractor or the Employer, under the other terms of the Contractor otherwise. Any amounts not insured or not recovered from the insurers shall be borne by the Contractor and/or the Employer in accordance with these obligations, liabilities or responsibilities. However, if the insuring Party fails to effect and keep in force an insurance which is available and which it is required to effect and maintain under the Contract, and the other Party neither approves the omission nor effects insurance for the coverage relevant to this default, any moneys which should have been recoverable under this insurance shall be paid by the insuring Party.

Payments by one Party to the other Party shall be subject to Sub-Clause 2.5 [*Employer's Claims*] or Sub-Clause 20.1 [*Contractor's Claims*], as applicable.

The second paragraph of this Sub-Clause envisages a meeting between the Employer and the Contractor, before the issue of the Letter of Acceptance, at which the terms of the insurance will be agreed. FIDIC recognise that there may be difficulties in obtaining the insurance as required by Clause 18 and it is certainly desirable that the terms should be agreed before the Letter of Acceptance is issued or the Contract Agreement is signed. However, it is preferable that any problems are resolved before the Base Date, in order that all Tenders are submitted on the same basis. If changes are agreed after the submission of the Tender then they must be recorded and attached to the Letter of Acceptance or Contract Agreement.

The Contractor is required to effect and maintain the insurances as required by Sub-Clauses 18.2, 18.3 and 18.4 unless it is stated in the Particular Conditions that the Employer will effect these insurances. It may be preferable for the Contractor to effect the insurances which cover his Equipment and Materials as well as matters for which he has obligations to the Employer. The Contractor may be able to take advantage of favourable terms from insurance companies who know his past record. However, in some circumstances the Employer may be able to obtain favourable terms for certain insurance cover and decide to effect parts of the insurances himself. When a project involves several Contracts, the Employer may prefer to take an overall insurance covering the separate Contracts. Any such arrangements require specialist insurance advice. The FIDIC Guide for the Preparation of Particular Conditions includes an example Clause, but warns that the Employer may not be aware of the details of the Contractor's Equipment. Any additional requirements, such as the use of insurance companies who are established in the Country, must be stated in the Particular Conditions.

The Appendix to Tender must give the number of days from the Commencement Date for the submission of evidence that the insurance has been effected and for submission of copies of the relevant policies. These periods will be determined to give the Contractor time to effect the insurances but the insurance will normally have been arranged before the Commencement Date. The Sub-Clause recognises that the insurance terms and details will probably have been discussed before the issue of the Letter of Acceptance. Any changes to the provisions of Clause 18 must be confirmed by the Contractor and accepted by the Employer in the Letter of Acceptance. The instructions to tenderers may have required insurance proposals to have been included with the Contractor's Tender.

Sub-Clause 18.2 requires the insurance for Works and Contractor's Equipment to be effective from the date by which the evidence is to be submitted, as stated in the Particular Conditions. The Contractor will need to ensure that he is properly insured for his own requirements up to this date. The insuring Party is also required to submit evidence of payment to the other Party and to the Engineer. For the initial premium this would be part of the evidence that the insurance has been effected, because insurance is not effective until the premium has been paid. However, the initial payment will probably be for one year only and it is important that evidence is provided of payment of the renewal premiums.

Sub-Clause 18.1 emphasises that the insurance requirements do not limit the obligations, liabilities or responsibilities for the Parties under the other terms of the Contract or otherwise. Either Party can claim from the other Party for any Cost which is not recoverable from the insurer. Any such claims must be submitted under Sub-Clause 2.5 for claims by the Employer or Sub-Clause 20.1 for claims by the Contractor, and will be determined by the Engineer in accordance with the provisions of the Contract.

18.2 Insurance for Works and Contractor's Equipment

The insuring Party shall insure the Works, Plant, Materials and Contractor's Documents for not less than the full reinstatement cost including the costs of demolition, removal of debris and professional fees and profit. This insurance shall be effective from the date by which the evidence is to be submitted under sub-paragraph (a) of Sub-Clause 18.1 [*General Requirements for Insurances*], until the date of issue of the Taking-Over Certificate for the Works.

The insuring Party shall maintain this insurance to provide cover until the date of issue of the Performance Certificate, for loss or damage for which the Contractor is liable arising from a cause occurring prior to the issue of the Taking-Over Certificate, and for loss or damage caused by the Contractor in the course of any other operations (including those under Clause 11 [*Defects Liability*]).

The insuring Party shall insure the Contractor's Equipment for not less than the full replacement value, including delivery to Site. For each item of Contractor's Equipment, the insurance shall be effective while it is being transported to the Site and until it is no longer required as Contractor's Equipment.

Unless otherwise stated in the Particular Conditions, insurances under this Sub-Clause:

(a) shall be effected and maintained by the Contractor as insuring Party;

(b) shall be in the joint names of the Parties, who shall be jointly entitled to receive payments from the insurers, payments being held or allocated between the Parties for the sole purpose of rectifying the loss or damage;

(c) shall cover all loss and damage from any cause not listed in Sub-Clause 17.3 [*Employer's Risks*];

(d) shall also cover loss or damage to a part of the Works which is attributable to the use or occupation by the Employer of another part of the Works, and loss or damage from the risks listed in sub-paragraphs (c), (g) and (h) of Sub-Clause 17.3 [*Employer's Risks*], excluding (in each case) risks which are not insurable at commercially reasonable terms, with deductibles per occurrence of not more than the amount stated in the Appendix to Tender (if an amount is not so stated, this sub-paragraph (d) shall not apply); and

(e) may however exclude loss of, damage to, and reinstatement of:

(i) a part of the Works which is in a defective condition due to a defect in its design, materials or workmanship (but cover shall include any other parts which are lost or damaged as a direct result of this defective condition and not as described in sub-paragraph (ii) below),

(ii) a part of the Works which is lost or damaged in order to reinstate any other part of the Works if this other part is in a defective condition due to a defect in its design, materials or workmanship,

(iii) a part of the Works which has been taken over by the Employer, except to the extent that the Contractor is liable for the loss or damage, and

(iv) Goods while they are not in the Country, subject to Sub-Clause 14.5 [*Plant and Materials intended for the Works*].

If, more than one year after the Base Date, the cover described in sub-paragraph (d) above ceases to be available at commercially reasonable terms, the Contractor shall (as insuring Party) give notice to the Employer, with supporting particulars. The Employer shall then (i) be entitled subject to Sub-Clause 2.5 [*Employer's Claims*] to payment of an amount equivalent to such commercially reasonable terms as the Contractor should have expected to have paid for such cover, and (ii) be deemed, unless he obtains the cover at commercially reasonable terms, to have approved the omission under Sub-Clause 18.1 [*General Requirements for Insurances*].

In the Yellow Book, the words 'and Clause 12 [*Tests after Completion*]' have been added at the end of the second paragraph.

The insurance must cover the full reinstatement Cost, as defined in the Sub-Clause, including professional fees and profit. The insurance must commence by the date by which the evidence of insurance must have been submitted as stated in the Appendix to Tender and Sub-Clause 18.1 sub-paragraph (a) and continue:

- until the date of issue of the Taking-Over Certificate for the Works, for all the cover as required by this Sub-Clause;
- until the date of issue of the Performance Certificate for loss or damage for which the Contractor is liable as defined at the second paragraph of this Sub-Clause.

If a Red Book Contract includes some design by the Contractor and requires Tests after Completion then the second paragraph should be amended in the Particular Conditions to follow the Yellow Book requirement. The insuring Party must notify the insurer of any changes or delays to either of these dates.

The requirements for this insurance are given at paragraphs (a) to (e), which may have been modified in the Particular Conditions. The insurance covers all causes not listed as Employer's risks at Sub-Clause 17.3, but the provisions of paragraph (d) are complex. The paragraph states that certain risks may be excluded if cover cannot be obtained 'at commercially reasonable terms' with deductibles per occurrence of not more than the amount stated in the Appendix to Tender. The risks listed, items (c), (g) and (h) of Sub-Clause 17.3 and certain loss or damage following use or occupation by the Employer of another part of the Works are all risks for which the Employer would be liable. The matter of whether cover can be obtained at commercially reasonable terms should be discussed and agreed, preferably before issue of the Letter of Acceptance.

The final paragraph of Sub-Clause 18.2 introduces a further complication to paragraph (d). If cover is no longer available at commercially reasonable rates more than one year from the Base Date, then the cover may be agreed to be omitted and the Employer can claim the sum which the Contractor would have allowed as premium, subject to the provisions of Sub-Clause 2.5. However, if the Employer is prepared to dispense with paragraph (d) insurance because of an increase in the premium, it might be queried whether it is necessary in the first place, or could be omitted from the Sub-Clause.

The exclusions at subparagraph (e) are the same in the Red Book and the Yellow Book, including the reference to design defects, although design may the responsibility of either the Employer or the Contractor. This requires further study when preparing the Particular Conditions in order to establish the Employer's requirements for this insurance.

18.3 Insurance against Injury to Persons and Damage to Property

The insuring Party shall insure against each Party's liability for any loss, damage, death or bodily injury which may occur to any physical property (except things insured under Sub-Clause 18.2 [*Insurance for Works and Contractor's Equipment*]) or to any person (except persons insured under Sub-Clause 18.4 [*Insurance for Contractor's Personnel*]), which may arise out of the Contractor's performance of the Contract and occurring before the issue of the Performance Certificate.

This insurance shall be for a limit per occurrence of not less than the amount stated in the Appendix to Tender, with no limit on the number of occurrences. If an amount is not stated in the Appendix to Tender, this Sub-Clause shall not apply.

Unless otherwise stated in the Particular Conditions, the insurances specified in this Sub-Clause:

(a) shall be effected and maintained by the Contractor as insuring Party;
(b) shall be in the joint names of the Parties;

(c)   shall be extended to cover liability for all loss and damage to the Employer's property (except things insured under Sub-Clause 18.2) arising out of the Contractor's performance of the Contract; and

(d)   may however exclude liability to the extent that it arises from:

   (i)   the Employer's right to have the Permanent Works executed on, over, under, in or through any land, and to occupy this land for the Permanent Works,

   (ii)   damage which is an unavoidable result of the Contractor's obligations to execute the Works and remedy any defects, and

   (iii)   a cause listed in Sub-Clause 17.3 [*Employer's Risks*], except to the extent that cover is available at commercially reasonable terms.

The minimum amount of third party insurance required by this Sub-Clause must be stated in the Appendix to Tender. If no amount is stated then the Sub-Clause will not apply. The Contractor will then need to ensure that he has adequate insurance to cover his liabilities to third parties.

No date is given for the cover to commence but the insurance covers events arising out of the Contractor's performance of the Contract and so must commence before the Contractor takes any action in connection with the Contract. The insurance must cover any such event up to the issue of the Performance Certificate.

The requirements for the insurance are given at paragraphs (a) to (d). Paragraph (d) refers to exclusion of circumstances where the Employer has some responsibility, but the exclusion of the Employer's risks listed at Sub-Clause 17.3 does not apply if cover is available at commercially reasonable terms. The meaning of 'commercially reasonable' could be open to debate and the matter should be discussed and agreed, as noted under Sub-Clause 18.2, preferably before the issue of the Letter of Acceptance.

18.4   Insurance for Contractor's Personnel

The Contractor shall effect and maintain insurance against liability for claims, damages, losses and expenses (including legal fees and expenses) arising from injury, sickness, disease or death of any person employed by the Contractor or any other of the Contractor's Personnel.

The Employer and the Engineer shall also be indemnified under the policy of insurance, except that this insurance may exclude losses and claims to the extent that they arise from any act or neglect of the Employer or of the Employer's Personnel.

The insurance shall be maintained in full force and effect during the whole time that these personnel are assisting in the execution of the

Works. For a Subcontractor's employees, the insurance may be effected by the Subcontractor, but the Contractor shall be responsible for compliance with this Clause.

The insurance to cover liabilities for claims concerning Contractor's Personnel must be maintained for the whole time that such persons are assisting with the execution of the Works.

Sub-Clauses 18.2 and 18.3 refer to 'the insuring Party', which is stated to be the Contractor but could be the Employer if this is required by the Particular Conditions. However, Sub-Clause 18.4 does not refer to the insuring Party but states that the insurance shall be effected by the Contractor.

Chapter 29

Clause 19: Force Majeure

Clause 19 includes a definition of 'Force Majeure' and gives the procedures that must be followed and the consequences if a Force Majeure event occurs. Force Majeure is a new concept for FIDIC Civil Engineering Contracts, but is covered by the law of many countries. Any provisions of the governing law which cover Force Majeure or refer to situations such as 'unexpected circumstances' must be checked.

Sub-Clause 19.7 refers to events or circumstances outside the control of the Parties and is not limited to the definition of Force Majeure. The procedures for payment on termination under Sub-Clauses 19.6 and 19.7 do not include provision for the resolution of any disputes, but the procedures of Sub-Clause 20.1 would apply.

The definition of Force Majeure at Sub-Clause 1.1.6.4 just refers back to Clause 19. Definitions at Sub-Clause 1.1 relevant to this Clause include:

    1.1.4.3   Cost
    1.1.5.2   Goods
    1.1.5.8   Works
    1.1.6.1   Contractor's Documents
    1.1.6.5   Laws
    1.1.6.8   Unforeseeable.

19.1 Definition of Force Majeure

In this Clause, 'Force Majeure' means an exceptional event or circumstance:

(a) which is beyond a Party's control;
(b) which such Party could not reasonably have provided against before entering into the Contract;
(c) which, having arisen, such Party could not reasonably have avoided or overcome; and

282

(d) which is not substantially attributable to the other Party.

Force Majeure may include, but is not limited to, exceptional events or circumstances of the kind listed below, so long as conditions (a) to (d) above are satisfied:

(i)   war, hostilities (whether war be declared or not), invasion, act of foreign enemies,

(ii) rebellion, terrorism, revolution, insurrection, military or usurped power, or civil war,

(iii) riot, commotion, disorder, strike or lockout by persons other than the Contractor's Personnel and other employees of the Contractor and Subcontractors,

(iv) munitions of war, explosive materials, ionising radiation or contamination by radio-activity, except as may be attributable to the Contractor's use of such munitions, explosives, radiation or radio-activity, and

(v)   natural catastrophes such as earthquake, hurricane, typhoon or volcanic activity.

Sub-Clause 19.1 gives the four conditions which must all be met for an event or circumstance to qualify as Force Majeure. The event or circumstance does not have to be Unforeseeable, but it must prevent the Party from performing one or more of its obligations.

These conditions are similar to the conditions for 'unexpected circumstances' which are included in the Civil Codes of some countries. A comparison with the conditions and consequences as given in the governing law, as stated in the Appendix to Tender, will be necessary. If the governing law is more advantageous to the Contractor then the claim may be submitted under these provisions, or as 'otherwise in connection with the Contract' under Sub-Clause 20.1.

A non-exclusive list of five examples is given, all of which are events outside the control of either Party. The list is significant as the Contractor's right to claim for Cost as well as delay depends on the category of the Force Majeure, as provided at Sub-Clause 19.4. The list includes events which are also listed at Sub-Clause 17.3 as 'Employer's risks'. The distinction is that the Employer's risk relates to loss or damage to the Works, Goods or Contractor's Documents together with delay or Cost from rectifying this loss or damage. Force Majeure refers to the situation when either Party is prevented from performing any of its obligations under the Contract.

For Force Majeure, the relevant forces of nature are described in more detail as 'such as earthquake, hurricane, lightning, typhoon or volcanic activity', although Force Majeure is not limited to these examples.

19.2 Notice of Force Majeure

If a Party is or will be prevented from performing any of its obligations under the Contract by Force Majeure, then it shall give notice to the other Party of the event or circumstances constituting the Force Majeure and shall specify the obligations, the performance of which is or will be prevented. The notice shall be given within 14 days after the Party became aware (or should have become aware), of the relevant event or circumstance constituting Force Majeure.

The Party shall, having given notice, be excused performance of such obligations for so long as such Force Majeure prevents it from performing them.

Notwithstanding any other provision of this Clause, Force Majeure shall not apply to obligations of either Party to make payments to the other Party under the Contract.

Sub-Clause 19.2 is reviewed together with Sub-Clause 19.3.

19.3 Duty to Minimise Delay

Each Party shall at all times use all reasonable endeavours to minimise any delay in the performance of the Contract as a result of Force Majeure.

A Party shall give notice to the other Party when it ceases to be affected by the Force Majeure.

Sub-Clauses 19.2 and 19.3 refer to the notices that must be given within 14 days of the Party becoming aware of the relevant event or circumstance, or when the Party should have become aware of it. Another notice must be given when the Party is no longer affected by the Force Majeure. The notice under Sub-Clause 19.2 may duplicate a notice given under another Sub-Clause. To avoid potential confusion and problems it is important that each notice refers to every Sub-Clause under which it is given and includes exactly the information that is stipulated in each Sub-Clause. If the Force Majeure prevents the performance of obligations by both Parties then they must each give the due notices to the other. For Force Majeure to apply the Party must be prevented from performing an obligation. It is not sufficient that performance may be more difficult or more expensive.

Sub-Clause 19.2 also includes the effect of the Force Majeure that:

The Party shall, having given notice, be excused performance of such obligations for so long as such Force Majeure continues.

For a Party to be excused from performing some obligation, it must be prevented from performing that particular obligation by the Force Majeure. All other obligations, which are not prevented by the Force

Majeure, must be performed as required by the Contract. In particular, the final paragraph of Sub-Clause 19.2 states that the obligation to make payments is not affected by the provisions for Force Majeure. If the Force Majeure has serious consequences for the Works as a whole then the Engineer may consider suspension under Sub-Clause 8.8.

There is apparently no need for the Engineer or other Party to confirm or agree that the event constitutes Force Majeure or the performance of the obligation has been prevented. However, it is clearly advisable for the Contractor to ensure that the Engineer agrees that the event constitutes Force Majeure before he assumes that he can be excused from some obligation and stops work on the relevant item of work. Under Sub-Clause 19.3 both Parties must use 'all reasonable endeavours' to minimise any delay in the performance of the Contract, which repeats the usual legal obligation to mitigate damage due to an event outside the Party's control. The application of the phrase 'all reasonable endeavours' is a subjective interpretation which may be argued and would be determined initially by the Engineer and then, if necessary, by the Dispute Adjudication Board.

19.4   Consequences of Force Majeure

If the Contractor is prevented from performing any of his obligations under the Contract by Force Majeure of which notice has been given under Sub-Clause 19.2 [*Notice of Force Majeure*], and suffers delay and/or incurs Cost by reason of such Force Majeure, the Contractor shall be entitled subject to Sub-Clause 20.1 [*Contractor's Claims*] to:

(a)   an extension of time for any such delay, if completion is or will be delayed, under Sub-Clause 8.4 [*Extension of Time for Completion*]; and

(b)   if the event or circumstance is of the kind described in subparagraphs (i) to (iv) of Sub-Clause 19.1 [*Definition of Force Majeure*] and, in the case of subparagraphs (ii) to (iv), occurs in the Country, payment of any such Cost.

After receiving this notice, the Engineer shall proceed in accordance with Sub-Clause 3.5 [*Determinations*] to agree or determine these matters.

If the Contractor suffers delay or additional Cost due to the Force Majeure then the rights to claim depend on which category of the list at Sub-Clause 19.1 is appropriate. An extension of time can be claimed, as Sub-Clause 8.4(b), if completion is, or will be, delayed. However, Cost can only be claimed following the warlike events at subparagraphs (i) to (iv) of Sub-Clause 19.1 and not as a consequence of natural catastrophes. If the event is a war, hostilities, invasion or act of foreign enemies, as paragraph (i) then the event may occur anywhere in the world, although it would be necessary to prove the effect on the Contract. Paragraphs (ii) to (iv) refer to more localised situations and only events in the Country are covered.

19.5   Force Majeure Affecting Subcontractor

If any Subcontractor is entitled under any contract or agreement relating to the Works to relief from force majeure on terms additional to or broader than those specified in this Clause, such additional or broader force majeure events or circumstances shall not excuse the Contractor's non-performance or entitle him to relief under this Clause.

It is important that all Subcontracts contain similar Force Majeure provisions to this Contract. The FIDIC Conditions of Subcontract for the previous Contracts do not include provision for Force Majeure.

19.6   Optional Termination, Payment and Release

If the execution of substantially all the Works in progress is prevented for a continuous period of 84 days by reason of Force Majeure of which notice has been given under Sub-Clause 19.2 [*Notice of Force Majeure*], or for multiple periods which total more than 140 days due to the same notified Force Majeure, then either Party may give to the other Party a notice of termination of the Contract. In this event, the termination shall take effect 7 days after the notice is given, and the Contractor shall proceed in accordance with Sub-Clause 16.3 [*Cessation of Work and Removal of Contractor's Equipment*].

Upon such termination, the Engineer shall determine the value of the work done and issue a Payment Certificate which shall include:

(a)   the amounts payable for any work carried out for which a price is stated in the Contract;

(b)   the Cost of Plant and Materials ordered for the Works which have been delivered to the Contractor, or of which the Contractor is liable to accept delivery; this Plant and Materials shall become the property of (and be at the risk of) the Employer when paid for by the Employer, and the Contractor shall place the same at the Employer's disposal;

(c)   any other Cost or liability which in the circumstances was reasonably incurred by the Contractor in the expectation of completing the Works;

(d)   the Cost of removal of Temporary Works and Contractor's Equipment from the Site and the return of these items to the Contractor's works in his country (or to any other destination at no greater cost); and

(e)   the Cost of repatriation of the Contractor's staff and labour employed wholly in connection with the Works at the date of termination.

Under Sub-Clause 19.6, either Party may give a notice of termination of the Contract. The procedures are a mixture of the provisions for termination of Clauses 15 and 16, which reflects the fact that Force Majeure is not caused by any default by either Party.

19.7 Release from Performance Under the Law

Notwithstanding any other provision of this Clause, if any event or circumstance outside the control of the Parties (including, but not limited to, Force Majeure) arises which makes it impossible or unlawful for either or both Parties to fulfil its or their contractual obligations or which, under the law governing the Contract, entitles the Parties to be released from further performance of the Contract, then upon notice by either Party to the other Party of such event or circumstance:

(a) the Parties shall be discharged from further performance, without prejudice to the rights of either Party in respect of any previous breach of the Contract; and

(b) the sum payable by the Employer to the Contractor shall be the same as would have been payable under Sub-Clause 19.6 [*Optional Termination, Payment and Release*] if the Contract had been terminated under Sub-Clause 19.6.

Sub-Clause 19.7 is much wider than the Force Majeure provisions of Sub-Clause 19.1 and acknowledges that situations can arise when it is impossible for the Contract to continue. This is a very serious action and should only be taken after legal advice and consideration of the applicable law.

Chapter 30

Clause 20: Claims, Disputes and Arbitration

Previous FIDIC Conditions included a requirement that any dispute must first be referred to the Engineer. Only after the Engineer had made a decision on the dispute under Clause 67 could it be referred to an outside dispute resolver for amicable settlement or arbitration. The 1996 Supplement to the Red Book introduced an option for a Dispute Adjudication Board (DAB) and in the 1999 Conditions the DAB is the standard procedure.

The FIDIC Guidance for the Preparation of Particular Conditions includes an alternative paragraph for Sub-Clause 20.4 which enables the Engineer to be appointed as the DAB, but this cannot be recommended. In practice, the Engineer tends to be regarded as an instrument of the Employer and in the 1999 Conditions he is defined as Employer's Personnel, which can only enhance this belief. Generally the Engineer will already have given a determination under Sub-Clause 3.5 and a decision in principle under Sub-Clause 20.1 before a dispute is referred to the DAB. This makes it virtually impossible for him to act as an independent DAB. The DAB, provided it is properly constituted, is the only way to obtain a fast and truly independent decision on a dispute.

Sub-Clauses 20.2 to 20.4 must be read together with the Appendix: General Conditions of Dispute Adjudication Agreement and the Annex: Procedural Rules, as well as the Appendix to Tender. The arrangement of information in these different documents is not always logical and all the documents must be read together in order to understand and apply the DAB procedures.

The Multilateral Development Bank Harmonised Edition of the Red Book (the MDB Edition) is reviewed in Part 4 of this book. In the introduction to the MDB Edition, FIDIC states that the changes to the DAB procedures, at Sub-Clauses 20.2 to 20.8 and the Appendix, are an improvement on the earlier wording and could be introduced into the Red Book. Any such change requires a check on other related Clauses and Rule 2 of the Annex: Procedural Rules should also be changed as in the MDB Edition.

Definitions at Sub-Clause 1.1 relevant to this Clause include:

1.1.1.3   Letter of Acceptance
1.1.1.4   Letter of Tender
1.1.2.9   DAB
1.1.3.2   Commencement Date.

20.1   Contractor's Claims

If the Contractor considers himself to be entitled to any extension of the Time for Completion and/or any additional payment, under any Clause of these Conditions or otherwise in connection with the Contract, the Contractor shall give notice to the Engineer, describing the event or circumstance giving rise to the claim. The notice shall be given as soon as practicable, and not later than 28 days after the Contractor became aware, or should have become aware, of the event or circumstance.

If the Contractor fails to give notice of a claim within such period of 28 days, the Time for Completion shall not be extended, the Contractor shall not be entitled to additional payment, and the Employer shall be discharged from all liability in connection with the claim. Otherwise, the following provisions of this Sub-Clause shall apply.

The Contractor shall also submit any other notices which are required by the Contract, and supporting particulars for the claim, all as relevant to such event or circumstance.

The Contractor shall keep such contemporary records as may be necessary to substantiate any claim, either on the Site or at another location acceptable to the Engineer. Without admitting the Employer's liability, the Engineer may, after receiving any notice under this Sub-Clause, monitor the record-keeping and/or instruct the Contractor to keep further contemporary records. The Contractor shall permit the Engineer to inspect all these records, and shall (if instructed) submit copies to the Engineer.

Within 42 days after the Contractor became aware (or should have become aware) of the event or circumstance giving rise to the claim, or within such other period as may be proposed by the Contractor and approved by the Engineer, the Contractor shall send to the Engineer a fully detailed claim which includes full supporting particulars of the basis of the claim and of the extension of time and/or additional payment claimed. If the event or circumstance giving rise to the claim has a continuing effect:

(a)   this fully detailed claim shall be considered as interim;
(b)   the Contractor shall send further interim claims at monthly intervals, giving the accumulated delay and/or amount claimed, and such further particulars as the Engineer may reasonably require; and

(c)   the Contractor shall send a final claim within 28 days after the end of the effects resulting from the event or circumstance, or within such other period as may be proposed by the Contractor and approved by the Engineer.

Within 42 days after receiving a claim or any further particulars supporting a previous claim, or within such other period as may be proposed by the Engineer and approved by the Contractor, the Engineer shall respond with approval, or with disapproval and detailed comments. He may also request any necessary further particulars, but shall nevertheless give his response on the principles of the claim within such time.

Each Payment Certificate shall include such amounts for any claim as have been reasonably substantiated as due under the relevant provision of the Contract. Unless and until the particulars supplied are sufficient to substantiate the whole of the claim, the Contractor shall only be entitled to payment for such part of the claim as he has been able to substantiate.

The Engineer shall proceed in accordance with Sub-Clause 3.5 [*Determinations*] to agree or determine (i) the extension (if any) of the Time for Completion (before or after its expiry) in accordance with Sub-Clause 8.4 [*Extension of Time for Completion*], and/or (ii) the additional payment (if any) to which the Contractor is entitled under the Contract.

The requirements of this Sub-Clause are in addition to those of any other Sub-Clause which may apply to a claim. If the Contractor fails to comply with this or another Sub-Clause in relation to any claim, any extension of time and/or additional payment shall take account of the extent (if any) to which the failure has prevented or prejudiced proper investigation of the claim, unless the claim is excluded under the second paragraph of this Sub-Clause.

Sub-Clause 20.1 includes the overall requirement that the Contractor shall give notice to the Engineer of any claim, either for time or money, for whatever reason, 'as soon as practicable and not later than 28 days after the Contractor became aware, or should have become aware, of the event or circumstance'. If the Contractor fails to give this notice then he loses any entitlement to additional time or money and 'the Employer shall be discharged from all liability in connection with the claim'. This is an extremely serious sanction for failing to submit a notice on time and it must be queried whether the sanction will be enforced by the Courts. It is particularly harsh when the claim may have caused by a default on the part of the Employer, or when the Employer will enjoy the benefit of some additional work, or when the Engineer initially recognised the validity of the claim but then withdrew his initial acceptance. If the Engineer rejects a claim on the basis of this paragraph then he must be prepared for the Contractor to pursue his claim and continue to follow the procedures under Clause 20. If the immediate decision is overturned by a later decision by a DAB or arbitration tribunal then the Employer will be at a considerable disadvantage if the Engineer has not checked, monitored and maintained the appropriate records.

In order to avoid losing the right to claim, many Contractors will use a standard form to submit notices for every imaginable event, many of which will not be followed by a detailed claim. It is also necessary to consider the meaning of the phrase 'event or circumstance'. These are not defined terms but, according to the dictionary, an event is the fact of something which happened. A circumstance seems to be a wider situation such as 'external conditions affecting or that might affect action'. Clearly there is scope for debate on what exactly was the 'event or circumstance giving rise to the claim'. There is also the possibility that the Contractor might not have been immediately aware that the event was going to entitle him to additional time and/or money. This sanction is bound to be controversial and Employers should consider whether it might be preferable to delete this paragraph and rely on the final paragraph of Sub-Clause 20.1. This paragraph results in a reduction in a claim if the Engineer was not given the opportunity to investigate the claim, but does not affect the entitlement in principle.

Whether a failure to give a notice or provide information can remove a legal entitlement is a matter which may depend on the applicable law. In any event, in order to avoid potential problems, this notice is obviously essential for the Contractor to establish his legal entitlements and must be given in writing, to the appropriate address, as required by Sub-Clause 1.3.

Sub-Clause 20.1 only refers to claims by the Contractor. The equivalent provision for claims by the Employer is at Sub-Clause 2.5, which is much less stringent in its requirements. A list of notices under Sub-Clauses 2.5 and 20.1 is to be included in the Contractor's monthly progress report under Sub-Clause 4.21.

The Sub-Clause 20.1 notice is in addition to the other requirements for similar notices, such as the Sub-Clauses that refer matters to the Engineer for a determination under Sub-Clause 3.5, the sequence of notices at Red Book Sub-Clause 1.9 and the notice hidden in Sub-Clause 8.3. Clearly these notices can be combined, but the supporting information that is required and the further actions by the Engineer and the Contractor vary for each notice.

These notices are important:

- to enable the Engineer to make his own observations and records of the problem;
- to enable the Engineer to consider possible actions to overcome the problem;

- to put the problem on record and make it possible for the Contractor to receive a prompt decision on his entitlements.

Sub-Clause 20.1 includes detailed requirements for the Contractor to submit contemporary records to substantiate the claim. Contemporary records are essential to substantiate any claim, regardless of whether it is being considered sympathetically by a resident Engineer, or if it will eventually be determined by an Arbitration Tribunal. The extent of records that are appropriate may be discussed with the Engineer but are the Contractor's responsibility, because it is the Contractor who will eventually have to prove his entitlement to additional time or money. Claims under a Yellow Book Contract may include additional Costs incurred in the design office. This will be away from the Site so the immediate submission of contemporary records becomes even more important.

The Engineer is entitled to inspect the contemporary records and to request copies. If the Engineer has any doubts about the accuracy of the records then he should raise any queries and give the Contractor the opportunity to discuss and justify the records. The Engineer may also keep his own records and is not obliged to show these records to the Contractor. However, if the Engineer fails to query the Contractor's records at the time it will be difficult for him to argue later that they are not accurate.

Having submitted all the appropriate notices and contemporary records the Contractor must now prepare his detailed claim, for submission within 42 days of when he became aware of the event. This may be just an interim evaluation of the claim but it is important for the Contractor to submit the principle that justifies the claim as soon as possible. The Engineer must then respond with approval or disapproval on the principles of the claim within a further 42 days. The Engineer must give detailed comments with his approval or disapproval. The Contract includes provisions for extending these periods but it is to everyone's advantage for the principle to be established as quickly as possible. If the principle is agreed, the Contractor will receive interim payments and can revise his programme to incorporate the decision. The Employer will know that he has an additional liability and that completion will be delayed.

Sub-Clause 20.1 includes a requirement for the Engineer to carry out a Sub-Clause 3.5 determination. However, the paragraph with this requirement is positioned after he has made his decision on the principles of the claim. The other claims clauses, such as Sub-Clause 2.1, simply state that the Contractor gives notice and 'after receiving this notice the Engineer shall proceed in accordance with Sub-Clause 3.5'. From a claims management point of view, the Sub-Clause 3.5 consultations should proceed as soon as possible after both sides have established their positions on the merits of the claim. In the opinion of this author, the Contract should state that the Engineer may proceed with his Sub-Clause 3.5 determination when he considers that the time is right, or at the request of either Party. The determination might cover just the principle, or also the details, as appropriate. It does not seem right for consultation and determination to wait for several months after the claim event and the Contractor's expenditure of money. Also, if the claim results in a dispute then it should be referred to the DAB as soon as possible.

20.2 (RB)   Appointment of the Dispute Adjudication Board
Disputes shall be adjudicated by a DAB in accordance with Sub-Clause 20.4 [*Obtaining Dispute Adjudication Board's Decision*]. The Parties shall jointly appoint a DAB by the date stated in the Appendix to Tender.

The DAB shall comprise, as stated in the Appendix to Tender, either one or three suitably qualified persons ('the members'). If the number is not so stated and the Parties do not agree otherwise, the DAB shall comprise three persons.

If the DAB is to comprise three persons, each Party shall nominate one member for the approval of the other Party. The Parties shall consult both these members and shall agree upon the third member, who shall be appointed to act as chairman.

However, if a list of potential members is included in the Contract, the members shall be selected from those on the list, other than anyone who is unable or unwilling to accept appointment to the DAB.

The agreement between the Parties and either the sole member ('adjudicator') or each of the three members shall incorporate by reference the General Conditions of Dispute Adjudication Agreement contained in the Appendix to these General Conditions, with such amendments as are agreed between them.

The terms of the remuneration of either the sole member or each of the three members, including the remuneration of any expert whom the DAB consults, shall be mutually agreed upon by the Parties when agreeing the terms of appointment. Each Party shall be responsible for paying one-half of this remuneration.

If at any time the Parties so agree, they may jointly refer a matter to the DAB for it to give its opinion. Neither Party shall consult the DAB on any matter without the agreement of the other Party.

If at any time the Parties so agree, they may appoint a suitably qualified person or persons to replace (or to be available to replace) any one or more members of the DAB. Unless the Parties agree otherwise, the appointment will come into effect if a member declines to act or is unable to act as a result of death, disability, resignation or termination of appointment.

If any of these circumstances occurs and no such replacement is available, a replacement shall be appointed in the same manner as the replaced person was required to have been nominated or agreed upon, as described in this Sub-Clause.

The appointment of any member may be terminated by mutual agreement of both Parties, but not by the Employer or the Contractor acting alone. Unless otherwise agreed by both Parties, the appointment of the DAB (including each member) shall expire when the discharge referred to in Sub-Clause 14.12 [*Discharge*] shall have become effective.

20.2 (YB)   Appointment of the Dispute Adjudication Board

Disputes shall be adjudicated by a DAB in accordance with Sub-Clause 20.4 [*Obtaining Dispute Adjudication Board's Decision*]. The Parties shall jointly appoint a DAB by the date 28 days after a Party gives notice to the other Party of its intention to refer a dispute to a DAB in accordance with Sub-Clause 20.4.

The DAB shall comprise, as stated in the Appendix to Tender, either one or three suitably qualified persons ('the members'). If the number is not so stated and the Parties do not agree otherwise, the DAB shall comprise three persons.

If the DAB is to comprise three persons, each Party shall nominate one member for the approval of the other Party. The Parties shall consult both these members and shall agree upon the third member, who shall be appointed to act as chairman.

However, if a list of potential members is included in the Contract, the members shall be selected from those on the list, other than anyone who is unable or unwilling to accept appointment to the DAB.

The agreement between the Parties and either the sole member ('adjudicator') or each of the three members shall incorporate by reference the General Conditions of Dispute Adjudication Agreement contained in the Appendix to these General Conditions, with such amendments as are agreed between them.

The terms of the remuneration of either the sole member or each of the three members, shall be mutually agreed upon by the Parties when agreeing the terms of appointment. Each Party shall be responsible for paying one-half of this remuneration.

If at any time the Parties so agree, they may appoint a suitably qualified person or persons to replace any one or more members of the DAB. Unless the Parties agree otherwise, the appointment will come into effect if a member declines to act or is unable to act as a result of death, disability, resignation or termination of appointment. The replacement shall be appointed in the same manner as the replaced person was required to have been nominated or agreed upon, as described in this Sub-Clause.

The appointment of any member may be terminated by mutual agreement of both Parties, but not by the Employer or the Contractor acting alone. Unless otherwise agreed by both Parties, the appointment of the DAB (including each member) shall expire when the DAB has given its decision on the dispute referred to it under Sub-Clause 20.4 [*Obtaining Dispute Adjudication Board's Decision*], unless other disputes have been referred to the DAB by that time under Sub-Clause 20.4, in which event the relevant date shall be when the DAB has also given decisions on those disputes.

The Red Book DAB procedure requires the appointment of the DAB at the start of the project and this is referred to as a 'full term' DAB. The DAB is kept informed about the project, makes regular visits to the Site and makes decision on any disputes arising. However, under the Yellow Book the DAB is appointed after a dispute has arisen and is referred to as an 'ad hoc' DAB. The ad hoc DAB is only appointed for that particular dispute, so it makes a decision on that dispute and has then completed its appointment. The FIDIC Contracts Guide advises that the two types of DAB are not intended to be particularly suitable for the Red Book and Yellow Book, respectively. If a Yellow Book Employer wishes to have a full term DAB then the Red Book DAB should be specified in the Particular Conditions. Similarly, a Yellow Book DAB could be specified in Red Book Particular Conditions. This is not just a matter of introducing Sub-Clause 20.2. All the DAB provisions must be reviewed and changed where necessary.

An ad hoc DAB may appear to be cheaper, because it saves the cost of the monthly retainer and Site visits. However:

- it is always more difficult to agree on the members of a DAB *after* a dispute has arisen;
- there will be a further delay before the DAB can actually consider the dispute;
- the DAB will charge for the time necessary to mobilise and familiarise itself with the background to the dispute and, perhaps most important;
- the Parties have lost the potential for the DAB to help to prevent the dispute from arising.

The DAB is an independent panel of three people, or a single person, who give decisions on any disputes. The DAB decision must be implemented but if either Party is not satisfied with the DAB decision it can refer the original dispute to arbitration. Sub-Clause 20.4 states specifically that the DAB does not act as arbitrators and so are not covered by any arbitration provisions in the governing law. It is necessary for the Contract to state the procedures, powers and authority of the DAB and the actions which can or must be taken by the Parties after the DAB has given its decision on a dispute. These procedures, powers and authority are given at Sub-Clauses 20.2 to 20.4, together with the Appendix and Annex that follow Clause 20 and the DAB Agreement printed at the end of the FIDIC document.

Experience has shown that DAB decisions are more likely to satisfy both Parties and be accepted than were decisions by Engineers under the previous FIDIC procedure. For the DAB to operate successfully it is essential that:

- the procedure for the selection of members of the DAB allows for people suggested separately by each Party and the people appointed are completely independent of both Parties;
- the DAB is appointed at the time stated in the Contract and Dispute Adjudication Agreements are signed by both parties and each member of the DAB;
- any decision by the DAB is implemented immediately.

Sub-Clause 20.2 (RB) requires the DAB to be appointed at the start of the Contract, within 28 days of the Commencement Date, as stated in the Appendix to Tender. Sub-Clause 20.2 (YB) requires the DAB to be appointed within 28 days of one Party giving notice to the other Party of its intention to refer a dispute to a DAB in accordance with Sub-Clause 20.4.

For a three-person DAB the Sub-Clause requires that each Party shall nominate one member, for the approval of the other Party. The Chairman is then agreed between the Parties, after consultation with the two members, or appointed by the appointing authority as Sub-Clause 20.3.

A one-person DAB is chosen by agreement or appointed by the appointing authority. Different procedures for the selection of the person to be nominated are envisaged in the Contract, as follows.

- Each Party could nominate one member for the other Party's agreement during the period after the submission of the Tender and before the Letter of Acceptance. The agreed names would be confirmed in the Letter of Acceptance.
- Sub-Clause 20.2 refers to the possibility that a list of potential members is included in the Contract. The FIDIC Guidance for the Preparation of Particular Conditions suggests that such a list could be useful if the DAB is not to be appointed at the commencement of the Contract, but emphasises that 'it is essential that candidates for this position (as DAB member) are not imposed by either Party on the other Party'. Hence, any such list would need to be prepared after the Employer has entered negotiations with the preferred tenderer. The list must not be prepared just by the Employer, but must include people suggested by the Contractor.

- One problem when preparing a list of potential DAB members is that people on the list may no longer be available when the appointment is actually made. It will also be necessary to check for any conflict of interest when the successful tenderer is known.
- The FIDIC example for the Letter of Tender allows the Contractor to accept or reject names proposed by the Employer and to include the Contractor's suggestions for his nominee. If this procedure is used it is essential that the tenderer does not feel under any pressure to accept the Employer's suggestions but feels free to add his own suggestions.
- Nominations can be submitted and agreed during the period after the Commencement Date. This is a last minute procedure which has the advantage, or possibly the disadvantage, that the individuals who will be working on the project can be involved in the selection procedure.
- If the Parties fail to agree then the FIDIC Appendix to Tender designates the President of FIDIC as the appointing authority. The Appendix to Tender may have been amended to designate a different appointing authority.

The FIDIC Guidance for the Preparation of Particular Conditions emphasises the importance of each Party being free to nominate one member and the benefits of appointing the DAB *before* the Letter of Acceptance.

It is important that any person appointed to a DAB has appropriate construction experience, including experience of claims and dispute resolution, knowledge of contract interpretation and knowledge of the DAB procedures. The DAB acts as a team, not as representatives of the Parties, so ideally there should be a balance of experience and professional expertise within the team. Whilst this may be difficult to achieve for the members nominated by the separate Parties, it should be considered in the choice of the Chairman. It is always useful for the Parties to discuss their prospective nominees before making a final decision.

Training courses for DAB members have already been established and no doubt will develop further as the 1999 FIDIC Contracts are used more extensively. Lists of suitable people have been prepared by several organisations, including FIDIC, The Institution of Civil Engineers (ICE) in London, The International Chamber of Commerce in Paris and other organisations in different countries.

The FIDIC Appendix to Tender names the President of FIDIC as the appointing authority but other organisations can be substituted in the Appendix to Tender for the particular Contract or by agreement between the Parties.

Having accepted the appointment, each member of the DAB signs an Agreement with both Parties. Standard forms for the Dispute Adjudication Agreement for a one-person and three-person DAB are included with the FIDIC Contract. The Agreement refers to the 'General Conditions of Dispute Adjudication Agreement' and the 'Procedural Rules', which are annexed to Clause 20. The Conditions and Rules give detailed procedures for the working of the DAB and emphasise the importance of the DAB being impartial.

In accordance with the final paragraph of Sub-Clause 20.2 (RB), a full term DAB's appointment will expire when the Contractor's discharge under Sub-Clause 14.12 becomes effective. This will normally be when the Contractor has received back his Performance Security, together with the amount due under the Final Payment Certificate. However, if the Engineer and the Contractor cannot agree on the Final Payment Certificate then the resulting dispute can be referred to the DAB, amicable settlement or arbitration. The discharge does not then become effective and the DAB would remain in place. The Parties might then agree to terminate the appointment of the DAB.

Sub-Clause 20.2 (YB) states that an ad hoc DAB's appointment will expire when it has given a decision on any disputes which have been referred to it.

Sub-Clause 20.2 (RB) includes a provision that the Parties may refer any matter to the DAB for an opinion at any time. The matter does not have to be a dispute, as defined at Sub-Clause 20.4, but may be a claim or a difference of opinion. This provision is important because an opinion from the DAB, or just the fact of preparing presentations to the DAB, may enable the staff on the Site to resolve their differences. Such a reference to the DAB must be with the agreement of both Parties. However, if one Party wants to refer some matter to the DAB for an opinion, the other Party should normally agree. If they do not agree to refer any matter to the DAB then the Party who wants an opinion can turn the problem into a dispute and ask the DAB to give a decision. This would mean a longer, more time consuming and hence more expensive procedure. If the DAB considers that matters are being referred unnecessarily, or frivolously, they can comment on this in their opinion. The Sub-Clause does not require the DAB opinion to be in writing, but Procedural Rule 3 requires the DAB to prepare a report on its activities before leaving the Site at the conclusion of each visit.

The provision for the DAB to give an opinion is not relevant to an ad hoc DAB so it has been omitted from Sub-Clause 20.2 (YB).

Sub-Clause 20.2 (YB) also omits the provision that the terms of remuneration of the DAB shall include the remuneration of any expert whom the DAB consults. The reason for this omission is not apparent and an ad hoc DAB would be well advised to ensure that the provision is included in their Agreements. Whilst an ad hoc DAB may be less likely to require expert advice than would a full term DAB, it is still a possibility.

20.3   Failure to Agree Dispute Adjudication Board
If any of the following conditions apply, namely:

(a)   the Parties fail to agree upon the appointment of the sole member of the DAB by the date stated in the first paragraph of Sub-Clause 20.2;

(b)   either Party fails to nominate a member (for approval by the other Party) of a DAB of three persons by such date;

(c)   the Parties fail to agree upon the appointment of the third member (to act as chairman) of the DAB by such date; or

(d)   the Parties fail to agree upon the appointment of a replacement person within 42 days after the date on which the sole member or one of the three members declines to act or is unable to act as a result of death, disability, resignation or termination of appointment;

then the appointing entity or official named in the Particular Conditions shall, upon the request of either or both of the Parties and after due consultation with both Parties, appoint this member of the DAB. This appointment shall be final and conclusive. Each Party shall be responsible for paying one-half of the remuneration of the appointing entity or official.

The Sub-Clause refers to the entity or official named in the Particular Conditions. The Appendix to Tender names the President of FIDIC, which should be confirmed in the Particular Conditions. If the Employer wishes to substitute the name of a different organisation then care must be taken to ensure that it is an organisation with a list of potential DAB members who are suitably qualified, trained and monitored.

The Employer may also wish to investigate the extent of consultation with the Parties which the appointing entity would normally carry out and the time it normally takes to make an appointment. An enquiry as to any particular requirements by either Party, or whether people on the appointing entity's list have already been considered and rejected by either Party, would be reasonable. However it is important that the appointment is not delayed by a reluctant Party deliberately prolonging the consultation process. This is an appointment, not a nomination or suggestion, so the Parties have to accept whoever the appointing entity decides to appoint. The Sub-Clause does not give any time limit for making this appointment, but it should be made within a matter of days, rather than weeks.

The fact that the appointing entity will make a final and conclusive appoint is in conflict with the opening paragraph which states that the Parties 'desire jointly to appoint the Member'. The member has already been selected and appointed by the appointing entity so there is no opportunity to negotiate fees or other details. The person appointed must also have studied and accepted the Procedural Rules, including warranties.

The Sub-Clause states that one half of the remuneration of the appointing entity is paid by each Party. In practice the Party that requests the appointment will pay the fee and recover one half from the other Party.

20.4   Obtaining Dispute Adjudication Board's Decision

If a dispute (of any kind whatsoever) arises between the Parties in connection with, or arising out of, the Contract or the execution of the Works, including any dispute as to any certificate, determination, instruction, opinion or valuation of the Engineer, either Party may refer the dispute in writing to the DAB for its decision, with copies to the other Party and the Engineer. Such reference shall state that it is given under this Sub-Clause.

For a DAB of three persons, the DAB shall be deemed to have received such reference on the date when it is received by the chairman of the DAB.

Both Parties shall promptly make available to the DAB all such additional information, further access to the Site, and appropriate facilities, as the DAB may require for the purposes of making a decision on such dispute. The DAB shall be deemed to be not acting as arbitrator(s).

Within 84 days after receiving such reference, or within such other period as may be proposed by the DAB and approved by both Parties, the DAB shall give its decision, which shall be reasoned and shall state that it is given under this Sub-Clause. The decision shall be binding on both Parties, who shall promptly give effect to it unless and until it shall be revised in an amicable settlement or an arbitral award as described below. Unless the Contract has already been abandoned, repudiated or terminated, the Contractor shall continue to proceed with the Works in accordance with the Contract.

If either Party is dissatisfied with the DAB's decision, then either Party may, within 28 days after receiving the decision, give notice to the other Party of its dissatisfaction. If the DAB fails to give its decision within the period of 84 days (or as otherwise approved) after receiving such reference, then either Party may, within 28 days after this period has expired, give notice to the other Party of its dissatisfaction.

In either event, this notice of dissatisfaction shall state that it is given under this Sub-Clause, and shall set out the matter in dispute and the reason (s) for dissatisfaction. Except as stated in Sub-Clause 20.7 [*Failure to Comply with Dispute Adjudication Board's Decision*] and Sub-Clause 20.8 [*Expiry of Dispute Adjudication Board's Appointment*], neither Party shall be entitled to commence arbitration of a dispute unless a notice of dissatisfaction has been given in accordance with this Sub-Clause.

If the DAB has given its decision as to a matter in dispute to both Parties, and no notice of dissatisfaction has been given by either Party within 28 days after it received the DAB's decision, then the decision shall become final and binding upon both Parties.

For an ad hoc DAB the payment procedures require an advance payment to the DAB, so the fourth paragraph of Sub-Clause 20.4 has been changed to the following.

Within 84 days after receiving such reference, or the advanced payment referred to in Clause 6 of the Appendix – General Conditions of the Dispute Adjudication Agreement, whichever date is later, or within such other period as may be proposed by the DAB and approved by both Parties, the DAB shall give its decision, which shall be reasoned and shall state that it is given under this Sub-Clause. However, if neither of the Parties has paid in full the invoices submitted by each member pursuant to Clause 6 of the Appendix, the DAB shall not be obliged to give its decision until such invoices have been paid in full. The decision shall be binding on both Parties, who shall promptly give effect to it unless and until it shall be revised in an amicable settlement or an arbitral award as described below. Unless the Contract has already been abandoned, repudiated or terminated, the Contractor shall continue to proceed with the Works in accordance with the Contract.

FIDIC does not define what is meant by the word 'Dispute'. Presumably the word will have its normal meaning, i.e. any statement, complaint, request, allegation or claim which has been rejected and the rejection is not acceptable to the person who made the original statement or complaint. It is clearly not necessary for a complaint to have been considered by the Engineer under the Sub-Clause 2.5 or 3.5 procedure in order to create a dispute, unless it refers to a subject about which notice must be given under the Contract. However, the DAB may suggest to the Parties that they should follow the Contract procedures before asking for a formal decision.

The strength of the DAB procedure is that whenever there is any problem between the people on Site – whether it is caused by a difference of opinion on a technical matter, a problem of interpretation of the Contract, communication or simply a misunderstanding – it can be referred quickly to an independent tribunal. The problem can then be resolved, with the assistance of the DAB, whether this requires an explanation, opinion or binding decision.

Sub-Clause 20.4 lays down the procedure for the DAB and further details are given in the FIDIC Annex: Procedural Rules, including the following.

- Both Parties make available to the DAB any information or facilities which it requires. The DAB may decide to conduct a hearing to consider submissions on the dispute from the Employer and the Contractor.
- The DAB gives its decision within 84 days or other agreed period, from the date the dispute reference is received by the chairman. The decision will be in writing, with reasons.
- Both Parties will comply immediately with the decision, which is binding until revised by agreement or arbitration.
- If either Party is dissatisfied with the decision, or the DAB fails to give a decision within the due period, it can give notice of dissatisfaction within 28 days.
- If no notice of dissatisfaction has been given within the due period, subject only to Sub-Clauses 20.7 and 20.8, the decision becomes final and binding on the Parties and they lose the right to refer that dispute to arbitration.

The requirement that both parties must comply immediately with the decision means that, if the DAB requires a sum of money to be paid, it must be paid immediately. The procedure for payment is not stated but some DABs may require that payment is made within, say, seven days. This may be impossible within the Employer's internal procedures and it is probably more realistic for payments during the construction period to be included in the next monthly payment certificate. The Contractor should include the payment in his next Statement under Sub-Clause 14.3. If for any reason payment is not certified or is not paid then the Contractor has the remedies under Sub-Clauses 14.8, 16.1 and 16.2.

Alternative to Sub-Clause 20.4

The FIDIC Guidance for the Preparation of Particular Conditions includes an alternative paragraph for Sub-Clause 20.4 for use if any disputes are to be referred to the Engineer for an initial decision. This requires the following changes.

- Delete Sub-Clauses 20.2 and 20.3.
- Delete the second paragraph of Sub-Clause 20.4 and substitute:

The Engineer shall act as the DAB in accordance with this Sub-Clause 20.4, acting fairly, impartially and at the cost of the Employer. In the event that the Employer intends to replace the Engineer, the Employer's notice under Sub-Clause 3.4 shall include detailed proposals for the appointment of a replacement DAB.

In this case the Engineer is required to follow the DAB procedures, acting fairly and impartially, but his fees are paid by the Employer. The DAB procedures impose duties and obligations on the Engineer which are different to his role under this Contract or under the equivalent Clause 67 in the fourth edition of the FIDIC Red Book. It is difficult to envisage that an Engineer can perform DAB duties having already given a determination under Sub-Clause 3.5 and a decision on the principles of the claim under Sub-Clause 20.1. Also, the Engineer DAB is paid by the Employer whereas the fact that DAB members are appointed and paid by both Parties adds considerably to their status and the creditability of their decision. An Engineer DAB who has had several decisions changed by an arbitration tribunal may find himself exposed to accusations of bad faith, impartiality or even negligence.

20.5   Amicable Settlement

Where notice of dissatisfaction has been given under Sub-Clause 20.4 above, both Parties shall attempt to settle the dispute amicably before the commencement of arbitration. However, unless both Parties agree otherwise, arbitration may be commenced on or after the fifty-sixth day after the day on which notice of dissatisfaction was given, even if no attempt at amicable settlement has been made.

Following issue of a notice of dissatisfaction there is a 56 day period before either Party can commence arbitration. Arbitration does not have to be started immediately. When the notice has been issued it may be preferable to leave arbitration proceedings until the construction has been completed. This enables all disputes to be dealt with in a single arbitration. Alternatively, there may be reasons why a claimant wants a final decision on the dispute as soon as possible and the arbitration can be started immediately after the amicable settlement period.

The amicable settlement period enables both Parties to consider their position, consult with their advisers and senior management, and put forward proposals to settle the dispute in order to avoid the additional cost and loss of management time, together with the frustration and deterioration in relationships that can result from arbitration.

The FIDIC Conditions require that the Parties shall attempt to settle the dispute amicably, but do not give guidance as to the procedure that might be used. When an Employer has a preference for a particular procedure, as a part of a sequence of dispute procedures, then details should be included in the Particular Conditions. Possible procedures include the following.

- *Direct negotiation.* The Contract procedures require the Engineer to consider claims and consult with both Parties. The Engineer has been closely involved in the analysis of the claim and any discussions. If the Contract procedures have failed to achieve agreement then direct negotiations between the Parties, without the involvement of the Engineer, may help to break the deadlock. The negotiations may be conducted between senior personnel from head office, rather than people who have been involved with the project on Site.
- *The Engineer.* The DAB's reasons for its decision may cause the Engineer to reconsider or revise his previous analysis and recommendations to his client. This may enable the Engineer to assist the Parties to reach a settlement.
- *Mediation.* Mediation is a procedure under which an independent person is appointed to help the Parties overcome their dispute and find an agreed settlement. The mediator meets the Parties, together and separately in confidence, discusses their views and the reasons why each Party is not prepared to accept the DAB decision. The mediator is looking for a solution that will be acceptable to both Parties, as distinct from the correct decision in accordance with the Contract.
- *Conciliation.* Conciliation can be similar to mediation, but is generally conducted under a set of rules or a published procedure. The Institution of Civil Engineers' Conciliation Procedure starts with a procedure similar to mediation, but if the Parties are not able to reach an agreed settlement the conciliator gives them his recommendation as to how the dispute should be settled. The recommendation is based on practical commercial considerations rather than the legal contractual situation. Some regional arbitration centres and Chambers of Commerce have published conciliation procedures. These may provide for either a tribunal or single conciliator who proposes and discusses alternative ways of settling the dispute.

Whilst the DAB has already performed a function as an independent tribunal, the mediator or conciliator is not just another independent person repeating a similar procedure. The DAB has collated and analysed the evidence in order to establish the rights and obligations of the Parties in accordance with the Contract. The mediator or conciliator is looking for a commercial agreement and has the additional benefit of confidential discussions with each Party separately and so can consider their aims and problems as well as their rights. Also, of course, one or both Parties may think that the DAB reached the wrong decision. A mediator or conciliator may have suggestions as to how any such situation could be resolved.

If provision for mediation or conciliation is included in the Particular Conditions it is necessary to name an appointing authority in case the Parties are not able to agree on a suitable person.

20.6   Arbitration

Unless settled amicably, any dispute in respect of which the DAB's decision (if any) has not become final and binding shall be finally settled by international arbitration. Unless otherwise agreed by both Parties:

(a)   the dispute shall be finally settled under the Rules of Arbitration of the International Chamber of Commerce;

(b)   the dispute shall be settled by three arbitrators appointed in accordance with these Rules; and

(c)   the arbitration shall be conducted in the language for communications defined in Sub-Clause 1.4 [*Law and Language*].

The arbitrator(s) shall have full power to open up, review and revise any certificate, determination, instruction, opinion or valuation of the Engineer, and any decision of the DAB, relevant to the dispute. Nothing shall disqualify the Engineer from being called as a witness and giving evidence before the arbitrator(s) on any matter whatsoever relevant to the dispute.

Neither Party shall be limited in the proceedings before the arbitrator(s) to the evidence or arguments previously put before the DAB to obtain its decision, or to the reasons for dissatisfaction given in its notice of dissatisfaction. Any decision of the DAB shall be admissible in evidence in the arbitration.

Arbitration may be commenced prior to or after completion of the Works. The obligations of the Parties, the Engineer and the DAB shall not be altered by reason of any arbitration being conducted during the progress of the Works.

If either Party is not prepared to accept the DAB decision and has issued a notice of dissatisfaction within the proper time period then the dispute will finally be settled by arbitration. It is the dispute itself that is referred to arbitration and not the decision of the DAB.

A detailed review of the procedures and legal aspects of arbitration is outside the scope of this book. Arbitration is a legal process, which leads to an enforceable award, and is subject to the applicable law. However, most legal systems recognise an agreement to refer disputes to arbitration and, when the Contract includes such an agreement, the Courts will not consider a dispute until it has been decided by arbitration.

Most international construction Contracts incorporate an arbitration agreement and most international Contractors prefer an independent arbitration to having to refer disputes to the local Courts of the Country of the project. Whilst most Court systems are reliable there is always likely to be some feeling that the Employer is from the same Country as the Courts. Also, arbitration is generally conducted in the same language as the Contract administration, whereas referral to the local Courts may require translation of a substantial number of documents and the use of interpreters during a hearing. All this can add to the costs and many international Contractors will increase their Tender price if the Contract does not include provision for arbitration.

The FIDIC Contract includes provision for arbitration under the Arbitration Rules of the International Chamber of Commerce in Paris, but the FIDIC Guidance for the Preparation of Particular Conditions allows that other rules or administering authorities can be named.

The procedures to be followed in arbitration are controlled by the arbitration rules designated in the Contract and arbitration law of the Country which is chosen as the place of arbitration. Arbitration rules vary considerably in the detailed procedures and must be studied carefully before being designated in the Contract. Most rules require that certain details are either stated in the Contract, agreed by the Parties after the dispute has arisen or, if the Parties cannot agree, decided by the administering authority. The details to be stated include the following.

- *Arbitration rules and administering authority.* Some organisations provide their rules and also act as administering authority. However, if the Contract designates rules such as the UNCITRAL Arbitration Rules, it is necessary to designate a separate administering authority.
- *The number of arbitrators in the tribunal.* The tribunal may be a single person, but is normally three people for a major construction dispute. One arbitrator is nominated by each Party and the Chairman is chosen by agreement or by the appointing authority.
- *The place of arbitration.* This should not be the Country of the Employer or the Contractor. Careful consideration must be given to the choice of the place of arbitration because the arbitration law of that country will control the administration of the arbitration and the enforcement of the award. A country should be chosen which has adopted a modern arbitration law and which permits the tribunal to proceed completely independently of the national Courts. Many countries have adopted the UNCITRAL Model Arbitration Law, or have modified the Model Law to suit their requirements. Any such modifications must be studied with care.

A country should be chosen which has ratified the 1958 New York Convention on the Recognition and Enforcement of Foreign Arbitral Awards, which will assist with the eventual enforcement of the tribunal's award.

20.7 Failure to Comply with Dispute Adjudication Board's Decision

In the event that:

(a) neither Party has given notice of dissatisfaction within the period stated in Sub-Clause 20.4 [*Obtaining Dispute Adjudication Board's Decision*];

(b) the DAB's related decision (if any) has become final and binding; and

(c) a Party fails to comply with this decision;

then the other Party may, without prejudice to any other rights it may have, refer the failure itself to arbitration Under Sub-Clause 20.6 [*Arbitration*]. Sub-Clause 20.4 [*Obtaining Dispute Adjudication Board's Decision*] and Sub-Clause 20.5 [*Amicable Settlement*] shall not apply to this reference.

Sub-Clause 20.7 covers the situation when the DAB decision has become final and binding but has not been implemented. This failure can be referred to arbitration without having to follow the procedures of Sub-Clauses 20.4 and 20.5.

20.8 Expiry of Dispute Adjudication Board's Appointment

If a dispute arises between the Parties in connection with, or arising out of, the Contract or the execution of the Works and there is no DAB in place, whether by reason of the expiry of the DAB's appointment or otherwise:

(a) Sub-Clause 20.4 [*Obtaining Dispute Adjudication Board's Decision*] and Sub-Clause 20.5 [*Amicable Settlement*] shall not apply; and

(b) the dispute may be referred directly to arbitration under Sub-Clause 20.6 [*Arbitration*].

If there is no DAB in place, for whatever reason, then any dispute can be referred direct to arbitration. This is a necessary provision in order to maintain a route for the resolution of disputes if there is no DAB.

Part 3

Appendices

Appendix A1

General Conditions of Dispute Adjudication Agreement

1   Definitions
Each 'Dispute Adjudication Agreement' is a tripartite agreement by and between:

(a)   the 'Employer';
(b)   the 'Contractor'; and
(c)   the 'Member' who is defined in the Dispute Adjudication Agreement as being:
  (i)   the sole member of the 'DAB' (or 'adjudicator') and, where this is the case, all references to the 'Other Members' do not apply, or
  (ii) one of the three persons who are jointly called the 'DAB' (or 'dispute adjudication board') and, where this is the case, the other two persons are called the 'Other Members'.

The Employer and the Contractor have entered (or intend to enter) into a contract, which is called the 'Contract' and is defined in the Dispute Adjudication Agreement, which incorporates this Appendix. In the Dispute Adjudication Agreement, words and expressions which are not otherwise defined shall have the meanings assigned to them in the Contract.

2   General Provisions
Unless otherwise stated in the Dispute Adjudication Agreement, it shall take effect on the latest of the following dates:

(a)   the Commencement Date defined in the Contract;
(b)   when the Employer, the Contractor and the Member have each signed the Dispute Adjudication Agreement; or
(c)   when the Employer, the Contractor and each of the Other Members (if any) have respectively each signed a dispute adjudication agreement.

311

When the Dispute Adjudication Agreement has taken effect, the Employer and the Contractor shall each give notice to the Member accordingly. If the Member does not receive either notice within six months after entering into the Dispute Adjudication Agreement, it shall be void and ineffective.

This employment of the Member is a personal appointment. At any time, the Member may give not less than 70 days' notice of resignation to the Employer and to the Contractor, and the Dispute Adjudication Agreement shall terminate upon the expiry of this period.

No assignment or subcontracting of the Dispute Adjudication Agreement is permitted without the prior written agreement of all the parties to it and of the Other Members (if any).

3   Warranties

The Member warrants and agrees that he/she is and shall be impartial and independent of the Employer, the Contractor and the Engineer. The Member shall promptly disclose, to each of them and to the Other Members (if any), any fact or circumstance which might appear inconsistent with his/her warranty and agreement of impartiality and independence.

When appointing the Member, the Employer and the Contractor relied upon the Member's representations that he/she is:

(a)   experienced in the work which the Contractor is to carry out under the Contract;

(b)   experienced in the interpretation of contract documentation; and

(c)   fluent in the language for communications defined in the Contract.

4   General Obligations of The Member

The Member shall:

(a)   have no interest financial or otherwise in the Employer, the Contractor or the Engineer, nor any financial interest in the Contract except for payment under the Dispute Adjudication Agreement;

(b)   not previously have been employed as a consultant or otherwise by the Employer, the Contractor or the Engineer, except in such circumstances as were disclosed in writing to the Employer and the Contractor before they signed the Dispute Adjudication Agreement;

(c)   have disclosed in writing to the Employer, the Contractor and the Other Members (if any), before entering into the Dispute Adjudication Agreement and to his/her best knowledge and recollection, any professional or personal relationships with any director, officer or employee of the Employer, the Contractor or the Engineer, and any previous involvement in the overall project of which the Contract forms part;

(d) not, for the duration of the Dispute Adjudication Agreement, be employed as a consultant or otherwise by the Employer, the Contractor or the Engineer, except as may be agreed in writing by the Employer, the Contractor and the Other Members (if any);

(e) comply with the annexed procedural rules and with Sub-Clause 20.4 of the Conditions of Contract;

(f) not give advice to the Employer, the Contractor, the Employer's Personnel or the Contractor's Personnel concerning the conduct of the Contract, other than in accordance with the annexed procedural rules;

(g) not while a Member enter into discussions or make any agreement with the Employer, the Contractor or the Engineer regarding employment by any of them, whether as a consultant or otherwise, after ceasing to act under the Dispute Adjudication Agreement;

(h) ensure his/her availability for all site visits and hearings as are necessary;

(i) become conversant with the Contract and with the progress of the Works (and of any other parts of the project of which the Contract forms part) by studying all documents received which shall be maintained in a current working file;

(j) treat the details of the Contract and all the DAB's activities and hearings as private and confidential, and not publish or disclose them without the prior written consent of the Employer, the Contractor and the Other Members (if any); and

(k) be available to give advice and opinions, on any matter relevant to the Contract when requested by both the Employer and the Contractor, subject to the agreement of the Other Members (if any).

5   General Obligations of the Employer and the Contractor

The Employer, the Contractor, the Employer's Personnel and the Contractor's Personnel shall not request advice from or consultation with the Member regarding the Contract, otherwise than in the normal course of the DAB's activities under the Contract and the Dispute Adjudication Agreement, and except to the extent that prior agreement is given by the Employer, the Contractor and the Other Members (if any). The Employer and the Contractor shall be responsible for compliance with this provision, by the Employer's Personnel and the Contractor's Personnel respectively.

The Employer and the Contractor undertake to each other and to the Member that the Member shall not, except as otherwise agreed in writing by the Employer, the Contractor, the Member and the Other Members (if any):

(a) be appointed as an arbitrator in any arbitration under the Contract;
(b) be called as a witness to give evidence concerning any dispute before arbitrator(s) appointed for any arbitration under the Contract; or
(c) be liable for any claims for anything done or omitted in the discharge or purported discharge of the Member's functions, unless the act or omission is shown to have been in bad faith.

The Employer and the Contractor hereby jointly and severally indemnify and hold the Member harmless against and from claims from which he/she is relieved from liability under the preceding paragraph.

Whenever the Employer or the Contractor refers a dispute to the DAB under Sub-Clause 20.4 of the Conditions of Contract, which will require the Member to make a site visit and attend a hearing, the Employer or the Contractor shall provide appropriate security for a sum equivalent to the reasonable expenses to be incurred by the Member. No account shall be taken of any other payments due or paid to the Member.

6   Payment
The Member shall be paid as follows, in the currency named in the Dispute Adjudication Agreement:

(a) a retainer fee per calendar month, which shall be considered as payment in full for:
   (i) being available on 28 days' notice for all site visits and hearings;
   (ii) becoming and remaining conversant with all project developments and maintaining relevant files;
   (iii) all office and overhead expenses including secretarial services, photocopying and office supplies incurred in connection with his duties; and
   (iv) all services performed hereunder except those referred to in subparagraphs (b) and (c) of this Clause.
   The retainer fee shall be paid with effect from the last day of the calendar month in which the Dispute Adjudication Agreement becomes effective; until the last day of the calendar month in which the Taking-Over Certificate is issued for the whole of the Works.

   With effect from the first day of the calendar month following the month in which Taking-Over Certificate is issued for the whole of the Works, the retainer fee shall be reduced by 50%. This reduced fee shall be paid until the first day of the calendar month in which the Member resigns or the Dispute Adjudication Agreement is otherwise terminated.
(b) a daily fee which shall be considered as payment in full for:
   (i) each day or part of a day up to a maximum of two days' travel time in each direction for the journey between the Member's

home and the site, or another location of a meeting with the Other Members (if any);

(ii) each working day on site visits, hearings or preparing decisions; and

(iii) each day spent reading submissions in preparation for a hearing.

(c) all reasonable expenses incurred in connection with the Member's duties, including the cost of telephone calls, courier charges, faxes and telexes, travel expenses, hotel and subsistence costs: a receipt shall be required for each item in excess of five percent of the daily fee referred to in sub-paragraph (b) of this Clause;

(d) any taxes properly levied in the Country on payments made to the Member (unless a national or permanent resident of the Country) under this Clause 6.

The retainer and daily fees shall be as specified in the Dispute Adjudication Agreement. Unless it specifies otherwise, these fees shall remain fixed for the first 24 calendar months, and shall thereafter be adjusted by agreement between the Employer, the Contractor and the Member, at each anniversary of the date on which the Dispute Adjudication Agreement became effective.

The Member shall submit invoices for payment of the monthly retainer and air fares quarterly in advance. Invoices for other expenses and for daily fees shall be submitted following the conclusion of a site visit or hearing. All invoices shall be accompanied by a brief description of activities performed during the relevant period and shall be addressed to the Contractor.

The Contractor shall pay each of the Member's invoices in full within 56 calendar days after receiving each invoice and shall apply to the Employer (in the Statements under the Contract) for reimbursement of one-half of the amounts of these invoices. The Employer shall then pay the Contractor in accordance with the Contract.

If the Contractor fails to pay to the Member the amount to which he/she is entitled under the Dispute Adjudication Agreement, the Employer shall pay the amount due to the Member and any other amount which may be required to maintain the operation of the DAB; and without prejudice to the Employer's rights or remedies. In addition to all other rights arising from this default, the Employer shall be entitled to reimbursement of all sums paid in excess of one-half of these payments, plus all costs of recovering these sums and financing charges calculated at the rate specified in Sub-Clause 14.8 of the Conditions of Contract.

If the Member does not receive payment of the amount due within 70 days after submitting a valid invoice, the Member may (i) suspend his/her services (without notice) until the payment is received, and/or (ii) resign his/her appointment by giving notice under Clause 7.

7   Termination

At any time: (i) the Employer and the Contractor may jointly terminate the Dispute Adjudication Agreement by giving 42 days' notice to the Member; or (ii) the Member may resign as provided for in Clause 2.

If the Member fails to comply with the Dispute Adjudication Agreement, the Employer and the Contractor may, without prejudice to their other rights, terminate it by notice to the Member. The notice shall take effect when received by the Member.

If the Employer or the Contractor fails to comply with the Dispute Adjudication Agreement, the Member may, without prejudice to his/her other rights, terminate it by notice to the Employer and the Contractor. The notice shall take effect when received by them both.

Any such notice, resignation and termination shall be final and binding on the Employer, the Contractor and the Member. However, a notice by the Employer or the Contractor, but not by both, shall be of no effect.

8   Default of the Member

If the Member fails to comply with any obligation under Clause 4, he/she shall not be entitled to any fees or expenses hereunder and shall, without prejudice to their other rights, reimburse each of the Employer and the Contractor for any fees and expenses received by the Member and the Other Members (if any), for proceedings or decisions (if any) of the DAB which are rendered void or ineffective.

9   Disputes

Any dispute or claim arising out of or in connection with this Dispute Adjudication Agreement, or the breach, termination or invalidity thereof, shall be finally settled under the Rules of Arbitration of the International Chamber of Commerce by one arbitrator appointed in accordance with these Rules of Arbitration.

The Dispute Adjudication Agreement is an agreement between the Employer, the Contractor and each member of the DAB. In addition to the General Conditions, FIDIC has published standard Dispute Adjudication Agreements for one-person and three-person DABs. These are the actual documents to be signed by the Employer, the Contractor and each member of the DAB and are printed at the end of the FIDIC document.

The General Conditions for the Agreement lay out extremely onerous requirements for the behaviour and duties of the DAB member, including the following.

- The Member must be impartial and independent of the Employer, the Contractor and the Engineer and must disclose anything that might appear inconsistent with this impartiality. This requirement is developed in a list of detailed stipulations.
- The Member must be fluent in the language defined in the Contract and experienced in the type of work and the interpretation of Contract documentation.
- The Member should study documents, become conversant with the progress of the Works and be available to give advice and opinions, but only when requested by both the Employer and the Contractor, with the agreement of the other Members.
- The Member is not permitted to be appointed arbitrator or to give evidence in any arbitration under the Contract except with the agreement of the Employer, Contractor and other Members.
- The Agreement includes figures for a monthly retainer and daily rate. The retainer is paid for keeping conversant with developments, being available for visits and for office expenses. The daily rate and expenses are paid for Site visits, hearings and preparing decisions, plus payment for travel time.
- The financial penalties for non-compliance with the obligations at Clause 4 are extremely severe. This emphasises the importance of the Member disclosing any previous involvement with either Party. Any problems or precedural changes must be confirmed in writing.

Appendix A2

Annex: Procedural Rules

1 Unless otherwise agreed by the Employer and the Contractor, the DAB shall visit the site at intervals of not more than 140 days, including times of critical construction events, at the request of either the Employer or the Contractor. Unless otherwise agreed by the Employer, the Contractor and the DAB, the period between consecutive visits shall not be less than 70 days, except as required to convene a hearing as described below.

2 The timing of and agenda for each site visit shall be as agreed jointly by the DAB, the Employer and the Contractor, or in the absence of agreement, shall be decided by the DAB. The purpose of site visits is to enable the DAB to become and remain acquainted with the progress of the Works and of any actual or potential problems or claims.

3 Site visits shall be attended by the Employer, the Contractor and the Engineer and shall be co-ordinated by the Employer in co-operation with the Contractor. The Employer shall ensure the provision of appropriate conference facilities and secretarial and copying services. At the conclusion of each site visit and before leaving the site, the DAB shall prepare a report on its activities during the visit and shall send copies to the Employer and the Contractor.

4 The Employer and the Contractor shall furnish to the DAB one copy of all documents which the DAB may request, including Contract documents, progress reports, variation instructions, certificates and other documents pertinent to the performance of the Contract. All communications between the DAB and the Employer or the Contractor shall be copied to the other Party. If the DAB comprises three persons, the Employer and the Contractor shall send copies of these requested documents and these communications to each of these persons.

5 If any dispute is referred to the DAB in accordance with Sub-Clause 20.4 of the Conditions of Contract, the DAB shall proceed in

accordance with Sub-Clause 20.4 and these Rules. Subject to the time allowed to give notice of a decision and other relevant factors, the DAB shall:

(a) act fairly and impartially as between the Employer and the Contractor, giving each of them a reasonable opportunity of putting his case and responding to the other's case; and

(b) adopt procedures suitable to the dispute, avoiding unnecessary delay or expense.

6 The DAB may conduct a hearing on the dispute, in which event it will decide on the date and place for the hearing and may request that written documentation and arguments from the Employer and the Contractor be presented to it prior to or at the hearing.

7 Except as otherwise agreed in writing by the Employer and the Contractor, the DAB shall have power to adopt an inquisitorial procedure, to refuse admission to hearings or audience at hearings to any persons other than representatives of the Employer, the Contractor and the Engineer, and to proceed in the absence of any party who the DAB is satisfied received notice of the hearing; but shall have discretion to decide whether and to what extent this power may be exercised.

8 The Employer and the Contractor empower the DAB, among other things, to:

(a) establish the procedure to be applied in deciding a dispute;

(b) decide upon the DAB's own jurisdiction, and as to the scope of any dispute referred to it;

(c) conduct any hearing as it thinks fit, not being bound by any rules or procedures other than those contained in the Contract and these Rules;

(d) take the initiative in ascertaining the facts and matters required for a decision;

(e) make use of its own specialist knowledge, if any;

(f) decide upon the payment of financing charges in accordance with the Contract;

(g) decide upon any provisional relief such as interim or conservatory measures; and

(h) open up, review and revise any certificate, decision, determination, instruction, opinion or valuation of the Engineer, relevant to the dispute.

9 The DAB shall not express any opinions during any hearing concerning the merits of any arguments advanced by the Parties. Thereafter, the DAB shall make and give notice to its decision in accordance with

Sub-Clause 20.4, or as otherwise agreed by the Employer and the Contractor in writing. If the DAB comprises three persons:

(a) it shall convene in private after a hearing, in order to have discussions and prepare its decision;

(b) it shall endeavour to reach a unanimous decision: if this proves impossible the applicable decision shall be made by a majority of the Members, who may require the minority Member to prepare a written report for submission to the Employer and the Contractor; and

(c) if a Member fails to attend a meeting or hearing, or to fulfil any required function, the other two Members may nevertheless proceed to make a decision, unless:

(i) either the Employer or the Contractor does not agree that they do so, or

(ii) the absent Member is the chairman and he/she instructs the other Members to not make a decision.

In the Yellow Book Rules 1 to 3 are omitted because they are not relevant to an ad hoc DAB. Rules 4 to 9 are thus renumbered 1 to 6.

Particular attention is drawn to the changes to Rule 2 in the MDB Edition, which are discussed at Part 4 and enable the DAB to use Site visits to try to prevent problems becoming disputes.

The Procedural Rules repeat much of the information which is given in Clause 20 and the General Conditions of Dispute Adjudication Agreement, with further details of procedures, including the following.

- Site visits by the full term DAB will normally be at intervals of not more than 140 days, with not less than 70 days between consecutive visits.

- Site visits enable the DAB to be informed about progress and any problems or claims. Before leaving the Site the DAB must prepare a report and send copies to both the Employer and the Contractor.

- The DAB has considerable powers to decide its own procedures and may decide to hold a hearing on a dispute, with written and oral arguments. The DAB may adopt an inquisitorial procedure, unless otherwise agreed in writing by the Employer and the Contractor. The alternative is presumably for the Parties to agree on an adversarial procedure with submissions from both sides. The DAB would then judge between the submissions, rather than reach a decision based on its own enquiries. This would create difficulties for the DAB and increase and length and cost of the hearing.

Appendix A3.1

Index of Sub-Clauses in the Conditions of Contract for Construction

Index of Sub-Clauses in the Conditions of Contract for Construction

Index of Sub-Clauses in the Conditions of Contract for Construction

Appendix A3.2

Index of Sub-Clauses in the Conditions of Contract for Plant and Design-Build

Appendix A4

Annexes and Forms

The Annexes and Forms which are included in the FIDIC Document have been reviewed under the Sub-Clause to which they relate.

Annexes   FORMS OF SECURITIES

Acceptable form(s) of security should be included in the tender documents: for Annex A and/or B, in the instructions to Tenderers; and for Annexes C to G, annexed to the Particular Conditions. The following example forms, which (except for Annex A) incorporate Uniform Rules published by the International Chamber of Commerce (the 'ICC', which is based at 38 Cours Albert 1er, 75008 Paris, France), may have to be amended to comply with the applicable law. Although the ICC publishes guides to these Uniform Rules, legal advice should be taken before the securities are written. Note that the guaranteed amounts should be quoted in all the currencies, as specified in the Contract, in which the guarantor pays the beneficiary.

Annex A   EXAMPLE FORM OF PARENT COMPANY GUARANTEE

[See page 3, and the comments on Sub-Clause 1.14]

Brief description of Contract ....

Name and address of Employer ....

(together with successors and assigns).

We have been informed that .... (hereinafter called the 'Contractor') is submitting an offer for such Contract in response to your invitation, and that the conditions of your invitation require his offer to be supported by a parent company guarantee.

In consideration of you, the Employer, awarding the Contract to the Contractor, we (*name of parent company*) .... irrevocably and unconditionally guarantee to you, as a primary obligation, the due performance of all the Contractor's obligations and liabilities under the Contract, including the Contractor's compliance with all its terms and conditions according to their true intent and meaning.

If the Contractor fails to so perform his obligations and liabilities and comply with the Contract, we will indemnify the Employer against and from all damages, losses and expenses (including legal fees and expenses) which arise from any such failure for which the Contractor is liable to the Employer under the Contract.

This guarantee shall come into full force and effect when the Contract comes into full force and effect. If the Contract does not come into full force and effect within a year of the date of this guarantee, or if you demonstrate that you do not intend to enter into the Contract with the Contractor, this guarantee shall be void and ineffective. This guarantee shall continue in full force and effect until all the Contractor's obligations and liabilities under the Contract have been discharged, when this guarantee shall expire and shall be returned to us, and our liability hereunder shall be discharged absolutely.

This guarantee shall apply and be supplemental to the Contract as amended or varied by the Employer and the Contractor from time to time. We hereby authorise them to agree any such amendment or variation, the due performance of which and compliance with which by the Contractor are likewise guaranteed hereunder. Our obligations and liabilities under this guarantee shall not be discharged by any allowance of time or other indulgence whatsoever by the Employer to the Contractor, or by any variation or suspension of the works to be executed under the Contract, or by any amendments to the Contract or to the constitution of the Contractor or the Employer, or by any other matters, whether with or without our knowledge or consent.

This guarantee shall be governed by the law of the same country (or other jurisdiction) as that which governs the Contract and any dispute under this guarantee shall be finally settled under the Rules of Arbitration of the International Chamber of Commerce by one or more arbitrators appointed in accordance with such Rules. We confirm that the benefit of this guarantee may be assigned subject only to the provisions for assignment of the Contract.

Date .... Signature(s) ....

Annex B   EXAMPLE FORM OF TENDER SECURITY

[See page 3]

Brief description of Contract ....

Name and address of Beneficiary ....

.... (whom the tender documents define as the Employer).

We have been informed that .... (hereinafter called the 'Principal') is submitting an offer for such Contract in response to your invitation, and that the conditions of your invitation (the 'conditions of invitation', which are set out in a document entitled Instructions to Tenderers) require his offer to be supported by a tender security.

At the request of the Principal, we (*name of bank*) .... hereby irrevocably undertake to pay you, the Beneficiary/Employer, any sum or sums not exceeding in total the amount of .... (say: ....) upon receipt by us of your demand in writing and your written statement (in the demand) stating that:

(a) the Principal has, without your agreement, withdrawn his offer after the latest time specified for its submission and before the expiry of its period of validity, or

(b) the Principal has refused to accept the correction of errors in his offer in accordance with such conditions of invitation, or

(c) you awarded the Contract to the Principal and he has failed to comply with sub-clause 1.6 of the conditions of the Contract, or

(d) you awarded the Contract to the Principal and he has failed to comply with sub-clause 4.2 of the conditions of the Contract.

Any demand for payment must contain your signature(s) which must be authenticated by your bankers or by a notary public. The authenticated demand and statement must be received by us at this office on or before (*the date 35 days after the expiry of the validity of the Letter of Tender*) ...., when this guarantee shall expire and shall be returned to us.

This guarantee is subject to the Uniform Rules for Demand Guarantees, published as number 458 by the International Chamber of Commerce, except as stated above.

Date .... Signature(s) ....

Annex C   EXAMPLE FORM OF PERFORMANCE SECURITY - DEMAND GUARANTEE

[See comments on Sub-Clause 4.2]

Brief description of Contract ....

Name and address of Beneficiary ....

.... (whom the Contract defines as the Employer).

We have been informed that .... (hereinafter called the 'Principal') is your contractor under such Contract, which requires him to obtain a performance security.

At the request of the Principal, we (*name of bank*) .... hereby irrevocably undertake to pay you, the Beneficiary/Employer, any sum or sums not exceeding in total the amount of .... (the 'guaranteed amount', say: ....) upon receipt by us of your demand in writing and your written statement stating:

    (a)   that the Principal is in breach of his obligation(s) under the Contract, and

    (a)   the respect in which the Principal is in breach.

[Following the receipt by us of an authenticated copy of the taking-over certificate for the whole of the works under clause 10 of the conditions of the Contract, such guaranteed amount shall be reduced by .... % and we shall promptly notify you that we have received such certificate and have reduced the guaranteed amount accordingly.] [1]

Any demand for payment must contain your [minister's/directors'] [1] signature(s) which must be authenticated by your bankers or by a notary public. The authenticated demand and statement must be received by us at this office on or before (*the date 70 days after the expected expiry of the Defects Notification Period for the Works*) .... (the 'expiry date'), when this guarantee shall expire and shall be returned to us.

We have been informed that the Beneficiary may require the Principal to extend this guarantee if the performance certificate under the Contract has not been issued by the date 28 days prior to such expiry date. We undertake to pay you such guaranteed amount upon receipt by us, within such period of 28 days, of your demand in writing and your written statement that the performance certificate has not been issued, for reasons attributable to the Principal, and that this guarantee has not been extended.

This guarantee shall be governed by the laws of .... and shall be subject to the Uniform Rules for Demand Guarantees, published as number 458 by the International Chamber of Commerce, except as stated above.

Date .... Signature(s) ....

---

[1]   *When writing the tender documents, the writer should ascertain whether to include the optional text, shown in parentheses [ ]*

Annex D　　**EXAMPLE FORM OF PERFORMANCE SECURITY - SURETY BOND**

[See comments on Sub-Clause 4.2]

Brief description of Contract ....

Name and address of Beneficiary ....

.... (together with successors and assigns, all as defined in the Contract as the Employer).

By this Bond, (*name and address of contractor*) ....
(who is the contractor under such Contract) as Principal and (*name and address of guarantor*)
.... as Guarantor are irrevocably held and firmly bound
to the Beneficiary in the total amount of .... (the 'Bond Amount', say:
......................................) for the due performance of all such Principal's obligations and liabilities
under the Contract. [Such Bond Amount shall be reduced by .... % upon the issue of the taking-
over certificate for the whole of the works under clause 10 of the conditions of the Contract.][1]

This Bond shall become effective on the Commencement Date defined in the Contract.

Upon Default by the Principal to perform any Contractual Obligation, or upon the occurrence of any of
the events and circumstances listed in sub-clause 15.2 of the conditions of the Contract, the Guarantor
shall satisfy and discharge the damages sustained by the Beneficiary due to such Default, event or
circumstances,[2] However, the total liability of the Guarantor shall not exceed the Bond Amount.

The obligations and liabilities of the Guarantor shall not be discharged by any allowance of time or
other indulgence whatsoever by the Beneficiary to the Principal, or by any variation or suspension
of the works to be executed under the Contract, or by any amendments to the Contract or to the
constitution of the Principal or the Beneficiary, or by any other matters, whether with or without the
knowledge or consent of the Guarantor.

Any claim under this Bond must be received by the Guarantor on or before (*the date six months after
the expected expiry of the Defects Notification Period for the Works*) .... (the 'Expiry
Date'), when this Bond shall expire and shall be returned to the Guarantor.

The benefit of this Bond may be assigned subject to the provisions for assignment of the Contract,
and subject to the receipt by the Guarantor of evidence of full compliance with such provisions.

This Bond shall be governed by the law of the same country (or other jurisdiction) as that which
governs the Contract. This Bond incorporates and shall be subject to the Uniform Rules for
Contract Bonds, published as number 524 by the International Chamber of Commerce, and words
used in this Bond shall bear the meanings set out in such Rules.

Wherefore this Bond has been issued by the Principal and the Guarantor on (*date*) ....

Signature(s) for and on behalf of the Principal ....

Signature(s) for and on behalf of the Guarantor ....

[1] *When writing the tender documents, the writer should ascertain whether to include the optional text,
shown in parentheses [ ]*

[2] *Insert:* [and shall not be entitled to perform the Principal's obligations under the Contract.]
　　Or:　　[or at the option of the Guarantor (to be exercised in writing within 42 days of receiving the claim
　　　　specifying such Default) perform the Principal's obligations under the Contract.]

Annex E   EXAMPLE FORM OF ADVANCE PAYMENT GUARANTEE

[*See comments on Sub-Clause 14.2*]

Brief description of Contract ....

Name and address of Beneficiary ....

.... (whom the Contract defines as the Employer).

We have been informed that .... (hereinafter called the 'Principal') is your contractor under such Contract and wishes to receive an advance payment, for which the Contract requires him to obtain a guarantee.

At the request of the Principal, we (*name of bank*) .... hereby irrevocably undertake to pay you, the Beneficiary/Employer, any sum or sums not exceeding in total the amount of .... (the 'guaranteed amount', say:..) upon receipt by us of your demand in writing and your written statement stating:

(a)   that the Principal has failed to repay the advance payment in accordance with the conditions of the Contract, and

(b)   the amount which the Principal has failed to repay.

This guarantee shall become effective upon receipt [of the first instalment] of the advance payment by the Principal. Such guaranteed amount shall be reduced by the amounts of the advance payment repaid to you, as evidenced by your notices issued under sub-clause 14.6 of the conditions of the Contract. Following receipt (from the Principal) of a copy of each purported notice, we shall promptly notify you of the revised guaranteed amount accordingly.

Any demand for payment must contain your signature(s) which must be authenticated by your bankers or by a notary public. The authenticated demand and statement must be received by us at this office on or before (*the date 70 days after the expected expiry of the Time for Completion*) .... (the 'expiry date'), when this guarantee shall expire and shall be returned to us.

We have been informed that the Beneficiary may require the Principal to extend this guarantee if the advance payment has not been repaid by the date 28 days prior to such expiry date. We undertake to pay you such guaranteed amount upon receipt by us, within such period of 28 days, of your demand in writing and your written statement that the advance payment has not been repaid and that this guarantee has not been extended.

This guarantee shall be governed by the laws of .... and shall be subject to the Uniform Rules for Demand Guarantees, published as number 458 by the International Chamber of Commerce, except as stated above.

Date .... Signature(s) ....

Annex F **EXAMPLE FORM OF RETENTION MONEY GUARANTEE**

[See comments on Sub-Clause 14.9]

Brief description of Contract ....

Name and address of Beneficiary ....

.... (whom the Contract defines as the Employer).

We have been informed that .... (hereinafter called the 'Principal') is your contractor under such Contract and wishes to receive early payment of [part of] the retention money, for which the Contract requires him to obtain a guarantee.

At the request of the Principal, we *(name of bank)* .... hereby irrevocably undertake to pay you, the Beneficiary/Employer, any sum or sums not exceeding in total the amount of .... (the 'guaranteed amount', say:..........................) upon receipt by us of your demand in writing and your written statement stating:

(a)   that the Principal has failed to carry out his obligation(s) to rectify certain defect(s) for which he is responsible under the Contract, and

(b)   the nature of such defect(s).

At any time, our liability under this guarantee shall not exceed the total amount of retention money released to the Principal by you, as evidenced by your notices issued under sub-clause 14.6 of the conditions of the Contract with a copy being passed to us.

Any demand for payment must contain your signature(s) which must be authenticated by your bankers or by a notary public. The authenticated demand and statement must be received by us at this office on or before *(the date 70 days after the expected expiry of the Defects Notification Period for the Works)* .... (the 'expiry date'), when this guarantee shall expire and shall be returned to us.

We have been informed that the Beneficiary may require the Principal to extend this guarantee if the performance certificate under the Contract has not been issued by the date 28 days prior to such expiry date. We undertake to pay you such guaranteed amount upon receipt by us, within such period of 28 days, of your demand in writing and your written statement that the performance certificate has not been issued, for reasons attributable to the Principal, and that this guarantee has not been extended.

This guarantee shall be governed by the laws of .... and shall be subject to the Uniform Rules for Demand Guarantees, published as number 458 by the International Chamber of Commerce, except as stated above.

Date.......................... Signature(s) ....

Annex G   EXAMPLE FORM OF PAYMENT GUARANTEE BY EMPLOYER

[See page 17: Contractor Finance]

Brief description of Contract   ....

Name and address of Beneficiary   ....

.... (whom the Contract defines as the Contractor).

We have been informed that .... (whom the Contract defines as the Employer and who is hereinafter called the 'Principal') is required to obtain a bank guarantee.

At the request of the Principal, we (*name of bank*) .... hereby irrevocably undertake to pay you, the Beneficiary/Contractor, any sum or sums not exceeding in total the amount of .... (say: ....) upon receipt by us of your demand in writing and your written statement stating:

(a)   that, in respect of a payment due under the Contract, the Principal has failed to make payment in full by the date fourteen days after the expiry of the period specified in the Contract as that within which such payment should have been made, and

(b)   the amount(s) which the Principal has failed to pay.

Any demand for payment must be accompanied by a copy of [*list of documents evidencing entitlement to payment*] .... in respect of which the Principal has failed to make payment in full.

Any demand for payment must contain your signature(s) which must be authenticated by your bankers or by a notary public. The authenticated demand and statement must be received by us at this office on or before (*the date six months after the expected expiry of the Defects Notification Period for the Works*) .... when this guarantee shall expire and shall be returned to us.

This guarantee shall be governed by the laws of .... and shall be subject to the Uniform Rules for Demand Guarantees, published as number 458 by the International Chamber of Commerce, except as stated above.

Date................................. Signature(s) ....

344

LETTER OF TENDER

NAME OF CONTRACT:

TO:

We have examined the Conditions of Contract, Specification, Drawings, Bill of Quantities, the other Schedules, the attached Appendix and Addenda Nos .... for the execution of the above-named Works. We offer to execute and complete the Works and remedy any defects therein in conformity with this Tender which includes all these documents, for the sum of (in currencies of payment) ....
....
or such other sum as may be determined in accordance with the Conditions of Contract.

We accept your suggestions for the appointment of the DAB, as set out in Schedule........................

> [*We have completed the Schedule by adding our suggestions for the other Member of the DAB, but these suggestions are not conditions of this offer*].*

We agree to abide by this Tender until .... and it shall remain binding upon us and may be accepted at any time before that date. We acknowledge that the Appendix forms part of this Letter of Tender.

If this offer is accepted, we will provide the specified Performance Security, commence the Works as soon as is reasonably practicable after the Commencement Date, and complete the Works in accordance with the above-named documents within the Time for Completion.

Unless and until a formal Agreement is prepared and executed this Letter of Tender, together with your written acceptance thereof, shall constitute a binding contract between us.

We understand that you are not bound to accept the lowest or any tender you may receive.

Signature .... in the capacity of ....

duly authorised to sign tenders for and on behalf of ....

....

Address: ....

....

Date: ....

* If the Tenderer does not accept, this paragraph may be deleted and replaced by:

> We do not accept your suggestions for the appointment of the DAB. We have included our suggestions in the Schedule, but these suggestions are not conditions of this offer. If these suggestions are not acceptable to you, we propose that the DAB be jointly appointed in accordance with Sub-Clause 20.2 of the Conditions of Contract.

APPENDIX TO TENDER

[Note: with the exception of the items for which the Employer's requirements have been inserted, the following information must be completed before the Tender is submitted]

Item	Sub-Clause	Data
Employer's name and address	1.1.2.2 & 1.3	_____ _____ _____
Contractor's name and address	1.1.2.3 & 1.3	_____ _____ _____
Engineer's name and address	1.1.2.4 & 1.3	_____ _____ _____
Time for Completion of the Works	1.1.3.3	_____ days
Defects Notification Period	1.1.3.7	365 days
Electronic transmission systems	1.3	_____
Governing Law	1.4	_____
Ruling language	1.4	_____
Language for communications	1.4	_____
Time for access to the Site	2.1	_____ days after Commencement Date
Amount of Performance Security	4.2	_____ % of the Accepted Contract Amount, in the currencies and proportions in which the Contract Price is payable
Normal working hours	6.5	_____
Delay damages for the Works	8.7 & 14.15(b)	_____ % of the final Contract Price per day, in the currencies and proportions in which the Contract Price is payable
Maximum amount of delay damages . .	8.7	_____ % of the final Contract Price
If there are Provisional Sums: Percentage for adjustment of Provisional Sums	13.5(b)	_____ %

Initials of signatory of Tender _____

If Sub-Clause 13.8 applies:
  Adjustments for Changes in Cost;
  Table(s) of adjustment data . . . . 13.8 . . . . for payments each
  month/[*YEAR*] in _____ (*currency*)

Coefficient; scope of index	Country of origin; currency of index	Source of index; Title/definition	Value on stated date(s)*	
			Value	Date
a= 0.10 Fixed				
b=_____ Labour				
c=_____				
d=_____				
e=_____				

* These values and dates confirm the definition of each index, but do not define Base Date indices

Total advance payment . . . . 14.2 . . . . _____% of the Accepted Contract Amount

Number and timing of instalments . . . . 14.2 . . . .

Currencies and proportions . . . . 14.2 . . . . _____ % in _____
  _____ % in _____

Start repayment of advance payment . 14.2(a) when payments are _____ %
  of the Accepted Contract Amount
  less Provisional Sums

Repayment amortisation of advance
payment . . . . 14.2(b) . . . . . _____ %

Percentage of retention . . . . 14.3 . . . . _____ %

Limit of Retention Money . . . . 14.3 . . . . ____ % of the Accepted Contract Amount

If Sub-Clause 14.5 applies:
  Plant and Materials for payment
  when shipped en route to the Site . . 14.5(b) . . . . . _____ [list]
  _____ [list]

  Plant and Materials for payment
  when delivered to the Site . . . . 14.5(c) . . . . . _____ [list]
  _____ [list]

Minimum amount of Interim Payment
Certificates . . . . 14.6 . . . . ____ % of the Accepted Contract Amount

If payments are only to be made in a currency/currencies named on the first page of the Letter of Tender:

  Currency/currencies of payment . . . . 14.15 . . . . . . as named in the Letters of Tender

_____

Initials of signatory of Tender _____

If some payments are to be made in a currency/currencies not named on the first page of the Letter of Tender:

Currencies of payment 14.15

Currency Unit	Percentage payable in the Currency	Rate of exchange: number of Local per unit of Foreign
Local: _____ [name]	_____	1.000
Foreign: _____ [name]	_____	_____
_____ [name]	_____	_____

Periods for submission of insurance:
(a) evidence of insurance . . . . 18.1 . . . .   ___ days
(b) relevant policies . . . . 18.1 . . . .   ___ days

Maximum amount of deductibles for
insurance of the Employer's risks . . . . 18.2(d) . . . . .   _____

Minimum amount of third party
insurance . . . . 18.3 . . . .   _____

Date by which the DAB shall be appointed . 20.2 . . . . 28 days after the Commencement Date

The DAB shall be . . . . 20.2 . . . . *Either:*
        ___ One sole Member/adjudicator
        Or:
        ___ A DAB of three Members

Appointment (if not agreed) to be
made by . . . . 20.3 . . . . The President of FIDIC or a person appointed by the President

If there are Sections:
Definition of Sections:

Description (Sub-Clause 1.1.5.6)	Time for Completion (Sub-Clause 1.1.3.3)	Delay Damages (Sub-Clause 8.7)
_____	_____	_____
_____	_____	_____
_____	_____	_____
_____	_____	_____

[*In the above Appendix, the text shown in italics is intended to assist the drafter of a particular contract by providing guidance on which provisions are relevant to the particular contract. This italicised text should not be included in the tender documents, as it will generally appear inappropriate to tenderers.*]

Initials of signatory of Tender _____

In the Yellow Book the Appendix to Tender is changed to suit the Sub-Clauses:

- the period for notifying unforeseeable errors, faults and defects in the Employer's Requirements is added for Sub-Clause 5.1;
- the date by which the DAB shall be appointed is deleted for Sub-Clause 20.2.

CONTRACT AGREEMENT

This Agreement made the _____ day of _____ 20 _____

Between _____ of _____ (hereinafter called 'the Employer') of the one part,
and _____ of _____ (hereinafter called 'the Contractor') of the other
part

Whereas the Employer desires that the Works known as_____ should be executed by
the Contractor, and has accepted a Tender by the Contractor for the execution and completion of
these Works and the remedying of any defects therein.

The Employer and the Contractor agree as follows:

1. In this Agreement words and expressions shall have the same meanings as are respectively
    assigned to them in the Conditions of Contract hereinafter referred to.

2. The following documents shall be deemed to form and be read and construed as part of this
    Agreement:

    (a) The Letter of Acceptance dated _____

    (b) The Letter of Tender dated _____

    (c) The Addenda nos. _____

    (d) The Conditions of Contract

    (e) The Specification

    (f) The Drawings, and

    (g) The completed Schedules.

3. In consideration of the payments to be made by the Employer to the Contractor as
    hereinafter mentioned, the Contractor hereby covenants with the Employer to execute and
    complete the Works and remedy any defects therein, in conformity with the provisions of the
    Contract.

4. The Employer hereby covenants to pay the Contractor, in consideration of the execution and
    completion of the Works and the remedying of defects therein, the Contract Price at the
    times and in the manner prescribed by the Contract.

In Witness whereof the parties hereto have caused this Agreement to be executed the day and
year first before written in accordance with their respective laws. _____

SIGNED by: _____   SIGNED by: _____

for and on behalf of the Employer in the presence   for and on behalf of the Contractor in the presence
of   of

Witness: _____   Witness: _____
Name: _____   Name: _____
Address: _____   Address: _____
Date: _____   Date: _____

In the Yellow Book the Contract Agreement is changed to suit the requirements of the Contract: At paragraph 2(e) 'The Specification' is replaced by 'Employer's Requirements'; at 2(f) 'Drawings' are replaced by 'completed Schedules'; at 2(g) 'completed Schedules' are replaced by 'Contractor's proposal'. This confirms that the Contractor's proposal, even if approved, does not supersede the Employer's Requirements. If particular items in the Contractor's proposal are intended to have priority than they must be confirmed as Variations.

DISPUTE ADJUDICATION AGREEMENT

[for a one-person DAB]

Name and details of Contract _____

Name and address of Employer _____

Name and address of Contractor _____

Name and address of Member _____

Whereas the Employer and the Contractor have entered into the Contract and desire jointly to appoint the Member to act as sole adjudicator who is also called the 'DAB'.

The Employer, Contractor and Member jointly agree as follows:

1. The conditions of this Dispute Adjudication Agreement comprise the 'General Conditions of Dispute Adjudication Agreement', which is appended to the General Conditions of the 'Conditions of Contract for Construction' First Edition 1999 published by the Fédération Internationale des Ingénieurs-Conseils (FIDIC), and the following provisions. In these provisions, which include amendments and additions to the General Conditions of Dispute Adjudication Agreement, words and expressions shall have the same meanings as are assigned to them in the General Conditions of Dispute Adjudication Agreement.

2. [*Details of amendments to the General Conditions of Dispute Adjudication Agreement, if any. For example:*

    In the procedural rules annexed to the General Conditions of Dispute Adjudication Agreement, Rule _ is deleted and replaced by: ' ... ']

3. In accordance with Clause 6 of the General Conditions of Dispute Adjudication Agreement, the Member shall be paid as follows:

    A retainer fee of _____ per calendar month,

    plus a daily fee of _____ per day.

4. In consideration of these fees and other payments to be made by the Employer and the Contractor in accordance with Clause 6 of the General Conditions of Dispute Adjudication Agreement, the Member undertakes to act as the DAB (as adjudicator) in accordance with this Dispute Adjudication Agreement.

5. The Employer and the Contractor jointly and severally undertake to pay the Member, in consideration of the carrying out of these services, in accordance with Clause 6 of the General Conditions of Dispute Adjudication Agreement.

6. This Dispute Adjudication Agreement shall be governed by the law of _____

SIGNED by: _____   SIGNED by: _____   SIGNED by: _____

for and on behalf of the Employer   for and on behalf of the Contractor   the Member in the presence of
in the presence of   in the presence of

Witness: _____	Witness: _____	Witness _____
Name: _____	Name: _____	Name: _____
Address: _____	Address: _____	Address: _____
Date: _____	Date: _____	Date: _____

DISPUTE ADJUDICATION AGREEMENT

[for each member of a three-person DAB]

Name and details of Contract _____

Name and address of Employer _____

Name and address of Contractor _____

Name and address of Member _____

Whereas the Employer and the Contractor have entered into the Contract and desire jointly to appoint the Member to act as one of the three persons who are jointly called the 'DAB' *[and desire the Member to act as chairman of the DAB].*

The Employer, Contractor and Member jointly agree as follows:

1.   The conditions of this Dispute Adjudication Agreement comprise the 'General Conditions of Dispute Adjudication Agreement', which is appended to the General Conditions of the 'Conditions of Contract for Construction' First Edition 1999 published by the Fédération Internationale des Ingénieurs-Conseils (FIDIC), and the following provisions. In these provisions, which include amendments and additions to the General Conditions of Dispute Adjudication Agreement, words and expressions shall have the same meanings as are assigned to them in the General Conditions of Dispute Adjudication Agreement.

2.   [*Details of amendments to the General Conditions of Dispute Adjudication Agreement, if any. For example:*

       In the procedural rules annexed to the General Conditions of Dispute Adjudication Agreement, Rule _ is deleted and replaced by: ' ... ']

3.   In accordance with Clause 6 of the General Conditions of Dispute Adjudication Agreement, the Member shall be paid as follows:

                     A retainer fee of _____ per calendar month,
                     plus a daily fee of _____ per day.

4.   In consideration of these fees and other payments to be made by the Employer and the Contractor in accordance with Clause 6 of the General Conditions of Dispute Adjudication Agreement, the Member undertakes to serve, as described in this Dispute Adjudication Agreement, as one of the three persons who are jointly to act as the DAB.

5.   The Employer and the Contractor jointly and severally undertake to pay the Member, in consideration of the carrying out of these services, in accordance with Clause 6 of the General Conditions of Dispute Adjudication Agreement.

6.   This Dispute Adjudication Agreement shall be governed by the law of _____

SIGNED by: _____   SIGNED by: _____   SIGNED by: _____

for and on behalf of the Employer   for and on behalf of the Contractor   the Member in the presence of
in the presence of   in the presence of

Witness: _____   Witness: _____   Witness _____
Name: _____   Name: _____   Name: _____
Address: _____   Address: _____   Address: _____
Date: _____   Date: _____   Date: _____

Part 4

MDB Harmonised Edition of the FIDIC Conditions of Contract for Construction

Chapter 31

The MDB Edition

31.1 Introduction

The Multilateral Development Banks (MDB) Harmonised Edition of the FIDIC Conditions of Contract for Construction, first edition 1999 (referred to here as 'the MDB Edition') incorporates standard changes that have been agreed by the group of MDBs and was first published in 2005. FIDIC stated that this edition must only be used for contracts that are financed by one of the Participating Banks. The Participating Banks are listed in the MDB Edition as:

African Development Bank
Asian Development Bank
Black Sea Trade and Development Bank
Caribbean Development Bank
European Bank for Reconstruction and Development
Inter-American Development Bank
International Bank for Reconstruction and Development
(The World Bank)
Islamic Bank for Development
Nordic Bank for Development.

The MDB Edition follows the same layout as the Red Book and most of the Clauses are identical. Changes have been introduced as required by the MDBs and agreed by FIDIC. Some of these changes are obviously based on experience of the use of the 1999 FIDIC Contracts as well as the specific requirements of the MDBs. Some of the changes are improvements which, where appropriate, could be incorporated into the Particular Conditions for other FIDIC Contracts.

The following review of the changes must be read in conjunction with the published MDB Edition (available on the FIDIC website) and the review of the 1999 Red Book at Parts 1 to 3 of this book. Sub-Clause numbers and references to the wording refer to the MDB Edition or the

1999 Red Book. The changes are reviewed in the following sections in this chapter.

- *General changes* – changes to terminology, which apply throughout the MDB Edition.
- *Bank changes* – changes and additional Clauses that relate to the role of the MDB.
- *Other changes* – changes and additional Clauses that do not specifically relate to the role of the MDB. These include changes to the Appendix, changes to Annex: Procedural Rules and changes to standard forms.

31.2 General changes

The following Sub-Clauses incorporate changes in terminology that apply throughout the MDB Edition. These are useful changes and an improvement on the traditional FIDIC terminology.

1.1 Definitions

- 1.1.1.4   Now states that the 'Letter of Tender' may be referred to as the Letter of Bid.
- 1.1.1.9   Was 1.1.1.10 and also refers to Schedule of Payment Currencies, as required by Sub-Clause 14.15.
- 1.1.1.10 Was 1.1.1.9. The Appendix to Tender is now called the Contract Data. It is Part A of the Particular Conditions and consists of information provided by the Employer.
- 1.1.2.9   The word Adjudication is deleted from Dispute Adjudication Board, so the DAB becomes DB throughout.

The change from 'Appendix to Tender' to 'Contract Data' is logical because the information in the document has been determined by the Employer. However, the change from DAB to DB must be regretted. The DB still act as Adjudicators, making a decision which must be implemented.

1.2 Interpretation

The word Bid has been introduced and is synonymous with the word Tender. The Red Book includes the phrase 'Cost plus reasonable profit', in relation to certain claims Clauses. The MDB Edition requires profit to be 5% of this Cost, unless otherwise indicated in the Contract Data. This means that wherever the Contract refers to 'Cost plus reasonable profit', the word 'reasonable' is deleted. The choice of 5% seems to be a reasonable compromise and the fact of stating a figure will avoid potential disagreement on Site.

1.5 Priority of Documents

The change from Appendix to Tender to Particular Conditions – Part A means a change in the order of priority. Particular Conditions – Part A is now priority (d). The FIDIC Particular Conditions is now part B and is priority (e).The previous points (e) to (h) become (f) to (i).

31.3 Bank changes

These changes give the financing Bank a named status in the Contract, although it is not a Party to the Contract. The Borrower is also named, as the organisation who has the financial agreement with the Bank and who may, or may not, be the Employer.

1.1 Definitions

The following new definitions have been added.

> 1.1.2.11 **'Bank'** means the financing institution (if any) named in the Contract Data.
> 1.1.2.12 **'Borrower'** means the person (if any) named as the borrower in the Contract Data.

1.15 Inspections and Audit by the Bank

The MDB Edition includes a new Sub-Clause 1.15:

> The Contractor shall permit the Bank and/or persons appointed by the Bank to inspect the Site and/or the Contractor's accounts and records relating to the performance of the Contract and to have such accounts and records audited by auditors appointed by the Bank if required by the Bank.

Financing institutions have always taken an interest in financial control and have often appointed their own consultant to work as a part of the Employer's team. This Sub-Clause increases the Bank's power to investigate and check the Contractor's use of money that has been provided by the Bank. The Sub-Clause could be controversial but presumably reflects a condition in the Bank's agreement with the Borrower.

2.4 Employer's Financial Arrangements

The MDB Edition includes a new second paragraph to Sub-Clause 2.4:

> In addition, if the Bank has notified to the Borrower that the Bank has suspended disbursements under its loan, which finances in whole or in part the execution of the Works, the Employer shall give notice of such suspension to the Contractor with detailed particulars, including the date

of such notification, with a copy to the Engineer, within 7 days of the Borrower having received the suspension notification from the Bank. If alternative funds will be available in appropriate currencies to the Employer to continue making payments to the Contractor beyond a date 60 days after the date of Bank notification of the suspension, the Employer shall provide reasonable evidence in such notice of the extent to which such funds will be available.

This Sub-Clause imposes an obligation on the Employer to notify the Contractor if the Bank suspends disbursements under the loan. Sub-Clauses 16.1 and 16.2 have also been amended to enable the Contractor to suspend work or terminate the Contract in these circumstances.

4.1 Contractor's General Obligations

The MDB Edition includes, as a new third paragraph to Sub-Clause 4.1, the following restriction on the countries from which equipment, material and services can be obtained. The MDB Edition does not include a list or definition of these countries, which may be different for different MDBs, but it must obviously be included in the Contract.

All equipment, material, and services to be incorporated in or required for the Works shall have their origin in any eligible source country as defined by the Bank.

14.1 The Contract Price

A new paragraph (e) has been added:

(e) Notwithstanding the provisions of subparagraph (b), Contractor's Equipment, including essential spare parts therefore, imported by the Contractor for the sole purpose of executing the Contract shall be exempt from the payment of import duties and taxes upon importation.

This provision for an exemption from import duties and taxes must have been agreed with the Government of the Country, presumably as a condition of the loan from the MDB.

14.7 Payment

The payment provisions at paragraphs (b) and (c) have been changed to allow for the situation if the Bank's loan or credit has been suspended. In this situation the Employer must pay the full amount of the Contractor's Statement, within 14 days of the Statement.

(b) the amount certified in each Interim Payment Certificate within 56 days after the Engineer receives the Statement and supporting documents or, at a time when the Bank's loan or credit (from which part of the payments to the Contractor is being made) is suspended, the amount shown on any statement submitted by the Contractor, within 14 days after such statement is submitted. Any discrepancy shall be rectified in the next payment to the Contractor; and

(c) the amount certified in the Final Payment Certificate within 56 days after the Employer receives this Payment Certificate or, at a time when the Bank's loan or credit (from which part of the payments to the Contractor is being made) is suspended, the undisputed amount shown in the Final Statement, within 56 days after the date of notification of the suspension in accordance with Sub-Clause 16.2.

15.6 Corrupt or Fraudulent Practices

A new Sub-Clause has been added to enable the Employer to terminate the Contract if he determines that the Contractor engaged in corrupt (or similar) practices in competing for or in executing the Contract. The decision to terminate appears to be made by the Employer, solely on the basis that the Employer has determined that the Contractor engaged in these practices. This is obviously a very serious accusation against the Contractor and the Employer must have strong evidence to support his determination, preferably a judgement by a Court or other third party. If the Contractor denies the charge then the dispute would go to the DB or, eventually to the Courts and an unjustified accusation would have very serious consequences.

If the Employer determines that the Contractor has engaged in corrupt, fraudulent, collusive or coercive practices, in competing for or in executing the Contract, then the Employer may, after giving 14 days notice to the Contractor, terminate the Contractor's employment under the Contract and expel him from the Site, and the provisions of Clause 15 shall apply as if such expulsion had been made under Sub- Clause 15.2.

For the purposes of this Sub-Clause:

(a) 'corrupt practice' means the offering, giving, receiving of soliciting of any thing of value to influence the action of a public official in the procurement process or in the Contract execution.

(b) 'fraudulent practice' means a misrepresentation of facts in order to influence a procurement process or the execution of the Contract to the detriment of the Borrower, and includes collusive practice among Bidders (prior to or after bid submission) designed to establish bid prices at artificial non-competitive levels and to deprive the Borrower of the benefits of free and open competition.

(c) 'collusive practice' means a scheme or arrangement between two or more bidders, with or without the knowledge of the Borrower, designed to establish bid prices at artificial, non-competitive levels.

(d) 'coercive practice' means harming or threatening to harm, directly or indirectly, persons or their property to influence their partici-pation in the procurement process or affect the execution of a contract.

16.1 Contractor's Entitlement to Suspend Work

A new paragraph has been added to confirm the right to suspend work if the Bank has suspended disbursements under its loan:

> Notwithstanding the above, if the Bank has suspended disbursements under its loan, which finances in whole or in part the execution of the Works, and no alternative funds are available as provided for in Sub-Clause 2.4 [*Employer's Financial Arrangements*], the Contractor may by notice suspend work or reduce the rate of work at any time, but not less than 7 days after the Borrower having received the suspension notification from the Bank.

16.2 Termination by Contractor

Paragraph (d) has been changed to ensure that the failing by the Employer has had the necessary consequence on the Contractor:

> (d) the Employer substantially fails to perform his obligations under the Contract in such manner as to materially and adversely affect the ability of the Contractor to perform the Contract.

A new paragraph (h) has been added to confirm the Contractor's rights if the Bank suspends its loan or credit:

> (h) In the event the Bank suspends the loan or credit from which part of the payments to the Contractor are being made, if the Contractor has not received the sums due to him upon expiration of the 14 days referred to in Sub-Clause 14.7 for payments under Interim Payment certificates, the Contractor may, without prejudice to the Contractor's entitlement to financing charges under Sub-Clause 14.8, immediately take one or both of the following actions, namely (i) suspend work or reduce the rate of work, and (ii) terminate his employment under the Contract by giving notice to the Employer, with a copy to the Engineer, such termination to take effect 14 days after the giving of the notice.

18.1 General Requirements for Insurances

A new paragraph has been added as the final paragraph of the Sub-Clause. It is not clear whether the statement that insurance may be placed with insurers from any eligible source country would ban insurers from all other countries. The list of eligible source countries will depend on the particular MDB and should be stated.

The Contractor shall be entitled to place all insurance relating to the Contract (including, but not limited to the insurance referred to Clause 18) with insurers from any eligible source country.

31.4 Other changes

Many of these changes have previously been introduced in the Particular Conditions of FIDIC Contracts and include some useful Sub-Clauses.

1.1 Definitions

- 1.1.3.6 'provisions of the Particular Conditions' is replaced by 'Specification'.
- 1.1.6.8 The text: 'and against which adequate preventative precautions could not reasonably be taken' is added after 'foreseeable'. The precise implications of this change are not clear and could result in arguments and disputes.

1.4 Law and Language

The wording of the Sub-Clause has been simplified such that the ruling language shall be stated in the Contract Data. The Language for Communications is that stated in the Contract Data or, if none is stated, then the ruling language will also be the Language for Communications.

1.8 Care and Supply of Documents

The phrase 'of a technical nature' is deleted from the fourth paragraph. All errors or defects, of whatever type, must be reported. This does not avoid the problem that the Contractor may notice an omission or conflict between documents, but will not be aware of an error in a statement that appears to be reasonable but does not reflect the Employer's intentions.

1.12 Confidential Details

A new paragraph has been added, which clarifies the requirement:

The Contractor shall treat the details of the Contract as private and confidential, except to the extent necessary to carry out the Contractor's obligations under the Contract or to comply with applicable Laws. The Contractor shall not publish or disclose any particulars of the Works without the previous agreement of the Employer. However, the Contractor shall be permitted to disclose any publicly available information, or information otherwise required to establish his qualifications to compete for other projects.

2.5 Employer's Claims

The phrase 'or should have become aware' has been added. This brings the Employer's claim procedure one step closer to the Sub-Clause 20.1 procedure for Contractor's claims. However, there is still no separation between notice and details and no 28 day time bar for Employer's claims.

3.1 Engineer's Duties and Authority

The final sentence of the third paragraph has been changed to read: 'The Employer shall promptly inform the Contractor of any change to the authority attributed to the Engineer.' For the Employer to change, and possibly reduce, the authority of the Engineer during the course of the project could have a serious impact on the administration of the Contract and lead to complaints and claims from the Contractor. On the other hand, if the Employer intends to change the Engineer under Sub-Clause 3.4, he now has the opportunity to change the authority during the notice period. Any such change could be construed by the Contractor as a Variation or a unilateral change to the Contract terms.

The following provisions shall apply:

The Engineer shall obtain the specific approval of the Employer before taking action under the-following Sub-Clauses of these Conditions:

(a) Sub-Clause 4.12: Agreeing or determining an extension of time and/ or additional cost.
(b) Sub-Clause 13.1: Instructing a Variation, except;
    (i)   in an emergency situation as determined by the Engineer, or
    (ii) if such a Variation would increase the Accepted Contract Amount by less than the percentage specified in the Contract Data.
(c) Sub-Clause 13.3: Approving a proposal for Variation submitted by the Contractor in accordance with Sub Clause 13.1 or 13.2.
(d) Sub-Clause 13.4: Specifying the amount payable in each of the applicable currencies.
(e) Notwithstanding the obligation, as set out above, to obtain approval, if, in the opinion of the Engineer, an emergency occurs affecting the safety of life or of the Works or of adjoining property, he may, without relieving the Contractor of any of his duties and responsibility under the Contract, instruct the Contractor to execute all such work or to do all such things as may, in the opinion of the Engineer, be necessary to abate or reduce the risk. The Contractor shall forthwith comply, despite the absence of approval of the Employer, with any

such instruction of the Engineer. The Engineer shall determine an addition to the Contract Price, in respect of such instruction, in accordance with Clause 13 and shall notify the Contractor accordingly, with a copy to the Employer.

These provisions restrict the power of the Engineer to commit the Employer to additional payments, or extension of time, without prior approval, except in an emergency. It is to be hoped that the Engineer will be able to convince the Employer to give his approval when the Contractor has a contractual entitlement to the additional time or money. They also show the limited extent of restrictions which the MDB consider to be necessary. Hopefully they will not permit Employers to introduce additional restrictions.

3.4 Replacement of the Engineer

This has always been a difficult requirement to express in a reasonable procedure. The MDB Edition shortens the notice period and improves the wording.

Notwithstanding Sub-Clause 3.1, if the Employer intends to replace the Engineer, the Employer shall, not less than 21 days before the intended date of replacement, give notice to the Contractor of the name, address and relevant experience of the intended replacement Engineer. If the Contractor considers the intended replacement Engineer to be unsuitable, he has the right to raise reasonable objection against him by notice to the Employer, with supporting particulars, and the Employer shall give full and fair consideration to this objection.

4.2 Performance Security

The MDB Edition has deleted the list of situations in which the Employer can claim on the Performance Security and so removes the anomalies that were discussed in Part 2 of this book. However, it still retains the indemnity by the Employer in the event that the Employer makes a claim to which he was not entitled. The MDB Edition also requires the Contractor to increase or decrease the value of the Performance Security if the Contract Price changes by more than 25% in certain circumstances. The new Sub-Clause reads as follows.

The Contractor shall obtain (at his cost) a Performance Security for proper performance, in the form, amount and currencies stated in the Contract Data. If an amount is not stated in the Contract Data, this Sub-Clause shall not apply.

The Contractor shall deliver the Performance Security to the Employer within 28 days after receiving the Letter of Acceptance, and shall send a copy to the Engineer. The Performance Security shall be issued by an entity and from within a country (or other jurisdiction) approved by the Employer, and shall be in the form annexed to the Particular Conditions or in another form approved by the Employer.

The Contractor shall ensure that the Performance Security is valid and enforceable until the Contractor has executed and completed the Works and remedied any defects. If the terms of the Performance Security specify its expiry date, and the Contractor has not become entitled to receive the Performance Certificate by the date 28 days prior to the expiry date, the Contractor shall extend the validity of the Performance Security until the Works have been completed and any defects have been remedied.

The Employer shall not make a claim under the Performance Security, except for amounts to which the Employer is entitled under the Contract. The Employer shall indemnify and hold the Contractor harmless against and from all damages, losses and expenses (including legal fees and expenses) resulting from a claim under the Performance Security to the extent to which the Employer was not entitled to make the claim.

The Employer shall return the Performance Security to the Contractor within 21 days after receiving a copy of the Performance Certificate.

Without limitation to the provisions of the rest of this Sub-Clause, whenever the Engineer determines an addition or a reduction to the Contract Price as a result of a change in cost and/or legislation or as a result of a Variation amounting to more than 25 percent of the portion of the Contract Price payable in a specific currency, the Contractor shall at the Engineer's request promptly increase, or may decrease, as the case may be, the value of the Performance Security in that currency by an equal percentage.

4.3 Contractor's Representative

The final paragraph of Sub-Clause 4.3 has been changed to require the Contractor to provide interpreters if his staff are not fluent in the language for communications.

> The Contractor's Representative shall be fluent in the language for communications defined in Sub-Clause 1.4 [*Law and Language*]. If the Contractor's Representative's delegates are not fluent in the said language, the Contractor shall make competent interpreters available during all working hours in a number deemed sufficient by the Engineer.

4.4 Subcontractors

The word 'solely' is added after 'suppliers' in paragraph (a). A new paragraph is added:

Where practicable, the Contractor shall give fair and reasonable opportunity for contractors from the Country to be appointed as Sub-contractors.

This paragraph attempts to encourage the use of local companies as Subcontractors. However, the Contractor is still responsible for his Subcontractors and will still want to submit an economic Tender in order to obtain the Contract, so the practical effect of this Sub-Clause is uncertain.

4.18 Protection of the Environment

The wording of this Sub-Clause has been improved.

6.1 Engagement of Staff and Labour

A new paragraph has been added. However, the MDB only encourages, rather than requires, the use of local staff and labour.

The Contractor is encouraged, to the extent practicable and reasonable, to employ staff and labour with appropriate qualifications and experience from sources within the Country.

6.2 Rates of Wages and Conditions of Labour

A new paragraph has been added, which requires the Contractor to inform his personnel and to carry out any obligations with respect to local taxation:

The Contractor shall inform the Contractor's Personnel about their liability to pay personal income taxes in the Country in respect of such of their salaries, wages and allowances as are chargeable under the Laws of the Country for the time being in force, and the Contractor shall perform such duties in regard to such deductions thereof as may be imposed on him by such Laws.

6.7 Health and Safety

The MDB Edition includes detailed procedures to combat the spread of HIV/AIDS. The Contractor is obliged to implement these procedures, probably through a specialist Subcontractor, and they will, presumably, be included as an item in the Bill of Quantities.

HIV/AIDS Prevention. The Contractor shall conduct an HIV/AIDS awareness programme via an approved service provider, and shall undertake such other measures as are specified in this Contract to reduce the risk of the transfer of the HIV virus between and among the

Contractor's Personnel and the local community, to promote early diagnosis and to assist affected individuals.

The Contractor shall throughout the contract (including the Defects Notification Period): (i) conduct Information, Education and Consultation Communication (IEC) campaigns, at least every other month, addressed to all the Site staff and labour (including all the Contractor's employees, all Sub-Contractors and Consultants' employees, and all truck drivers and crew making deliveries to Site for construction activities) and to the immediate local communities, concerning the risks, dangers and impact, and appropriate avoidance behaviour with respect to of Sexually Transmitted Diseases (STD) – or Sexually Transmitted Infections (STI) in general and HIV/AIDS in particular; (ii) provide male or female condoms for all Site staff and labour as appropriate; and (iii) provide for STI and HIV/AIDS screening, diagnosis, counselling and referral to a dedicated national STI and HIV/AIDS programme, (unless otherwise agreed) of all Site staff and labour.

The Contractor shall include in the programme to be submitted for the execution of the Works under Sub-Clause 8.3 an alleviation programme for Site staff and labour and their families in respect of Sexually Transmitted Infections (STI) and Sexually Transmitted Diseases (STD) including HIV/AIDS. The STI, STD and HIV/AIDS alleviation programme shall indicate when, how and at what cost the Contractor plans to satisfy the requirements of this Sub-Clause and the related specification. For each component, the programme shall detail the resources to be provided or utilized and any related sub-contracting proposed. The programme shall also include provision of a detailed cost estimate with supporting documentation. Payment to the Contractor for preparation and implementation this programme shall not exceed the Provisional Sum dedicated for this purpose.

6.12–6.22 Additional Staff and Labour Sub-Clauses

The MDB Edition includes additional Sub-Clauses that cover different aspects of the local and welfare requirements for the employment of staff and labour. The Sub-Clauses must be considered in relation to the governing law and regulations, which may cover the same requirements. Several of these Sub-Clauses have been in use in other MDB Contracts and are included in the Guidance for the Preparation of Particular Conditions in the 1999 Red Book.

6.12 Foreign Personnel

The Contractor may bring in to the country any foreign personnel who are necessary for the execution of the Works to the extent allowed by the applicable Laws. The Contractor shall ensure that these personnel are provided with the required residence visas and work permits. The Employer will, if requested by the Contractor, use his best endeavours in a timely and expeditious manner to assist the Contractor in obtaining any local, state, national, or government permission required for bringing in the Contractor's personnel.

The Contractor shall be responsible for the return of these personnel to the place where they were recruited or to their domicile. In the event of the death in the Country of any of these personnel or members of their families, the Contractor shall similarly be responsible for making the appropriate arrangements for their return or burial.

6.13   Supply of Foodstuffs

The Contractor shall arrange for the provision of a sufficient supply of suitable food as may be stated in the Specification at reasonable prices for the Contractor's Personnel for the purposes of or in connection with the Contract.

6.14   Supply of Water

The Contractor shall, having regard to local conditions, provide on the Site an adequate supply of drinking and other water for the use of the Contractor's Personnel.

6.15   Measures against Insect and Pest Nuisance

The Contractor shall at all times take the necessary precautions to protect the Contractor's Personnel employed on the Site from insect and pest nuisance, and to reduce their danger to health. The Contractor shall comply with all the regulations of the local health authorities, including use of appropriate insecticide.

6.16   Alcoholic Liquor or Drugs

The Contractor shall not, otherwise than in accordance with the Laws of the Country, import, sell, give barter or otherwise dispose of any alcoholic liquor or drugs, or permit or allow importation, sale, gift barter or disposal thereto by Contractor's Personnel.

6.17   Arms and Ammunition

The Contractor shall not give, barter, or otherwise dispose of, to any person, any arms or ammunition of any kind, or allow Contractor's Personnel to do so.

6.18   Festivals and Religious Customs

The Contractor shall respect the Country's recognized festivals, days of rest and religious or other customs.

6.19   Funeral Arrangements

The Contractor shall be responsible, to the extent required by local regulations, for making any funeral arrangements for any of his local employees who may die while engaged upon the Works.

6.20   Prohibition of Forced or Compulsory Labour

The contractor shall not employ 'forced or compulsory labour' in any form. 'Forced or compulsory labour' consists of all work or service, not voluntarily performed, that is extracted from an individual under threat of force or penalty.

6.21   Prohibition of Harmful Child Labour

The Contractor shall not employ any child to perform any work that is economically exploitative, or is likely to be hazardous to, or to interfere with, the child's education, or to be harmful to the child's health or physical, mental, spiritual, moral, or social development.

6.22   Employment Records of Workers

The Contractor shall keep complete and accurate records of the employment of labour at the Site. The records shall include the names, ages, genders, hours worked and wages paid to all workers. These records shall be summarized on a monthly basis and shall be available for inspection by the Engineer during normal working hours. These records shall be included in the details to be submitted by the Contractor under Sub-Clause 6.10 [Records of Contractor's Personnel and Equipment].

8.4 Extension of Time for Completion

The words 'on the Site' have been deleted from paragraph (e). The Employer will take responsibility for delays caused by his other Contractors, whether or not they are working on the same Site.

12.3 Evaluation

A new paragraph has been added, which confirms the attitude already taken by many Engineers:

Any item of work included in the Bill of Quantities for which no rate or price was specified shall be considered as included in other rates and prices in the Bill of Quantities and will not be paid for separately.

In subparagraphs (a) (i) and (ii) the figures 10% and 0.10% are replaced by 25% and 0.25% respectively. These is a recognition that the previous figures were not realistic for the requirement to consider a new rate or price.

13.7 Adjustments for Changes on Legislation

A new paragraph has been added to avoid duplication between this and other Sub-Clauses.

Notwithstanding the foregoing, the Contractor shall not be entitled to such an extension of time if the same shall already have been taken into account in determining an extension and such Cost shall not be separately paid if the same shall already have been taken into account in the indexing of any inputs to the table of adjustment data in accordance with the provisions of Sub-Clause 13.8.

13.8 Adjustments for Changes in Cost

The reference to the Appendix to Tender in the definition of 'Pn' is changed to refer to local and foreign currencies in the Schedules.

14.2 Advance Payment

The wording of the repayment procedures has been improved and the amortisation rate is to be stated in the Contract Data.

Unless stated otherwise in the Contract Data, the advance payment shall be repaid through percentage deductions from the interim payments determined by the Engineer in accordance with Sub-Clause 14.6 [*Issue of Interim Payment Certificates*], as follows:

(a) deductions shall commence in the next interim Payment Certificate following that in which the total of all certified interim payments (excluding the advance payment and deductions and repayments of retention) exceeds 30 percent of the Accepted Contract Amount less Provisional Sums; and

(b) deductions shall be made at the amortisation rate stated in the Contract Data of the amount of each Interim Payment Certificate (excluding the advance payment and deductions and repayments of retention) in the currencies and proportions of the advance payment until such time as the advance payment has been repaid;

provided that the advance payment shall be completely repaid prior to the time when 80 percent of the Accepted Contract Amount less Provisional Sums has been certified for payment.

14.5 Plant and Materials intended for the Works

The references to the 'Appendix to Tender' at paragraphs (b) (i) and (c) (i) have been changed to refer to 'Schedules'.

14.9 Payment of Retention Money

Two paragraphs have been added to entitle the Contractor to provide guarantees for the release of the Retention Money, unless otherwise stated in the Particular Conditions.

Unless otherwise stated in the Particular Conditions, when the Taking-Over Certificate has been issued for the Works and the first half of the Retention Money has been certified for payment by the Engineer, the Contractor shall be entitled to substitute a guarantee, in the form annexed to the Particular Conditions or in another form approved by the Employer and provided by an entity approved by the Employer, for the second half of the Retention Money. The Contractor shall ensure that the guarantee is in the amounts and currencies of the second half of the Retention Money and is valid and enforceable until the Contractor has executed and completed the Works and remedied any defects, as specified for the Performance Security in Sub-Clause 4.2. On receipt by the Employer of the required guarantee, the Engineer shall certify and the Employer shall pay the second half of the Retention Money. The release of the second half of the Retention Money against a guarantee shall then be in lieu of the release under the second paragraph of this Sub-Clause. The Employer shall return the guarantee to the Contractor within 21 days after receiving a copy of the Performance Certificate.

If the Performance Security required under Sub-Clause 4.2 is in the form of a demand guarantee, and the amount guaranteed under it when the Taking-Over Certificate is issued is more than half of the Retention Money, then the Retention Money guarantee will not be required. If the amount guaranteed under the Performance Security when the Taking-Over Certificate is issued is less than half of the Retention Money, the Retention Money guarantee will only be required for the difference between half of the Retention Money and the amount guaranteed under the Performance Security.

14.13 Issue of Final Payment Certificate

Paragraph (a) is changed to refer to 'the amount which he fairly determines is due'.

14.15 Currencies of Payment

The references to the 'Appendix to Tender' are changed to refer to the 'Schedule of Payment Currencies'.

15.5 Employer's Entitlement to Termination for Convenience

The Sub-Clause heading has been changed to reflect its content and the phrase 'or to avoid a termination of the Contract by the Contractor under Clause 16.2 [*Termination by Contractor*]' has been added to the first paragraph. Both of these are improvements on the previous wording.

16.4 Payment on Termination

The provision for loss of profit has been deleted from subparagraph (c). This seems unfair to the Contractor because the termination was caused by a default by the Employer.

17.1 Indemnities

Paragraph (b) has been changed to read:

> (b)   damage to or loss of any property, real or personal (other than the Works), to the extent that such damage or loss arises out of or in the course of or by reason of the Contractor's design (if any), the execution and completion of the Works and the remedying of any defects, unless and to the extent that any such damage or loss is attributable to any negligence, wilful act or breach of the Contract by the Employer, the Employer's Personnel, their respective agents, or anyone directly or indirectly employed by any of them.

The revised paragraph is probably more logical than the original version in that the indemnity by the Contractor does not require negligence, wilful act or breach of Contract by the Contractor, but is excluded by negligence, wilful act or breach of Contract by the Employer.

17.3 Employer's Risks

The Sub-Clause is changed so that the risks only apply if they directly affect the execution of the Works in the Country. This seems a logical clarification.

Subparagraphs (b) and (c) are changed to exclude sabotage by the Contractor's Personnel, which is logical. The change to subparagraph (c) only deletes a repetition because the definition of Contractor's Personnel, at Sub-Clause 1.1.2.7, includes employees of the Contractor and Subcontractors.

17.6 Limitation of Liability

The Sub-Clause is revised as follows.

> Neither Party shall be liable to the other Party for loss of use of any Works, loss of profit, loss of any contract or for any indirect or consequential loss or damage which may be suffered by the other Party in connection with the Contract, provided that this exclusion shall not apply to any obligation of the Contractor to pay Delay Damages to the Employer under Sub-Clause 8.7 [*Delay Damages*].
>
> The total liability of the Contractor to the Employer, under or in connection with the Contract other than under Sub-Clause 4.19 [*Electricity, Water and Gas*], Sub-Clause 4.20 [*Employer's Equipment and Free-Issue Material*], Sub-Clause 17.1 [*Indemnities*] and Sub-Clause 17.5 [*Intellectual and Industrial Property Rights*], shall not exceed the sum resulting from the application of a multiplier (less or greater than one) to the Accepted Contract Amount, as stated in the Contract Data, or (if such multiplier or other sum is not so stated), the Accepted Contract Amount.
>
> This Sub-Clause shall not limit liability in any case of fraud, deliberate default or reckless misconduct by the defaulting Party.

This Sub-Clause remains controversial and legal advice should always be sought.

19.1 Definition of Force Majeure

Subparagraph (ii) now includes sabotage by persons other than the Contractor's Personnel. The change to subparagraph (iii) only deletes the reference to other employees of the Contractor or Subcontractors, who are already included in Contractor's Personnel.

19.2 Notice of Force Majeure

In the first paragraph the MDB Edition restricts Force Majeure to events which prevent a Party from performing 'its substantial obligations' rather than 'any of its obligations'. In the second paragraph the phrase 'such obligations' is changed to 'its obligations'. These changes restrict the application of Force Majeure to the really serious events.

The meaning of the word 'substantial' could be controversial but, as the Party is prevented from performing the obligation, it has no choice but to stop performance. The precise meaning and extent of the performance which must stop will then be the subject of debate and possibly a dispute.

19.4 Consequences of Force Majeure

The first paragraph of the Sub-Clause has been changed to include the word 'substantial' as in Sub-Clause 19.2.

19.6 Optional Termination, Payment and Release

At subparagraph (c) the Cost or liability must be 'necessarily', as well as reasonably, incurred. This is a stricter standard that may exclude some of the Costs which would be claimed by the Contractor.

20.2 Appointment of the Dispute Board

The MDB Sub-Clauses 20.2 to 20.4 incorporate the general changes of wording to change from DAB to DB. However, MDB Sub-Clause 20.2 includes several significant changes. These changes are presumably based on the MDBs' experience of the use of DBs. Most of the changes, such as the changes to the selection procedures, are improvements. The removal of the right of the Parties to refer a matter to the DB for an opinion may seem surprising, but it has been replaced by the improved provision at the second of the Procedural Rules in the Annex, concerning the prevention of problems or claims from becoming disputes. The main changes can be summarised as follows.

- Some of the qualities for the DB member, which are given in the Appendix, have been repeated in the Sub-Clause.
- The Parties must first consider together who shall serve as the DB and it is only if they have not jointly appointed the DB 21 days before the date stated in the Contract Data that each Party proposes a member for a three-person DB. This enables the Parties to agree on a balance of skills in the DB.
- The first two members have an obligation to recommend someone to be appointed as the third member, who will act as chairman for the Parties' agreement.
- The provision for a list of potential members for a three-person board to be included in the Contract has been deleted. The Contract Data includes provision for suggestions for a sole member, but this is not clear in the revised Sub-Clause 20.2.
- It has been clarified that the Parties must agree on the terms of appointment of any expert whom the DB consults, as well as the remuneration.
- The provision for the Parties to refer a matter to the DB for an opinion has been deleted, but there is a new requirement at Rule 2 in the Annex that, during the Site visits, the DB shall endeavour to prevent potential problems or claims from becoming disputes.
- The wording of the procedure for the appointment of a replacement member has been improved.

Disputes shall be referred to a DB for decision in accordance with Sub-Clause 20.4 [*Obtaining Dispute Board's Decision*]. The Parties shall appoint a DB by the date stated in the Contract Data.

The DB shall comprise, as stated in the Contract Data, either one or three suitably qualified persons ('the members'), each of whom shall be fluent in the language for communication defined in the Contract and shall be a professional experienced in the type of construction involved in the Works and with the interpretation of contractual documents. If the number is not so stated and the Parties do not agree otherwise, the DB shall comprise three persons, one of whom shall serve as chairman.

If the Parties have not jointly appointed the DB 21 days before the date stated in the Contract Data and the DB is to comprise three persons, each Party shall nominate one member for the approval of the other Party. The first two members shall recommend and the Parties shall agree upon the third member, who shall act as chairman.

The agreement between the Parties and either the sole member or each of the three members shall incorporate by reference the General Conditions of Dispute Board Agreement contained in the Appendix to these General Conditions, with such amendments as are agreed between them.

The terms of the remuneration of either the sole member or each of the three members, including the remuneration of any expert whom the DB consults, shall be mutually agreed upon by the Parties when agreeing the terms of appointment of the member or such expert (as the case may be). Each Party shall be responsible for paying one-half of this remuneration.

If a member declines to act or is unable to act as a result of death, disability, resignation or termination of appointment, a replacement shall be appointed in the same manner as the replaced person was required to have been nominated or agreed upon, as described in this Sub-Clause.

The appointment of any member may be terminated by mutual agreement of both Parties, but not by the Employer or the Contractor acting alone. Unless otherwise agreed by both Parties, the appointment of the DB (including each member) shall expire when the discharge referred to in Sub-Clause 14.12 [*Discharge*] shall have become effective.

20.3 Failure to Agree on the Composition of the Dispute Board

The heading of the MDB version has been changed to reflect its content. Subparagraph (b) has been changed to provide for reference to the appointing entity if one Party fails to approve a member nominated by the other Party. This closes a gap in the Red Book provisions.

20.4 Obtaining Dispute Board's Decision and 20.5 Amicable Settlement

In Sub-Clauses 20.4 and 20.5 the provision for a notice of dissatisfaction with the DBs decision must also refer to the Party's intention to commence arbitration.

20.6 Arbitration

The arbitration requirements have been changed in the MDB Edition such that the arbitration procedure will be stated in the Particular Conditions. This enables the Employer to decide whether to use the ICC, or a different set of rules. If no procedure is stated then the ICC rules will apply.

20.7 Failure to Comply with Dispute Board's Decision

This Sub-Clause has been revised such that a failure to comply with a DB decision, which has become final and binding as the final paragraph of Sub-Clause 20.4, can be referred to arbitration, whether or not a notice of dissatisfaction has been issued.

> In the event that a Party fails to comply with a DB decision which has become final and binding, then the other Party may, without prejudice to any other rights it may have, refer the failure itself to arbitration under Sub-Clause 20.6 [*Arbitration*]. Sub-Clause 20.4 [*Obtaining Dispute Board's Decision*] and Sub-Clause 20.5 [*Amicable Settlement*] shall not apply to this reference.

31.5 Changes in the Appendix

The heading of the Appendix has been changed to 'General Conditions of Dispute Board Agreement', consistent with the general omission of the word 'Adjudication'.

2 General Provisions

The MDB Edition has omitted the paragraph which states that the Agreement shall be void and ineffective if the Member has not been notified by both Parties, within six months of signing, that it has taken effect. This notice should be a formality, if copies of the signed Agreement have been circulated to the Member and the Parties. However, if the Member has not received the signed copies he could be uncertain, perhaps for some considerable time, as to whether the Agreement has come into effect.

The ban on assignment or subcontracting has also been deleted. However, the previous paragraph is clear that this employment is a personal appointment so assignment or subcontracting would not be possible.

5 General Obligations of the Employer and the Contractor

The first paragraph of this section includes a ban on either Party requesting advice or consultation from the Member, except in the normal course of the DB's activities. The paragraph is revised in the MDB Edition such that the Parties and the other Members are not permitted to give their prior agreement.

6 Payment

Subparagraph (a) (iv) has been revised so that the retainer is only reduced by one third, rather than 50%, after the Taking-Over Certificate has been issued.

Subparagraph (c) has been reworded to impose restrictions on the expenses and now reads:

> (c) all reasonable expenses including necessary travel expenses (air fare in less than first class, hotel and subsistence and other direct travel expenses) incurred in connection with the Member's duties, as well as the cost of telephone calls, courier charges, faxes and telexes: a receipt shall be required for each item in excess of five percent of the daily fee referred to in subparagraph (b) of this Clause.

A new paragraph has been added to this section to resolve a situation if the Parties and the Member cannot agree to the retainer or daily fee – it will be determined by the appointing entity or official named in the Contract Data.

> If the parties fail to agree on the retainer fee or the daily fee of the appointing entity or official named in the Contract Data shall determine the amount of the fees to be used.

8 Default of the Member

This section has been revised to separate the procedural parts of Clause 4, items (e) to (k), from the parts which refer to the Member's relations with the Parties, items (a) to (d). The penalty in respect of failure to comply with items (e) to (k) is restricted to fees and expenses from the date and to the extent of the non-compliance. Also, the penalties only apply to proceedings or decisions that were rendered ineffective by the failure to comply.

> If the Member fails to comply with any of his obligations under Clause 4 (a)–(d) above, he shall not be entitled to any fees or expenses hereunder and shall, without prejudice to their other rights, reimburse each of the Employer and the Contractor for any fees and expenses received by the Member and the Other Members (if any), for proceedings or decisions (if any) of the DB which are rendered void or ineffective by the said failure to comply.
>
> If the Member fails to comply with any of his obligations under Clause 4 (e)–(k) above, he shall not be entitled to any fees or expenses hereunder

from the date and to the extent of the non-compliance and shall, without prejudice to their other rights, reimburse each of the Employer and the Contractor for any fees and expenses already received by the Member, for proceedings or decisions (if any) of the DB which are rendered void or ineffective by the said failure to comply.

9 Disputes

The Parties to the Dispute Board Agreement can agree on an arbitration institution or, if no institution is agreed, that the Rules of the ICC will apply.

31.6 Changes to Annex: Procedural Rules

Rule 2 has been revised to include provision for the Site visit to, as far as possible, endeavour to prevent potential problems or claims from becoming disputes. This is a wider requirement than the provision for an opinion from the DB which has been deleted from Sub-Clause 20.2. It remains to be seen how this procedure will work in practice.

2   The timing of and agenda for each site visit shall be as agreed jointly by the DB, the Employer and the Contractor, or in the absence of agreement, shall be decided by the DB. The purpose of site visits is to enable the DB to become and remain acquainted with the progress of the Works and of any actual or potential problems or claims, and, as far as reasonable, to endeavour to prevent potential problems or claims from becoming disputes.

31.7 Changes to standard forms

The MDB Edition publication includes standard forms for the Particular Conditions, the Letters of Bid and Acceptance, the Agreements, and the Forms of Security and Guarantee. The following notes should be read together with the full text in the MDB Edition.

- The Particular Conditions – Part A: Contract Data

  The Contract Data replaces the Appendix to Tender in other FIDIC Contracts. It includes the same items, modified to suit the wording of MDB Edition, and all the information must be provided by the Employer.

- The Particular Conditions – Part B: Specific Provisions

  Additional specific provisions could be added to suit the particular requirements of the project.

- Sample Forms

  The MDB Edition includes 11 sample forms. These are similar to the FIDIC sample forms, modified to suit the MDB requirements. The differences should be studied to check whether they could be of value for the particular requirements of other FIDIC Contracts. The MDB standard forms are provided in three sections:

  1. **Forms of letter of Bid, Letter of Acceptance, Contract Agreement and Dispute Board Agreement.**

     Annex A Letter of Bid
     Annex B Letter of Acceptance
     Annex C Contract Agreement
     Annex D Dispute Board Agreement (one-person DB)
     Annex E Dispute Board Agreement (each person of a three-person DB).

  2. **Forms of Security annexed to the Particular Conditions**

     Annex F Performance Security: Demand Guarantee
     Annex G Performance Security: Performance Bond
     Annex H Advance Payment Security: Demand Guarantee
     Annex I Retention Money Security: Demand Guarantee.

  3. **Forms of Guarantee annexed to the Instructions to Tenderers**
     Annex J Parent Company Guarantee
     Annex K Bid Security: Bank Guarantee.

Part 5

Sub-Clause comparison

A comparison of Sub-Clause numbers between the fourth edition of 'The Red Book' and the 1999 Conditions of Contract for Construction

A schedule of comparison of Sub-Clause numbers between the 1999 Yellow Book (The Conditions of Contract for Plant and Design-Build) and the previous Yellow Book (The Conditions of Contract for Electrical and Mechanical Works) would not serve any useful purpose because there is no direct comparison between the Sub-Clauses. However, the list of Sub-Clauses in the 1999 Yellow Book is almost identical to the list of Sub-Clauses in the previous Orange Book (The Conditions of Contract for Design-Build and Turnkey) so a direct comparison can be made for each Sub-Clause.

Clauses in the fourth edition of the 'Red Book'	*Equivalent Sub-Clause in 1999 Conditions of Contract for Construction*
PART 1: GENERAL CONDITIONS	
Definitions and Interpretation	
1.1 Definitions	1.1
1.2 Headings and Marginal Notes	1.2
1.3 Interpretation	1.2
1.4 Singular and Plural	1.2
1.5 Notices, Consents, Approvals, Certificates and Determinations	1.3
Engineer and Engineer's Representative	
2.1 Engineer's Duties and Authority	3.1
2.2 Engineer's Representative	3.2
2.3 Engineer's Authority to Delegate	3.2
2.4 Appointment of Assistants	3.2
2.5 Instructions in Writing	3.3
2.6 Engineer to Act Impartially	3.1
Assignment and Subcontracting	
3.1 Assignment of Contract	1.7

Labour

Materials, Plant and Workmanship

Suspension

Commencement and Delays

Defects Liability

Alterations, Additions and Omissions

Procedure for Claims

Contractor's Equipment, Temporary Works and Materials

Index

Index by page numbers. Flow charts and Tables are indicated by *italic page numbers*, Definitions by initial capitals (except 'day' and 'year') + **emboldened page numbers**; 'RB' means '1999 Red Book' [Construction], 'YB' is '1999 Yellow Book' [Plant and Design–Build], and 'MDB' is 'Multilateral Development Banks Harmonised Conditions of Contract for Construction'